Student Solutions Manual to Accompany
Gillespie, Humphreys, Baird, and Robinson

CHEMISTRY

N. Colin Baird
UNIVERSITY OF WESTERN ONTARIO

Andrew E. Scott
UNIVERSITY OF WESTERN ONTARIO

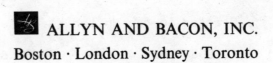 ALLYN AND BACON, INC.
Boston · London · Sydney · Toronto

ISBN 0-205-08754-X

Printed in the United States of America.

10 9 8 7 6 5 4   90 89 88 87

CONTENTS

A NOTE TO THE STUDENT

In arriving at the numerical answers to problems we have adopted the following conventions in this book:

1) Where intermediate results are shown, they are rounded to the appropriate number of significant figures before being used in subsequent steps. Thus if you do a problem all in one step, your final value may differ slightly (i.e. in the last significant figure) from that given - do not be concerned!

2) All atomic masses used are from Table B.1 of Appendix B of the text, and are first rounded to 2 decimal places before being added to obtain molecular or molar masses. Thus there is no need to deduce the appropriate number of significant figures for a molar mass, and no ambiguity is introduced concerning the stage of the calculation at which rounding occurs.

3) For reasons of clarity, formal charges on atoms are not circled as they are in the text. Furthermore, in the later chapters nonbonding electron pairs on atoms usually are not shown explicitly unless the atom is the central one in the structure.

ACKNOWLEDGEMENTS

The authors are grateful to Professors R.G. Gillespie and E.A. Robinson for useful discussions, and to Janis Zaborniak and Anne Donovan-Graham for their efficiency and patience in typing the manuscript.

1. a) The elements listed in this question are drawn from
        those for which you should memorize the symbols.
        Therefore you should be able to write the following
        answers without recourse to the text:

hydrogen H	carbon C	oxygen O	nitrogen N
chlorine Cl	sodium Na	potassium K	krypton Kr
iron Fe	nickel Ni	chromium Cr	silicon Si
barium Ba	lead Pb	uranium U	

    b) Similarly, you should be able to identify from their
    symbols the following atoms:

He - Helium	P - Phosphorus	Co - Cobalt	Br - Bromine
Ne - Neon	S - Sulphur	Cu - Copper	Ag - Silver
F - Fluorine	Ca - Calcium	Zn - Zinc	Pt - Platinum
Mg - Magnesium	Fe - Iron	As - Arsenic	Au - Gold
Al - Aluminum	Mn - Manganese	K - Potassium	

2. You should recognize (b) iron and (g) sulfur as elements,
    and (a) water, (d) sugar and (f) salt as compounds. Since
    (c) beer and (e) wine contains both alcohol and water, they
    are mixtures as is (h) milk.

3. | Material | Color | State | Electrical Conductivity |
    |---|---|---|---|
    | Water | colorless | liquid | very little (when pure) |
    | Sugar | white | solid | none |
    | Mercury | silver | liquid | high |
    | Copper | brown | solid | high |
    | Maple syrup | light brown | liquid | very little |
    | Oxygen | colorless | gas | none |
    | Glass | colorless | solid | none |
    | Bromine | orange-brown | liquid | none |

4. | Material | Chemical Properties (example) |
    |---|---|
    | Water | Reacts with many metals to give H_2 |
    | Copper | Dissolves in nitric acid |
    | Iron | Dissolves in many acids |
    | Magnesium | Reacts with steam |
    | Carbon dioxide | Reacts with limewater |
    | Hydrogen peroxide | Bleaches color |
    | Hydrogen | Reacts with oxygen to give water |

5. i) The pure substances are nitrogen, iron, carbon, sodium
        chloride, nylon, carbon dioxide, oxygen, diamond and
        distilled water; the rest are mixtures.

ii) Of the pure substances, you should recognize nitrogen, iron, carbon and oxygen as elements; the rest are compounds. Of the mixtures, those clearly heterogeneous by visual inspection are milk, cottage cheese, vegetable soup, wet sand, salad dressing. The homogeneous mixtures are amalgam, black coffee, iodized table salt, filtered sea water, gasoline, a dime, 14 carat gold, coca cola and perhaps smog. Diamond is mainly elemental carbon, but contains some impurities and so it is a homogeneous mixture.

6. Coca cola, black coffee, (clean) snow and clouds are homogeneous.

7. Sugar and water: Boil the solution and condense the steam; the sugar stays in the original solution and is recovered once all the water has boiled off.

   Water and gasoline: Let the mixture settle. Two phases will result – the top one is gasoline. Simply decant off the gasoline to separate.

   Iron filings and sawdust: Use a magnet passed through the mixture to attract the iron.

   Sugar and Glass: Add water to the mixture; only the sugar dissolves. (The sugar can be recovered from the water as described above.) The glass-water mixture can be poured through a filter to separate them.

   Gasoline and kerosene: Use fractional distillation.

   Food Colouring in water: Add powdered charcoal to absorb the food colouring.

8. a) Test the liquids for electrical conductivity using a battery and a lamp; the salt solution wil give a much brighter light.

   b) Add a little water to each; the chalk does not dissolve in water.

9. a) Molecular = As_4 (the subscript gives the number of atoms in a molecule).
   The empirical formula is the simplest set of integers that yields the correct <u>ratio</u> of atoms; thus for any element X, the empirical formula simply is X. Thus for arsenic, the empirical formula is As.

   b) Molecular = C_3H_6. For its empirical formula, we can divide both 3 and 6 by the common integer 3 to obtain C_1H_2, or simply CH_2 = empirical formula.

   c) Molecular is P_4O_{10}. Dividing by 2 gives P_2O_5, the empirical formula.

   d) Molecular is XeF_4. Since there exists no integer factor common to 1 and 4 (other than unity), the empirical formula also is XeF_4.

2

10.

Molecular	Empirical	Explanation
H_2O_2	HO	Divide both 2's by 2.
H_2O	H_2O	No common divisor for 2 and 1.
Li_2CO_3	Li_2CO_3	No common divisor of 2 and 3.
$C_2H_4O_2$	CH_2O	Common divisor is 2
S_8	S	(See Q. 9a)
C_6H_{12}	CH_2	Common divisor of 6 and 12 is 6.
B_2H_6	BH_3	Common divisor of 2 and 6 is 2.
O_3	O	(See Q. 9a)
S_3O_9	SO_3	Common divisor is 3.
N_2O_3	N_2O_3	No common divisor.

11.

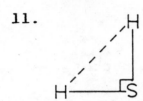

By Pythagorus' theorem,
$$R_{HH}^2 = R_{SH}^2 + R_{SH}^2 = 2R_{SH}^2$$
$$= 2 \times (134 \text{ pm})^2$$
Taking the square root of each side, we obtain
$$R_{HH} = 190 \text{ pm}$$

12. a)

$$\overset{74}{H - H} \qquad \overset{121}{O - O} \qquad \overset{109}{N - N} \qquad \overset{113}{C - O}$$

b)

Linear means all 3 atoms lie in a row; the C is in the middle since both CO distances are 116 pm.

c)

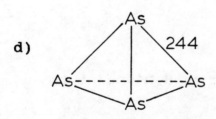

d)

As
244
As------As
As

13. H_2O is <u>angular</u>, since the three atoms are not in a line.
XeF_2 is <u>linear</u>, since the three atoms are in a line.
PH_3 is <u>pyramidal</u>, since the P atom stands above the plane of the three H atoms.

14. Define the corners of a cube by the Cartesian coordinates
±a, ±a, ±a. Two of the alternate corners of the tetrahedron
therefore have the coordinates a, a, a and −a, −a, a, and

the cube's center has coordinates 0, 0, 0. The distance
between the alternate corners is therefore $\sqrt{(2a)^2 + (2a)^2} =$
$2a\sqrt{2}$ and between either corner and the center of the cube is
$\sqrt{a^2 + a^2 + a^2} = a\sqrt{3}$. Thus we have the triangle

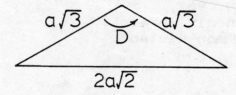

Draw a line from the top point to the midpoint of the bottom
line to obtain a right-angled triangle:

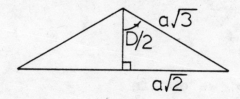

From trigonometry, $\sin(D/2) = \dfrac{a\sqrt{2}}{a\sqrt{3}} = 0.8165$

Using INV SIN on a calculator with the argument 0.8165 yields

$D/2 = 54.74°$, and thus $D = 109.5°$.

15. The geometry given for the triangle formed by the two
    hydrogens and oxygen is

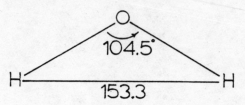

Draw a line from the oxygen to the H -----H midpoint to
obtain a right-angled triangle:

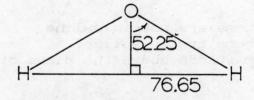

From trigonometry, $\sin 52.25° = 76.65/R_{OH}$
Thus $R_{OH} = 76.65 \text{ pm}/\sin 52.25 = 96.9 \text{ pm}$

4

16. In each case, we move the decimal until there is one non-zero digit which precedes it. If moved n places to the left, we multiply the resultant number by 10^n; if moved to the right, we multiply by 10^{-n}. Thus

    a)   12000 becomes 1.2×10^4

    b)   1740312.29 becomes 1.74031229×10^6

    c)   0.00404 becomes 4.04×10^{-3}

    d)   -0.04900 becomes -4.9×10^{-2}

17. In each example, the process of Q.16 is reversed.
    a) 3.0×10^2 becomes 300

    b) 1.162×10^5 becomes 116200

    c) 4.8×10^{-3} becomes 0.0048

    d) -6.44×10^{-2} becomes -0.0644

18. First we follow the procedure of Q.16 to write each number in scientific notation, then perform the multiplication and division operators. In these examples, no calculation is required.

    a)   becomes $(4 \times 10^{-6}) \times (1 \times 10^{-3}) \times (5 \times 10^3) =$
       20×10^{-6}, i.e. 2×10^{-5}. Note that $10^n \times 10^m = 10^{n+m}$.

    b) $(1.2 \times 10^{-4})/(6 \times 10^{-2}) = 0.2 \times 10^{-2}$, i.e.
       2×10^{-3}. Note that $10^n/10^m = 10^{n-m}$.

    c) $(2.0 \times 10^2)^3 \times (9 \times 10^{-4})^{\frac{1}{2}} =$
       $(8 \times 10^6)(3 \times 10^{-2}) = 24 \times 10^4$, i.e. 2.4×10^5.
       Note that $(10^{2n})^{\frac{1}{2}} = 10^n$.

    d)   becomes $\dfrac{(2 \times 10^{-2}) \times (6 \times 10^2) \times (5 \times 10^1)}{(3 \times 10^{-3}) \times (5 \times 10^2)} = 4 \times 10^2$.

    e) $(9.0 \times 10^{-6})^{\frac{1}{2}} \times (2.0 \times 10^1)^2 = (3.0 \times 10^{-3}) \times (4.0 \times 10^2) = 1.2$

19. a)   We can perform the multiplication and division of the powers of 10 above by using $10^n \times 10^m = 10^{n+m}$, and $10^n/10^m = 10^{n-m}$.

       Thus $\dfrac{10^{-6} \times 10^{14}}{10^3 \times 10^6} = \dfrac{10^8}{10^9} = 10^{-1}$

       Now $\dfrac{6 \times 3}{2 \times 1} = 9$

       Thus the answer is 9×10^{-1}.

    b)   Simple addition gives 6.099×10^{23}

c) As in (a), we obtain 1.0×10^6

d) We obtain, with the help of a calculator, 2.0×10^{-10}.

e) Simple addition yields 3.2332037×10^2, but to consider significant figures (see Appendix to text) we first convert to a common base, here 10^0:

$$
\begin{array}{r}
119.2 \\
204.12 \\
\underline{0.0003734} \\
323.3
\end{array}
$$

Thus the answer to the correct number of significant figures is 3.233×10^2.

20. a) By definition 1 km = 10^3 m.

$$2.998 \times 10^7 \text{ km} \times \frac{10^3 \text{m}}{1 \text{ km}} = 2.998 \times 10^{10} \text{ m}$$

b) By definition 1 pm = 10^{-12} m

Thus $143 \text{ pm} \times \frac{10^{-12} \text{m}}{1 \text{ pm}} = 1.43 \times 10^{-10} \text{ m}$

c) By definition 1 nm = 10^{-9} km

$$0.001 \text{ nm} \times \frac{10^{-9} \text{m}}{1 \text{ nm}} = 1 \times 10^{-12} \text{ m}$$

d) We know $1\text{Å} = 10^{-10}$ m
Thus to convert 1.54Å to m, we multiply by the unit factor which contains m in the numerator and Å in the denominator so that the units cancel:

$$1.54\text{Å} \times \frac{10^{-10} \text{m}}{1\text{Å}} = 1.54 \times 10^{-10} \text{ m}.$$

21. a) We know 1 mg = 10^{-3} g and 1 kg = 10^3 g; thus to convert mg to kg, first use a unit factor to convert mg to g, then another to convert g to kg:

$$5.84 \times 10^{-3} \text{ mg} \times \frac{10^{-3}\text{g}}{1 \text{ mg}} \times \frac{1 \text{ kg}}{10^3\text{g}} = 5.84 \times 10^{-9} \text{ kg}$$

b) By definition 1 Mg = 10^6 g, and 1 kg = 10^3 g

$$54.34 \text{ Mg} \times \frac{10^6\text{g}}{1 \text{ Mg}} \times \frac{1 \text{ kg}}{10^3 \text{ g}} = 5.434 \times 10^4 \text{ kg}$$

c) By definition 1 kg = 10^3 g

$$0.354 \text{ g} \times \frac{1 \text{ kg}}{10^3 \text{ g}} = 3.54 \times 10^{-4} \text{ kg}$$

6

d) Similarly to part c,

$$1.673 \times 10^{-21} \text{ g} \times \frac{1 \text{ kg}}{1000 \text{ g}} = 1.673 \times 10^{-24} \text{ g}$$

22. a) The SI base unit for distance is the meter and for time is the second; thus we convert Gm to m by using the equivalence

$$1 \text{ Gm} = 10^9 \text{ m}$$

Thus $0.0001998 \times 10^3 \text{ Gm s}^{-1} \times \frac{10^9 \text{ m}}{1 \text{ Gm}} = 1.998 \times 10^8 \text{ m}$

b) The SI base unit for mass is the kilogram: $1 \text{ kg} = 10^3 \text{ g}$. Thus we multiply

$$6.022 \times 10^{23} \times 1.673 \times 10^{-24} \text{ g} \times \frac{1 \text{ kg}}{10^3 \text{ g}}$$

$$= 1.007 \times 10^{-3} \text{ kg}$$

c) The base unit for distance is m, and $1\text{Å} = 10^{-10}$ m. The base unit for time is s, and 1 min = 60 s. Thus

$$\frac{32150 \text{Å}}{1 \text{ min}} \times \frac{1 \text{ min}}{60 \text{ s}} \times \frac{10^{-10} \text{ m}}{1 \text{Å}} = 5.358 \times 10^{-8} \text{ m s}^{-1}$$

d) Now $1 \text{ mL} = 1 \text{ cm}^3$, and since the SI base unit for length is the meter, and since $1 \text{ cm} = 10^{-2}$ m, we have

$$22.41 \text{ mL} \times \frac{1 \text{ cm}^3}{1 \text{ mL}} \times \left(\frac{10^{-2} \text{ m}}{1 \text{ cm}}\right)^3 = 2.241 \times 10^{-5} \text{ m}^3$$

Notice that 1 cm^3 means $(1 \text{ cm})^3$; this should be kept in mind in planning conversions. Thus the cm to m unit factor is cubed to convert 1 cm^3 to m^3.

23. a) Since 1 km = 0.6214 mile, and $1 \text{ km} = 10^3$ m,

thus $24000 \text{ miles} \times \frac{1 \text{ km}}{0.6214 \text{ mile}} \times \frac{1000 \text{ m}}{1 \text{ km}} = 3.9 \times 10^7 \text{ m.}$

b) Since 1 kg = 2.205 lb,

$$150 \text{ lb.} \times \frac{1 \text{ kg}}{2.205 \text{ lb}} = 68 \text{ kg}$$

c) Since 1 kg = 2.205 lb, and 1 inch = 2.540 cm,

thus $\frac{14 \text{ lb}}{1 \text{ in}^2} \times \frac{1 \text{ kg}}{2.205 \text{ lb}} \times \left(\frac{1 \text{ inch}}{2.540 \text{cm}}\right)^2 \times \left(\frac{1 \text{ cm}}{10^{-2} \text{m}}\right)^2$

$$= 9.8 \times 10^3 \text{ kg m}^{-2}$$

d) Since 1 km = 0.6214 miles,

$$\frac{60 \text{ miles}}{1 \text{ hour}} \times \frac{1 \text{ km}}{0.6214 \text{ miles}} \times \frac{1 \text{ hour}}{60 \text{ min}} \times \frac{1 \text{ min}}{60 \text{ sec}} =$$

$$= 2.7 \times 10^{-2} \text{ km sec}^{-1}$$

7

24. Using conversion factors in Table 1.3, we obtain:
The moon is at a distance of 384,400 km from the earth and revolves around it with a period of 2.360×10^6 seconds. The moon's radius is 1740 km and its mass is estimated to be 7.3×10^{22} kg.
The miles-to-kilometers conversions are done by multiplying the number of miles by the unit factor (1 km/0.6214 miles). The tons-to-kilograms conversion is accomplished by first

converting tons to pounds, using $\dfrac{2000 \text{ lb}}{1 \text{ ton}} = 1$

then converting pounds to grams using $\dfrac{453.6 \text{ g}}{1 \text{ lb}} = 1$

25. It is simplest to convert separately miles to kilometers and gallons to litres:

$$25.4 \text{ miles} \times \dfrac{1 \text{ km}}{0.6214 \text{ miles}} = 40.9 \text{ km}$$

To obtain litres from gallons, first convert gallons to

quarts and then use a unit factor based upon 1 L = 1.06

quart:

$$1 \text{ gallon} \times \dfrac{4 \text{ quarts}}{1 \text{ gallon}} \times \dfrac{1 \text{ L}}{1.06 \text{ quart}} = 3.77 \text{ L}$$

Thus the gasoline consumption is 3.77 L/40.9 km, which is 0.0922 L/km, or 9.2 L per 100 km.

26. Jupiter is approximately 7.79×10^{11} meters from the sun, and revolves around it with a period of 3.74×10^8 seconds. The average density of the planet is 1.330×10^3 kg m^{-3}.

27. An advantage is that one would not have to memorize different conversion factors for time units (e.g. how many minutes in an hour, how many days in a year, etc.) since there would only be one unit. Disadvantages are many, including the fact that the day and year are natural intervals which do not differ by a power of ten.

28. a) To convert inches to feet, the factor based on 12 in = 1 ft must have feet in the numerator and inches in the denominator,

    i.e. $\dfrac{1 \text{ foot}}{12 \text{ inch}} = 1$

b) Similarly, $\dfrac{12 \text{ inches}}{1 \text{ foot}} = 1$

c) Similarly, $\dfrac{1 \text{ km}}{0.6214 \text{ mile}} = 1$

d) Similarly, $\dfrac{0.6214 \text{ mile}}{1 \text{ km}} = 1$

e) Recall that 1 mL = 1 cm^3. Thus

$$1 \text{ m}^3 \times \left(\frac{1 \text{ cm}}{10^{-2}\text{m}}\right)^3 = 1 \times 10^6 \text{ cm}^3 \times \frac{1 \text{ mL}}{1 \text{ cm}^3} = 1 \times 10^6 \text{ mL},$$

i.e. 1 m^3 = 1 × 10^6 mL

The factor must have units of mL/m^3; thus

$$\frac{10^6 \text{ mL}}{1 \text{ m}^3} = 1$$

f) From Table 1.3, 0.6214 mile = 1 km

$$(1 \text{ mile})^2 \times \left(\frac{1 \text{ km}}{0.6214 \text{ mile}}\right)^2 = 2.590 \text{ km}^2$$

i.e. 1 mile^2 = 2.590 km^2

The factor must have units of km^2/mile^2; thus

$$\frac{2.590 \text{ km}^2}{1 \text{ mile}^2} = 1$$

g) Similarly

$$1 \text{ cm}^2 \times \left(\frac{10^{-2}\text{m}}{1 \text{ cm}}\right)^2 = 10^{-4} \text{ m}^2 \quad \text{i.e. } 1 \text{ cm}^2 = 10^{-4} \text{ m}^2$$

The factor is $\dfrac{10^{-4} \text{ m}^2}{1 \text{ cm}^2} = 1$

29. $4.0 \text{ light year} \times \dfrac{365 \text{ day}}{1 \text{ year}} \times \dfrac{24 \text{ hr}}{1 \text{ day}} \times \dfrac{60 \text{ min}}{1 \text{ hr}} \times \dfrac{60 \text{ s}}{1 \text{ min}} \times \dfrac{3.00 \times 10^8 \text{ m}}{1 \text{ s}}$
  = 3.8 × 10^{16} m
  = 3.8 × 10^{13} km
  = 2.4 × 10^{13} miles

30. 1.69518829544 × 10^{29}

31. a) 3   b) −3   c) −2   d) −12   e) −6

32. a) kilo   b) deci   c) centi   d) micro
    e) pico

33.

	Canada	U.S.	Australia	U.K.
Population:	2.3845×10^7	2.2009×10^8	1.451×10^7	5.5819×10^7
Areas:	9.976139×10^6	9.519617×10^6	7.686849×10^6	2.244013×10^5
Density:	2.3902	23.120	1.888	248.75

where each density = population/area, and has units of people km^{-2}.

34. a) From Table 1.6, the density of sodium chloride is 2.16 $g\ cm^{-3}$. To convert from mass to volume, we use the conversion factor

$$(\frac{1\ cm^3}{2.16\ g}) = 1$$

   Thus $1.34\ mg \times \frac{10^{-3}\ g}{1\ mg} \times \frac{1\ cm^3}{2.16\ g} = 6.20 \times 10^{-4}\ cm^3$

   b) $21.34\ g \times \frac{1\ cm^3}{13.6\ g} = 1.57\ cm^3$

   c) Similarly,

   $1.00\ kg \times \frac{10^3\ g}{1\ kg} \times \frac{1\ cm^3}{0.880\ g} = 1.14 \times 10^3\ cm^3$

   d) From Table 1.3, 1 L = 1.06 quart. To convert to cm^3, recall that $1\ mL = 1\ cm^3$, thus $1\ L = 10^3\ cm^3$:

   $1.00\ quart \times \frac{1\ L}{1.06\ quart} \times \frac{10^3\ cm^3}{1\ L} = 943\ cm^3$

35. To convert a volume into a mass, we multiply volume by the density, which has units of mass/volume, i.e.

   $$volume\ sample \times \frac{mass}{volume} = mass\ of\ sample$$

   a) $1\ L \times \frac{1000\ cm^3}{1\ L} \times \frac{1.84\ g}{1\ cm^3} \times \frac{1\ kg}{1000\ g} = 1.84\ kg$

   b) $25.00\ mL \times \frac{1\ cm^3}{1\ mL} \times \frac{0.785\ g}{1\ cm^3} \times \frac{1\ kg}{1000\ g} = 0.0196\ kg$

   c) $1\ quart \times \frac{1\ L}{1.06\ quart} \times \frac{1000\ cm^3}{1\ L} \times \frac{1.000\ g}{1\ cm^3} \times \frac{1\ kg}{1000\ g}$

   $= 0.943\ kg$

   d) $1\ in^3 \times (\frac{2.54\ cm}{1\ in})^3 \times \frac{2.16\ g}{1\ cm^3} \times \frac{1\ kg}{1000\ g} = 0.0354\ kg$

36. To deduce density, we require both the volume and mass since density = mass/volume.
   Now volume = length x width x depth
   $= 40\ cm \times 25\ cm \times 15\ cm = 15000\ cm^3$
   mass $= 157.5\ kg \times \frac{1000\ g}{1\ kg} = 157,500\ g$

   Therefore density $= 157500\ g/15000\ cm^3 = 10.5\ g\ cm^{-3}$

37. We convert mass in g to volume in cm³ by multiplying the mass by a unit factor based upon the density, with units of cm³/g:

$$75.0 \text{ g} \times \frac{1 \text{ cm}^3}{1.49 \text{ g}} = 50.3 \text{ cm}^3$$

38. To obtain mass, we can multiply volume by a unit factor from the density, with units of g L^{-1}. First we compute the volume and convert it to L, each of which is 1 dm³:

Volume $= 8.5 \text{ m} \times 13.5 \text{ m} \times 2.8 \text{ m} = 320 \text{ m}^3$

$$320 \text{ m}^3 \times \left(\frac{1 \text{ dm}}{0.1 \text{ m}}\right)^3 = 3.2 \times 10^5 \text{ dm}^3, \text{ i.e. } 3.2 \times 10^5 \text{ L}$$

Finally, $3.2 \times 10^5 \text{ L} \times \frac{1.19 \text{ g}}{1 \text{ L}} = 3.8 \times 10^5 \text{ g}$

and, $3.8 \times 10^5 \text{ g} \times \frac{1 \text{ kg}}{1000 \text{ g}} = 380 \text{ kg}$

39. Here we convert volume from gallons to quarts and then to litres, and pounds to grams

$$\frac{6.56 \text{ lb}}{1 \text{ gallon}} \times \underbrace{\frac{1 \text{ gallon}}{4 \text{ quarts}} \times \frac{1.06 \text{ quart}}{1 \text{ L}} \times \frac{1 \text{ L}}{1000 \text{ cm}^3}}_{\substack{\text{conversions of} \\ \text{gallons to cm}^3}} \times \underbrace{\frac{453.6 \text{ g}}{1 \text{ lb}}}_{\substack{\text{conversion of} \\ \text{mass}}}$$

$= 0.789 \text{ g cm}^{-3}$

40. $10{,}000 \text{ gallon} \times \underbrace{\frac{4 \text{ quarts}}{1 \text{ gallon}} \times \frac{1 \text{ L}}{1.06 \text{ quart}} \times \frac{1000 \text{ cm}^3}{1 \text{ L}}}_{\substack{\text{conversion of gallons} \\ \text{to cm}^3}} \times \underbrace{\frac{0.785 \text{ g}}{1 \text{ cm}^3}}_{\substack{\text{conversion of} \\ \text{volume to mass} \\ \text{by unit factor} \\ \text{from density}}}$

$= 2.96 \times 10^7 \text{ g}$

41. From the radius we can calculate the Earth's volume, assuming that it is a perfect sphere:

$$\begin{aligned} V &= (4/3)\pi r^3 \\ &= (4/3) \times 3.14 \times (6.34 \times 10^3 \text{ km})^3 \\ &= 1.07 \times 10^{12} \text{ km}^3 \end{aligned}$$

Now density $\begin{aligned} &= \text{mass/volume} \\ &= 6.00 \times 10^{24} \text{ kg}/1.07 \times 10^{12} \text{ km}^3 \\ &= 5.61 \times 10^{12} \text{ kg/km}^3 \end{aligned}$

Convert to g/cm³:

$$\frac{5.61 \times 10^{12} \text{ kg}}{1 \text{ km}^3} \times \frac{1000 \text{ g}}{1 \text{ kg}} \times \left(\frac{1 \text{ km}}{10^3 \text{ m}}\right)^3 \times \left(\frac{1 \text{ m}}{10^2 \text{ cm}}\right)^3 = 5.61 \text{ g cm}^{-3}$$

42. In each case,

$$\text{mass \%} = 100\% \times \frac{\text{mass of that component in a sample}}{\text{total mass of all components}}$$

a) $100\% \times \dfrac{5.34}{5.34 + 121.51} = 4.21\%$

b) $100\% \times \dfrac{18.12}{250} = 7.25\%$

c) Mass % HCl $= 100\% \times \dfrac{30.1}{30.1 + 3.42 + 250} = 10.6\%$

   Mass % NaCl $= 100\% \times \dfrac{3.42}{30.1 + 3.42 + 250} = 1.21\%$

d) To obtain mass of solution, we use a unit factor based upon the density:

   $250 \text{ mL} \times (\dfrac{1.35 \text{ g}}{1 \text{ mL}}) = 338 \text{ g (since 1 cm}^3 \equiv 1 \text{ mL)}$

   Mass % $H_3PO_4 = 100\% \times \dfrac{178}{338} = 52.7\%$

e) The density of water is 1.00 g cm ; thus 100 mL of it has a mass of 100 g.

   Mass of water $= 100\% \times \dfrac{100}{21.35 + 100} = 82.4\%$

43. To convert mass of vinegar to mass of acetic acid, we multiply the former by a unit factor with units
$$\frac{\text{mass acetic acid}}{\text{mass vinegar}}$$

Since vinegar is 5% acetic acid, we have

$1 \text{ kg vinegar} \times \dfrac{5 \text{ kg acetic acid}}{100 \text{ kg vinegar}} = 0.05 \text{ kg acetic acid}$

44. We have 500 mL of a solution, and wish to transform that information to grams of sulfuric acid. We first convert volume of solution to mass of solution by using a unit factor based upon the density.

$500 \text{ mL solution} \times \dfrac{1.84 \text{ g solution}}{1 \text{ mL solution}} = 920 \text{ g solution}$

Next we convert mass of solution to mass sulfuric acid by using a unit factor based upon the % composition:

$920 \text{ g solution} \times \dfrac{95 \text{ g sulfuric acid}}{100 \text{ g solution}} = 874 \text{ g sulfuric acid}$

12

45. We wish to transform the mass of NaOH into volume of solution. First we transform mass of NaOH to mass of solution by using a unit factor based upon the composition:

$$20 \text{ g NaOH} \times \frac{100 \text{ g solution}}{50 \text{ g NaOH}} = 40 \text{ g solution}$$

Next we convert mass solution into volume solution by a unit factor based upon the density:

$$40 \text{ g solution} \times \frac{1 \text{ cm}^3 \text{ solution}}{1.53 \text{ g solution}} = 26 \text{ cm}^3 \text{ solution}$$

46. By use of a unit factor based upon the concentration, we can transform the given mass of O_2 to mass of seawater:

$$1.00 \text{ g } O_2 \times \frac{1,000,000 \text{ g seawater}}{6.22 \text{ g } O_2} = 161,000 \text{ g seawater}$$

To obtain volume from mass, multiply by a unit factor based upon the density:

$$161,000 \text{ g seawater} \times \frac{1 \text{ cm}^3 \text{ seawater}}{1.03 \text{ g seawater}} = 156,000 \text{ cm}^3 \text{ seawater}$$

CHAPTER 2

1. The number of protons is equal to the atomic number, which
    is given as the leading subscript to the atomic symbol. The
    number of electrons equals the number of protons. The
    number of neutrons equals the mass number, i.e. the leading
    superscript, minus the number of protons.

Atom	Electrons and Protons	Number of Neutrons
$_{1}^{2}H$	1	1
$_{9}^{19}F$	9	10
$_{20}^{40}Ca$	20	20
$_{48}^{112}Cd$	48	64
$_{50}^{117}Sn$	50	67
$_{54}^{131}Xe$	54	77

2. The atom symbol has, as leading subscript, the atomic
    number which is also equal to the number of protons and
    of electrons. The leading superscript is the mass number;
    the number of neutrons can be deduced by subtracting the
    atomic number from the mass number.

Atom symbol	Mass number	Atomic number	Number of protons	Number of electrons	Number of neutrons
$_{4}^{9}Be$	9	4	4	4	5
$_{7}^{15}N$	15	7	7	7	8
$_{8}^{18}O$	18	8	8	8	10
$_{6}^{12}C$	12	6	6	6	6
$_{11}^{23}Na$	23	11	11	11	12

3. By logic similar to that used in problem 2, we obtain the following results:

Atom symbol	Mass number	Atomic number	Number of protons	Number of electrons	Number of neutrons
$^{24}_{12}Mg$	24	12	12	12	12
$^{106}_{47}Ag$	106	47	47	47	59
$^{137}_{56}Ba$	137	56	56	56	81

4. The number of protons in the nucleus is equal to the atomic number. By consulting the periodic table, which lists the atomic number along with the symbol for each element, we deduce that the elements are respectively:
Boron (B), Fluorine (F), Germanium (Ge), Xenon (Xe), and Uranium (U).

5. The element is identified in each case from the Periodic Table. For example, element 19 is potassium, K. The mass number is listed as a leading superscript, and the atomic number as a leading subscript:

a) $^{40}_{19}K$ b) $^{30}_{14}Si$ c) $^{40}_{18}Ar$ d) $^{15}_{7}N$

6. First we convert all distances to cm and masses to grams.

Approximate radius of proton $= 10^{-15}$ m x $\dfrac{1\ cm}{10^{-2}m} = 10^{-13}$ cm.

Approximate radius of the hydrogen atom
$$= 140\ pm\ x\ \dfrac{1\ m}{10^{12}pm}\ x\ \dfrac{1\ cm}{10^{-2}m}$$

$$= 1.40\ x\ 10^{-8}\ cm$$

Approximate mass of the proton
$$= 1.67\ x\ 10^{-27}\ kg\ x\ \dfrac{1000\ g}{1\ kg}$$

$$= 1.67\ x\ 10^{-24}\ g$$

Approximate mass of the hydrogen atom
$$= 1.67\ x\ 10^{-27}\ kg\ x\ \dfrac{1000\ g}{1\ kg}$$

$$= 1.67\ x\ 10^{-24}\ g.$$

a) Approximate volume of proton $= \dfrac{4\pi r^3}{3}$

$$= (4/3) \times 3.14 \times (10^{-13} \text{ cm})^3$$
$$= 4.2 \times 10^{-39} \text{ cm}^3$$

Approximate density of proton $= \dfrac{\text{mass}}{\text{volume}}$

$$= \dfrac{1.7 \times 10^{-24} \text{ g}}{4.2 \times 10^{-39} \text{ cm}^3}$$
$$= 4.0 \times 10^{14} \text{ g cm}^{-3}$$

b) Approximate volume of the hydrogen atom

$$= (4/3) \times 3.14 \times (1.4 \times 10^{-8} \text{ cm})^3$$
$$= 1.1 \times 10^{-23} \text{ cm}^3$$

Approximate density of hydrogen atom $= \dfrac{\text{mass}}{\text{volume}}$

$$= \dfrac{1.7 \times 10^{-24} \text{ g}}{1.1 \times 10^{-23} \text{ cm}^3}$$
$$= 0.15 \text{ g cm}^{-3}$$

c) The density of water is approximately 1.0 g cm^{-3}. Thus the proton is approximately 4×10^{14} times as dense as water while the hydrogen atom is only about one seventh the density of water, emphasizing in dramatic manner the extreme minuteness of the nucleus.

7. The formula for water is H_2O. Each hydrogen could be one of the two isotopes ^1H and ^2H, and the oxygen could be any of the three ^{16}O, ^{17}O, and ^{18}O. The possibilities are
$^1H^1H^{16}O$ and corresponding ones for ^{17}O and ^{18}O
$^2H^1H^{16}O$ and corresponding ones for ^{17}O and ^{18}O
$^2H^2H^{16}O$ and corresponding ones for ^{17}O and ^{18}O
Thus there are a total of nine isotopically-different molecules. (Note that $^2H^1HO$ is the same as $^1H^2HO$ since it does not matter the order in which we list the components.)

8. By definition, molecular mass = sum of atomic masses
For this example, then, Mass of BrCl = Mass of Br + Mass of Cl; thus Mass of Br = Mass of BrCl - Mass of Cl
There are six possibilities for the mass of the Br atom, corresponding to combining the BrCl masses (114,116,118) with the Cl masses (35,37):

16

(1)	(114-35)u	=	79u
(2)	(114-37)u	=	77u
(3)	(116-35)u	=	81u
(4)	(116-37)u	=	79u
(5)	(118-35)u	=	83u
(6)	(118-37)u	=	81u

In this list there are only four discrete values for the isotopic masses of Br, i.e. 77u, 79u, 81u and 83u. However we must exclude 77 and 83 since each appears only once; if they were actual isotopes of bromine, they would each appear twice (as do 79 and 81) corresponding to combinations of Br with each isotope of chlorine. Thus we conclude that bromine consists of the isotopes

$$^{79}_{35}Br \qquad ^{81}_{35}Br$$

The possible isotopic forms of BrCl correspond to all possible combinations of a Br isotope mass with one for Cl:

$$^{79}Br^{35}Cl, \quad ^{79}Br^{37}Cl, \quad ^{81}Br^{35}Cl, \quad ^{81}Br^{37}Cl$$

9. To determine the average atomic mass, we create the following product for each isotope and sum them:
   fractional abundance x isotopic mass
   i.e. Average mass = Sum over isotopes of (fractional abundance x isotope mass)
   Fractional abundances are percent abundances divided by 100. Thus for boron

   Average mass = 0.1977 x 10.01294u + 0.8023 x 11.00931u
              = 10.81u

10. (a) The leading subscript, 12, gives the atomic number whereas the leading superscript, 23, gives the mass number.
    (b) Convert each % abundance to a fraction and evaluate the weighted average. Thus the average atomic mass of magnesium is given by
    0.7860 x 23.993 + 0.1011 x 24.994 + 0.1129 x 25.991
    = 24.320 u.

11. See textbook for definitions.
    Regarding the copper isotope problem, the unknowns are the fractional abundances, called X and Y for convenience, of the two isotopes of copper. By definition we know
          X + Y = 1
    From the definition of (average) atomic mass, we know
    Average mass of Cu = Sum of the products of Fractional
                        Abundance x Isotopic Mass
    Thus 63.54 = 62.9298X + 64.9278Y
    Substituting Y = 1 - X, we have
    63.54 = 62.9298X + 64.9278(1-X)
    Solving for X, we obtain
          X = 0.695
      and Y = 1-X = 0.305
    Thus the percentage abundances are 69.5% and 30.5%

17

respectively.

12. The isotopes of Ga will have the symbols
$^{69}_{31}$Ga and $^{71}_{31}$Ga since mass number gives the isotopic
mass to the closest whole number.

$^{69}_{31}$Ga contains 31 protons and 69-31 = 38 neutrons

$^{71}_{31}$Ga contains 31 protons and 71-31 = 40 neutrons.

Average atomic mass = weighted isotopic average
mass. Let x = fraction of $^{69}_{31}$Ga present; thus 1-x is
the fraction of $^{71}_{31}$Ga present since the fractions must
add up to unity. Thus
$$68.926x + 70.926 (1-x) = 69.72.$$
Solving for x we obtain x = 0.603; and 1-x = 0.397.
The natural abundances of the Gallium isotopes
are one hundred times the fractional abundances; i.e.
60.3% for $^{69}_{31}$Ga   39.7% for $^{71}_{31}$Ga

13. Let the fraction of ^{235}U in naturally occurring Uranium
be x. Thus the fraction of ^{238}U in naturally occurring
Uranium is 1-x, since the fractions must add up to one.
The average molar mass of naturally occurring Uranium is
given by the weighted average of its isotopic masses and so
$$234.044x + 238.051(1-x) = 238.03$$
Thus x = 0.007.
The % abundance of ^{235}U is, therefore, 0.007 x 100%,
i.e. 0.7%.

14. The charge on both the proton and electron is 1.6022 x
10^{-19} coulombs per entity. The total charge per mole of
protons or electrons will be this value times Avogadro's
constant:

$$1.6022 \times 10^{-19} \frac{\text{Coulomb}}{\text{entity}} \times \frac{6.022 \times 10^{23} \text{entities}}{1 \text{ mole}}$$

$$= 9.648 \times 10^4 \text{ Coulombs/mole}$$

15. Since the atomic mass of Hg is 200.6u, one mole of it has
a mass of 200.6 g. We also know that the number of atoms
in one mole is Avogadro's constant:
1 mole Hg = 6.022 x 10^{23} atoms Hg
We can convert the mass Hg to moles Hg and then the latter

to atoms Hg by using conversion factors based upon the molar mass and upon the equation above:

$$1 \text{ g Hg} \times \frac{1 \text{ mole Hg}}{200.6 \text{g Hg}} \times \frac{6.022 \times 10^{23} \text{ atoms Hg}}{1 \text{ mole Hg}} = 3.00 \times 10^{21} \text{ atoms Hg}$$

16. As in Q.15, we can deduce molecules of O_2 from the molar mass of O_2, i.e. 32.00 g, and Avogadro's constant:

$$2.00 \text{ g } O_2 \times \frac{1 \text{ mole } O_2}{32.00 \text{g } O_2} \times \frac{6.022 \times 10^{23} \text{ molecules } O_2}{1 \text{ mole } O_2}$$

$$= 3.76 \times 10^{22} \text{ molecules } O_2$$

To deduce the moles of O atoms, we note that each mole of O_2 produces two moles of O atoms:

$$2.00 \text{ g } O_2 \times \frac{1 \text{ mole } O_2}{32.00 \text{g } O_2} \times \frac{2 \text{ moles O}}{1 \text{ mole } O_2} = 0.125 \text{ moles O}$$

17. a) The entities in 1 mole of any substance is 6.022×10^{23}; thus

$$1 \text{ mole cells} = 6.022 \times 10^{23} \text{ cells}$$

$$4 \times 10^9 \text{ persons} \times \frac{6 \times 10^{13} \text{cells}}{1 \text{ person}} \times \frac{1 \text{ mole cells}}{6.022 \times 10^{23} \text{ cells}} = 0.4 \text{ moles cells}$$

b) $$65,000 \text{g person}^{-1} \times \frac{80 \text{g } H_2O}{100 \text{g person}^{-1}} \times \frac{1 \text{ mole } H_2O}{18.02 \text{g } H_2O}$$

$$\times \frac{6.022 \times 10^{23} \text{ molecules } H_2O}{1 \text{ mole } H_2O} = 1.7 \times 10^{27} \text{ molecules } H_2O$$

18. We can deduce the mass of CO by multiplying the fatal concentration, in g L^{-1}, by the garage's volume converted to L:

$$150 \text{ m}^3 \times (\frac{10 \text{ dm}}{1 \text{ m}})^3 = 1.50 \times 10^5 \text{ dm}^3, \text{ i.e. } 1.50 \times 10^5 \text{ L since}$$

$$1L = 1 \text{ dm}^3.$$

$$2.38 \times 10^{-4} \frac{g}{L} \times 1.50 \times 10^5 \text{ L} = 35.7 \text{ g CO}$$

We now transform mass CO to moles CO, and the latter to molecules of CO using Avogadro's constant:

$$35.7 \text{ g CO} \times \frac{1 \text{ mole CO}}{28.01 \text{g CO}} \times \frac{6.022 \times 10^{23} \text{ molecules CO}}{1 \text{ mole CO}}$$
$$= 7.68 \times 10^{23} \text{ molecules CO}$$

19. The molar mass of salt, NaCl, = 22.99 + 35.45 = 58.44 g mol^{-1}

The molar mass of sugar, $C_{12}H_{22}O_{11}$ = 12 x 12.01 + 22 x 1.01 + 11 x 16.00 = 342.34 g mol^{-1}

In 1 kg of each there will be $\dfrac{1000 \text{ g}}{58.5 \text{ g mol}^{-1}}$ = 17.1 mol of NaCl

and $\dfrac{1000 \text{ g}}{342.34 \text{ g mol}^{-1}}$ = 2.9 mol of sugar

Clearly salt will be the cheaper commodity per mole.

20. To calculate molar masses of molecules, we add the molar masses of the atoms of which they are composed:

H_2O: 2(1.01) + 16.00   = 18.02 g mol^{-1}
H_2O_2:   2(1.01) + 2(16.00) = 34.04 g mol^{-1}
NaCl: 22.99 + 35.45   = 58.44 g mol^{-1}
$MgBr_2$:   24.31 + 2(79.91) = 184.13 g mol^{-1}
CO: 12.01 + 16.00   = 28.01 g mol^{-1}
CO_2:   12.01 + 2(16.00) = 44.01 g mol^{-1}
CH_4:   12.01 + 4(1.01)   = 16.05 g mol^{-1}
C_2H_6:   2(12.01) + 6(1.01) = 30.08 g mol^{-1}
NH_3:   14.01 + 3(1.01)   = 17.04 g mol^{-1}
HCl: 1.01 + 35.45   = 36.46 g mol^{-1}

21. a) To convert mass to moles, we multiply by the conversion factor which we know from atomic masses to be valid for 1 mole, i.e. 1 mole SO_2 = 64.06 g SO_2

Thus 0.0280g SO_2 x $\dfrac{1 \text{ mole } SO_2}{64.06 \text{g } SO_2}$ = 4.37 x 10^{-4} moles SO_2

b) To convert moles SO_2 to mass SO_2, we use the inverse of the conversion factor used in part a:

3 moles SO_2 x $\dfrac{64.06 \text{g } SO_2}{1 \text{ mole } SO_2}$ = 192.2 g SO_2

22. a) To convert mass C to moles C, we use a conversion factor.
Since   1 atom C = 12.011 u C
thus   1 mole C = 12.011 g C

1.00 g C x $\dfrac{1 \text{ mole C}}{12.011 \text{g C}}$ = 0.0833 moles C

b) Similarly to part a,

12.00 g C = 0.9992 mol C

c) Use Avogadro's constant to convert atoms C to moles C:

1.500 x 10^{21} atoms C x $\dfrac{1 \text{ mole C}}{6.022 \text{x} 10^{23} \text{ atoms C}}$ = 2.491x10^{-3} mol C

20

23. The molecular mass for benzene is the sum of its average atomic masses, i.e. $6 \times 12.01u + 6 \times 1.01u = 78.12u$. From the volume and density information, we can deduce the mass in 1 cm³:

$$1 \text{ cm}^3 \times \frac{0.880g}{1 \text{ cm}^3} = 0.880 \text{ g}$$

To deduce molecules of benzene, we convert mass to moles using a conversion factor based on the molar mass of 78.12g, and then moles to molecules via Avogadro's constant:

$$0.880g \times \frac{1 \text{ mole } C_6H_6}{78.12g} \times \frac{6.022 \times 10^{23} \text{ molecules } C_6H_6}{1 \text{ mole } C_6H_6}$$

$$= 6.78 \times 10^{21} \text{ molecules } C_6H_6$$

Finally, we convert molecules C_6H_6 to atoms by noting that each molecule contains 12 atoms:

$$6.78 \times 10^{21} \text{ molecules } C_6H_6 \times \frac{12 \text{ atoms}}{1 \text{ molecule } C_6H_6} = 8.14 \times 10^{22} \text{ atoms}$$

24. In each case,

$$\text{mass \% of an element X} = \frac{\text{mass of X in 1 mole of compound}}{\text{molar mass of compound}} \times 100\%$$

Thus for the hydrogen in H_2O,

$$\text{mass \% H} = \frac{\text{mass of 2 moles H}}{\text{mass of 1 mole } H_2O} \times 100\% = \frac{2 \times 1.01g}{18.02g} \times 100\% = 11.2\% \text{H}$$

$$\text{mass \% O} = \frac{1 \times 16.00g}{18.02g} \times 100\% = 88.8\% \text{ O}$$

Similarly,

NaCl: 58.45 g NaCl contains 22.99 g Na and 35.45 g Cl.

Thus, Na $= \dfrac{22.99g}{58.44g} \times 100\% = 39.34\%$: Cl $= \dfrac{35.45g}{58.44g} \times 100\% = 60.66\%$

C_2H_6: 30.08g C_2H_6 contains 24.02 g C and 6.06 g H

Thus, C $= \dfrac{24.02g}{30.08g} \times 100\% = 79.85\%$: H $= \dfrac{6.06g}{30.08g} \times 100\% = 20.15\%$

$MgBr_2$: 184.13 g $MgBr_2$ contains 24.31 g Mg and 159.82 g Br.

Thus, Mg $= \dfrac{24.31g}{184.13g} \times 100\% = 13.20\%$: Br $= \dfrac{159.82g}{184.13g} \times 100\% = 86.80\%$

CO_2: 44.01 g CO_2 contains 12.01 g C and 32.00 g O

Thus, C $= \dfrac{12.01g}{44.01g} \times 100\% = 27.29\%$: O $= \dfrac{32.00g}{44.01g} \times 100\% = 72.71\%$

25. By the same techniques as for problem 24, we have:

NH_3: 17.04 g NH_3 contains 14.01 g N and 3.03 g H

Thus, $N = \dfrac{14.01g}{17.04g} \times 100\% = 82.22\%$: $H = \dfrac{3.03g}{17.04g} \times 100\% = 17.8\%$.

Cl_2: contains 100% chlorine atoms Cl.

NaOH: 40.00 g NaOH contains 22.99 Na, 16.00g O and 1.01g H.

Thus, $Na = \dfrac{22.99g}{40.00g} \times 100\% = 57.48\%$: $O = \dfrac{16.00g}{40.00g} \times 100\% = 40.00\%$,

and $H = \dfrac{1.01g}{40.00g} \times 100\% = 2.52\%$.

C_2H_6O: 46.08 C_2H_6O contains 24.02 g C, 6.06 g H and 16.00 g O.

Thus, $C = \dfrac{24.02g}{46.08g} \times 100\% = 52.13\%$: $H = \dfrac{6.06g}{46.08g} \times 100\% = 13.1\%$ and

$O = \dfrac{16.00g}{46.08g} \times 100\% = 34.72\%$.

$C_6H_5NO_2$: Molar mass $= 6 \times 12.01 + 5 \times 1.01 + 14.01 + 2 \times 16.00$

$$= 123.12$$

Thus 123.1g $C_6H_5NO_2$ contains 72.06 g C, 5.05 g H, 14.01 g N

and 32.00 g O.

Thus, $C = \dfrac{72.06g}{123.12g} \times 100\% = 58.53\%$: $H = \dfrac{5.05g}{123.12g} \times 100\% = 4.10\%$

$N = \dfrac{14.01g}{123.12g} \times 100\% = 11.38\%$: $O = \dfrac{32.00g}{123.12g} \times 100\% = 25.99\%$.

26. From the formula, we know
    1 molecule HNO_3 contains 3 atoms O
    i.e. 1 mole HNO_3 contains 3 moles O atoms.
    Now the mass of 1 mole of HNO_3 is 63.02g, and that of three
    moles of O is 48.00g. Thus we have the equivalence
    63.02 g HNO_3 = 48.00 g O
    We create a conversion factor based on this to transform
    mass HNO_3 to mass O:

    3.40 g HNO_3 $\times$ $\dfrac{48.00 \text{ g O}}{63.02g \text{ } HNO_3}$ = 2.59 g O

27. The molar mass of ammonium sulphate $(NH_4)_2SO_4$ is given by
    $2(14.01) + 8(1.01) + 32.06 + 4(16.00) = 132.16g$
    which contains $2(14.01) = 28.02g$ N
    The percentage by mass of nitrogen in the compound is thus

    $\dfrac{28.02g \text{ N}}{132.16g \text{ } (NH_4)_2SO_4}$ $\times$ 100% = 21.20% nitrogen by mass

    The mass of ammonium sulphate required to supply 100 g

    of nitrogen may be obtained by utilizing the unit conversion factor

$$\left(\frac{100g\ (NH_4)_2SO_4}{21.20g\ N} \right)$$

$$100g\ N \left(\frac{100g\ (NH_4)_2SO_4}{21.20g\ N} \right) = 472\ g\ (NH_4)_2SO_4$$

28. $\%S$ in $Sb_2S_3 = \dfrac{\text{Mass S in 1 mole of } Sb_2S_3}{\text{Molar mass of } Sb_2S_3} \times 100\%$

$$= \frac{3 \times 32.06g \times 100\%}{339.68\ g} = 28.31\%$$

To deduce the mass of sulfur in 28.4 g of the compound, we can use a conversion factor based on the result above; i.e.

$$100\ g\ Sb_2S_3 \cong 28.31\ g\ S$$

Thus

$$28.4\ g\ Sb_2S_3 \times \frac{28.31g\ S}{100g\ Sb_2S_3} = 8.04\ g\ S$$

To deduce the mass of compound from a given mass S, we use the inverse of this conversion factor:

$$64.4\ g\ S \times \frac{100g\ Sb_2S_3}{28.31\ g\ S} = 227\ g\ Sb_2S_3$$

29. To deduce an empirical formula from percent mass in formation, we can take a sample of 100 g and deduce the mass and then the moles of each element. The atom ratio is equal to the mole ratio:

	C	Br
Percentage	7.00%	93.00%
Mass in 100g in compound	7.00 g	93.00 g
Moles of atoms	$7.00g\ C\ (\frac{1\ mol\ C}{12.01g\ C})$	$93.00g\ Br\ (\frac{1\ mol\ Br}{79.91g\ Br})$
	= 0.583 mol	= 1.164 mol
Mole ratio = Atomic ratio	$\frac{0.583}{0.583}$	$\frac{1.164}{0.583}$
	= 1.00	= 2.00

The empirical formula will be CBr_2 with an empirical formula mass of 171.83 u.

30. Since we are given specific information regarding masses of elements in a sample, we can convert them directly to moles:

	N	O
Mass	3.04 g	6.95 g

Moles of atoms   3.04g N $(\frac{1 \text{ mol N}}{14.01 \text{g N}})$ 6.95g O $(\frac{1 \text{ mol}}{16.00 \text{g O}})$

$\qquad\qquad\qquad$ = 0.217 mol $\qquad\qquad$ = 0.434 mol

Mole ratio = $\qquad\qquad \frac{0.217}{0.217} \qquad\qquad\qquad \frac{0.434}{0.217}$
Atomic ratio

$\qquad\qquad\qquad\qquad$ 1.00 $\qquad\qquad\qquad\qquad$ 2.00

The empirical formula is NO_2 with empirical formula mass
14.01 + 2(16.00) = 46.01u. This is approximately one half
of the determined molecular mass. Thus the molecular
formula is $(NO_2)_2$, i.e. N_2O_4.

31. We proceed as in problems 29 and 30:

	C	O	F
Percentage	21.7%	9.6%	68.7%
Mass	21.7g	9.6g	68.7g

Moles of   21.7g C $(\frac{1 \text{ mol C}}{12.01 \text{gC}})$ 9.6g O $(\frac{1 \text{ mol O}}{16.00 \text{gO}})$ 68.7g F $(\frac{1 \text{ mol F}}{19.00 \text{gF}})$
atoms

$\qquad\qquad\qquad$ 1.81 mol $\qquad\qquad$ 0.60 mol $\qquad\qquad$ 3.62 mol

Mole ratio $\qquad \frac{1.81}{0.60} \qquad\qquad\qquad \frac{0.60}{0.60} \qquad\qquad\qquad \frac{3.62}{0.60}$
= atomic ratio

$\qquad\qquad\qquad\qquad$ 3.0 $\qquad\qquad\qquad\qquad$ 1.0 $\qquad\qquad\qquad\qquad$ 6.0

The empirical formula of the compound is C_3OF_6, and its
empirical formula mass is 166.03 u.

32. The mass of carbon may be determined, using the appropriate
unit conversion factors, from the mass of CO_2 since one
mole of carbon dioxide contains one mole of carbon. Thus,

0.660g CO_2 x $\frac{1 \text{ mol } CO_2}{44.01 \text{g } CO_2}$ x $\frac{1 \text{ mol C}}{1 \text{ mol } CO_2}$ x $\frac{12.01 \text{g C}}{1 \text{ mol C}}$

= 0.180g C

Thus by difference the mass of hydrogen in the sample of
hydrocarbon must be (0.210 − 0.180) = 0.030 g H.

	C	H
Mass	0.180 g	0.030 g

Moles of atoms   0.180g C $(\frac{1 \text{ mol C}}{12.01 \text{g C}})$ 0.0300g H $(\frac{1 \text{ mol H}}{1.01 \text{g H}})$

$\qquad\qquad\qquad$ 0.0150 mol $\qquad\qquad$ 0.030 mol

Mole ratio = $\qquad \frac{0.0150}{0.0150} \qquad\qquad\qquad \frac{0.030}{0.0150}$
Atomic ratio
$\qquad\qquad\qquad$ 1.00 $\qquad\qquad\qquad$ 2.0

The empirical formula of the hydrocarbon is, therefore, CH_2.

33. For a 100g sample, we deduce the mass and then the moles of
each element. By dividing by the smallest number of moles,
we obtain the ratio of atoms.

	C	H	N	O
Percentage	49.5%	5.20%	28.8%	16.5%
Mass in 100 g of compound	49.5g	5.20g	28.8g	16.5g
Moles of element	4.12	5.15	2.06	1.03
Ratio of atoms	4.00	5.00	2.00	1.00

Thus the empirical formula is $C_4H_5N_2O$.

34. By using appropriate unit conversion factors we obtain the masses of carbon, hydrogen and nitrogen from the masses of CO_2, H_2O and NO_2 respectively. Remember that while one mole of carbon dioxide and nitrogen dioxide each contain one mole of carbon and one mole of nitrogen respectively, one mole of water contains two moles of hydrogen atoms.

Mass of Carbon

$$264g\ CO_2 \times \frac{1\ mol\ CO_2}{44.01g\ CO_2} \times \frac{1\ mol\ C}{1\ mol\ CO_2} \times \frac{12.01g\ C}{1\ mol\ C} = 72.0\ g\ C$$

Mass of Hydrogen

$$63.0g\ H_2O \times \frac{1\ mol\ H_2O}{18.02g\ H_2O} \times \frac{2\ mol\ H}{1\ mol\ H_2O} \times \frac{1.01g\ H}{1\ mol\ H} = 7.06g\ H$$

Mass of Nitrogen

$$46.0g\ NO_2 \times \frac{1\ mol\ NO_2}{46.01g\ NO_2} \times \frac{1\ mol\ N}{1\ mol\ NO_2} \times \frac{14.01g\ N}{1\ mol\ N} = 14.0g\ N$$

	C	H	N
Masses	72.0 g	7.06 g	14.0 g
Moles of atoms	72.0g C ($\frac{1\ mol\ C}{12.01g\ C}$)	7.06g H ($\frac{1\ mol\ H}{1.01g\ H}$)	14.0g N ($\frac{1\ mol\ N}{14.01gN}$)
= atoms in 1 molecule	= 6.00 mol	6.99 mol	1.00 mol

Thus the empirical formula is C_6H_7N.

35. From the mass of CO_2, we can compute the moles and mass of C; similarly from the mass of H_2O, we can obtain the moles and mass of H. The mass of O can be obtained then by difference, and the moles O determined. The ratio of moles of atoms will then yield the formula.

$$5.19g\ CO_2 \times \frac{1\ mole\ CO_2}{44.01g\ CO_2} \times \frac{1\ mole\ C}{1\ mole\ CO_2} = 0.118\ moles\ C \times \frac{12.01g\ C}{1\ mole\ C}$$

$$= 1.42g\ C$$

$$2.83g\ H_2O \times \frac{1\ mole\ H_2O}{18.02g\ H_2O} \times \frac{2\ moles\ H}{1\ mole\ H_2O} = 0.314\ moles\ H \times \frac{1.01g\ H}{1\ mole\ H}$$

$$= 0.32g\ H$$

Mass O = Mass Sample - Mass C - Mass H

$$= 3.62 - 1.42 - 0.32$$

$$= 1.88g \times \frac{1\ mole\ O}{16.00g\ O} = 0.118\ moles\ O$$

The moles of C, H, O are then 0.118, 0.314, and 0.118 which when all divided by the smallest yield the ratio 1.00:2.66:1.00. Multiplying by two does not yield all whole numbers, but multiplying each by three yields the ratio 3.00:7.98:3.00. Thus the empirical formula is $C_3H_8O_3$.

36. Methodology is the same as for Q. 35.

$$4.40g\ CO_2 \times \frac{1\ mole\ CO_2}{44.01g\ CO_2} \times \frac{1\ mole\ C}{1\ mole\ CO_2} = 0.100\ moles\ C \times \frac{12.01g\ C}{1\ mole\ C}$$

$$= 1.20g\ C$$

$$2.70g\ H_2O \times \frac{1\ mole\ H_2O}{18.02g\ H_2O} \times \frac{2\ moles\ H}{1\ mole\ H_2O} = 0.300\ moles\ H \times \frac{1.01g\ H}{1\ mole\ H}$$

$$= 0.30g\ H$$

Mass O = $3.10 - 1.20 - 0.30 = 1.60g\ O \times \frac{1\ mole\ O}{16.00g\ O} = 0.100\ moles\ O$

Dividing by smallest number of moles, we obtain
C:H:O atom ratio = 1.00:3.00:1.00
Thus the empirical formula is CH_3O, with an empirical formula mass of 31.04u. Since this is half the molar mass given in the information, the molecular formula is $(CH_3O)_2$, i.e. $C_2H_6O_2$.

37. For methodology, see Q. 31 or 33.

	C	H	N
Percentage	74.0%	8.7%	17.3%
Mass	74.0g	8.7g	17.3g
Moles of atoms:	74.0g C $(\frac{1\ mol\ C}{12.01gC})$	8.7g H $(\frac{1\ mol\ H}{1.01g\ H})$	17.3g N $(\frac{1\ mol\ N}{14.01gN})$
	= 6.16 mol	= 8.6 mol	= 1.23 mol
Mole ratio = Atomic ratio	$\frac{6.16}{1.23}$	$\frac{8.6}{1.23}$	$\frac{1.23}{1.23}$
	5.01	7.0	1.00

The empirical formula of nicotine therefore is C_5H_7N with an empirical formula mass of $5(12.01) + 7(1.01) + 14.01 = 81.13$ u. The molar mass of nicotine is 162 g, thus the molecular mass is 162 u, which is twice the empirical formula mass. The molecular formula of nicotine will therefore be $(C_5H_7N)_2$, i.e. $C_{10}H_{14}N_2$.

38.   See Q. 29 for methodology.

	C	H
Percentages	94.33%	5.67%
Mass in 100g sample	94.33g	5.67g
Moles	$94.33g\ C\ (\frac{1\ mol\ C}{12.01g\ C})$	$5.67g\ H\ (\frac{1\ mol\ H}{1.01g\ H})$
	= 7.854 mol	= 5.61 mol

Mole ratio = atomic ratio	$\frac{7.854}{5.61}$	$\frac{5.61}{5.61}$
	1.40	1.00

5 is lowest factor which converts 1.40 to an integer	5(1.40) 7.00	5(1.00) 5.00

The empirical formula of anthracene is C_7H_5.
The empirical formula mass is 7(12.01) + 5(1.01) = 89.12 u.

39.   The mass of copper in both oxides is the same and equals
      that of 2.542 g in the final product. Thus the mass of
      oxygen in each oxide will be
      1.   Red copper oxide: 2.862 - 2.542 = 0.320 g oxygen.
      2.   Black copper oxide: 3.182 - 2.542 = 0.640 g oxygen.
      We can calculate the empirical formula of the red copper
      oxide in the usual way

	Cu	O
Mass	2.542g	0.320g
Moles	$2.542g\ Cu\ (\frac{1\ mol\ Cu}{63.54g\ Cu})$	$0.320g\ O\ (\frac{1\ mol\ O}{16.00g\ O})$
	= 0.04000 mol	= 0.0200 mol

Mole ratio = atomic ratio	$\frac{0.04000}{0.0200}$	$\frac{0.0200}{0.0200}$
	2.00	1.00

The empirical formula for red copper oxide is thus Cu_2O.
We can repeat the same procedure for black copper oxide.

	Cu	O
Mass	2.542g	0.640g
Moles	$2.542g\ Cu\ (\frac{1\ mol\ Cu}{63.54g\ Cu})$	$0.640g\ O\ (\frac{1\ mol\ O}{16.00g\ O})$
	= 0.04000 mol	= 0.0400 mol

Mole ratio = atomic ratio	$\frac{0.04000}{0.0400}$	$\frac{0.0400}{0.0400}$
	= 1.00	= 1.00

The empirical formula of black copper oxide is CuO.

40. We note that both compounds formed by reaction with chlorine, HCl and CCl$_4$, each contain one mole of hydrogen and carbon atoms per mole. Using the appropriate unit conversion factors, therefore, we can deduce the masses of H and C in the original compound:

$$21.9 \text{ g HCl} \times \frac{1 \text{ mol HCl}}{36.46 \text{ g HCl}} \times \frac{1 \text{ mol H}}{1 \text{ mol HCl}} \times \frac{1.01 \text{ g H}}{1 \text{ mol H}} = 0.607 \text{ g H.}$$

$$30.8 \text{ g CCl}_4 \times \frac{1 \text{ mol CCl}_4}{153.81 \text{ g CCl}_4} \times \frac{1 \text{ mol C}}{1 \text{ mol CCl}_4} \times \frac{12.01 \text{ g C}}{1 \text{ mol C}} = 2.40 \text{ g C}$$

Total mass of compound = 6.20 g; thus by difference the mass of sulphur must be 6.20 − (0.607 + 2.40) = 3.19 g S. We now convert the masses of atoms to moles in order to deduce the mole ratio and hence the formula:

	C	H	S
Mass	2.41g	0.607g	3.18g
Moles of atoms	2.41g C $\left(\frac{1 \text{ mol C}}{12.01 \text{g C}}\right)$	0.607g H $\left(\frac{1 \text{ mol H}}{1.01 \text{g H}}\right)$	3.18g S $\left(\frac{1 \text{ mol S}}{32.06 \text{g S}}\right)$
	= 0.201	= 0.601	= 0.0992
Mole ratio = atomic ratio	$\frac{0.201}{0.0992}$	$\frac{0.600}{0.0992}$	$\frac{0.0992}{0.0992}$
	2.03	6.05	1.00

The empirical formula is, therefore, C$_2$H$_6$S.

41. For two aspirin samples, the relative mass of aspirin must equal the relative mass of CO$_2$ produced upon its combustion; thus

$$\frac{\text{Mass aspirin in antacid}}{\text{Mass aspirin in pure sample}} = \frac{\text{Mass CO}_2 \text{ from antacid}}{\text{Mass CO}_2 \text{ from pure sample}}$$

i.e. $$\frac{\text{Mass aspirin in antacid}}{1.00 \text{ g}} = \frac{1.80 \text{ g CO}_2}{1.96 \text{ g CO}_2}$$

Mass aspirin in antacid = 0.918 g

Thus mass % of aspirin in antacid = $\frac{0.918 \text{ g}}{2.00 \text{ g}} \times 100\% = 45.9\%$

42. The methodology here is similar to that in Q. 29. The compound contains sulphur and fluorine only and so the percentage (by mass) of sulphur must be (100.0 − 70.3) = 29.7%.

	S	F
Percentage	29.7%	70.3%
Mass in 100g of compound	29.7g	70.3g
Moles of Atoms	29.7g S $\left(\frac{1 \text{ mol S}}{32.06 \text{g S}}\right)$	70.3g F $\left(\frac{1 \text{ mol F}}{19.00 \text{g F}}\right)$

$$= 0.926 \text{ mol} \qquad\qquad = 3.70 \text{ mol}$$

Mole ratios = atomic ratios	$\dfrac{0.926}{0.926}$	$\dfrac{3.70}{0.926}$
	1.00	4.00

Thus the empirical formula for the compound is SF_4.

43. By difference, the mass of H_2O contained in 3.25 g of the hydrated compound is 3.25 g − 2.80 g = 0.45 g. To deduce the formula, convert this mass and that of pure Li_2SO_4 to moles and calculate the mole ratio:

$$0.45 \text{ g } H_2O \times \frac{1 \text{ mole } H_2O}{18.02 \text{g } H_2O} = 0.025 \text{ moles } H_2O$$

$$2.80 \text{ g } Li_2SO_4 \times \frac{1 \text{ mole } Li_2SO_4}{109.94 \text{g } Li_2SO_4} = 0.0255 \text{ moles } Li_2SO_4$$

Since the mole ratio is 1:1, thus the value of x = 1.

44. The molecular mass of the compound $KClO_x$ is 39.10 + 35.45 + 16.00x, i.e. (74.55 + 16.00x)u. Since this compound is known to contain 28.9% by mass of chlorine we can write an equation which expresses this result:

$$\frac{35.45 \text{ u}}{(74.55 + 16.00x)u} \times 100\% = 28.9\%$$

Solving the equation for x we have
$$3545 = 38.9 (74.55 + 16.00x)$$
$$= 2154 + 462.4x$$
Thus $462.4x = 1391$
$$x = 3.01$$
Thus the value of x is 3.

45. The "PCB" has the formula $C_{12}H_mCl_{10-m}$ and the formula mass 12(12.01) + 1.01m + 35.45(10−m), i.e. 498.6 − 34.44m. This formula mass contains 35.45(10−m) of Cl, which amounts to 58.9% of the total mass. Thus if we write an equation for the percent Cl,
$$\frac{354.5 - 35.45m}{498.6 - 34.44m} \times 100\% = 58.9\%$$

Solving for m, we obtain m = 4.01.
Thus the value of m is 4, and the empircal formula is $C_{12}H_4Cl_6$.

46. a) To determine whether or not the equation is balanced, check the balancing for each atom.
$$2SO_2 + H_2O + O_2 \rightarrow 2H_2SO_4$$
This equation is not balanced in oxygen, or in hydrogen. Since oxygen appears more often, we balance hydrogen first by placing a 2 in front of H_2O:
$$2SO_2 + 2H_2O + O_2 \rightarrow 2H_2SO_4$$
The equation now is completely balanced.

29

b) The equation
$$CH_3OH + 2O_2 \rightarrow CO_2 + 2H_2O$$
is balanced in all elements except oxygen. Since 4 O atoms appear on the left and five appear on the right, the simplest way to balance here is to reduce the O_2 coefficient to 3/2:
$$CH_3OH + 3/2\ O_2 \rightarrow CO_2 + 2H_2O$$
In terms of integer coefficients, we would obtain
$$2CH_3OH + 3O_2 \rightarrow 2CO_2 + 4H_2O$$

c) The equation
$$H_2O_2 \rightarrow H_2O + O_2$$
is balanced in hydrogen but not in O. As in Q. 49c, it is easiest to change the O_2 coefficient, here to 1/2, to balance O.
$$H_2O_2 \rightarrow H_2O + 1/2\ O_2$$
In terms of integer coefficients,
$$2H_2O_2 \rightarrow 2H_2O + O_2$$

d) The equation already is balanced.

47. a) Choose either element to start (both appear twice) in the initial equation.
$$S + O_2 \rightarrow SO_3$$
Balancing O requires a 3 in front of O_2 and a 2 in front of SO_3 to give 6 O on both sides.
$$S + 3O_2 \rightarrow 2SO_3$$
Finally to balance S, multiply it on left by 2.

b) In the initial equation, $C_2H_2 + O_2 \rightarrow CO + H_2O$ carbon appears twice, oxygen three times and hydrogen twice. Choosing C to start, we multiply CO by 2 to obtain 2 C's on both sides.
$$C_2H_2 + O_2 \rightarrow 2CO + H_2O$$
The H is balanced (2 per side) so we proceed to oxygen, for which there are 2 on the left and 3 on the right side. Multiplying O_2 by 3 and both (2CO) and (H_2O) by 2 gives
$$C_2H_2 + 3O_2 \rightarrow 4CO + 2H_2O$$
Return and rebalance carbon, now 2 on left and 4 on right, by multiplying C_2H_2 by 2:
$$2C_2H_2 + 3O_2 \rightarrow 4CO + 2H_2O$$
Hydrogen is still balanced (4 per side) as is oxygen, and so the entire equation is balanced.

c) In the initial equation
$$Na_2CO_3 + Ca(OH)_2 \rightarrow NaOH + CaCO_3$$
the element Na appears 2 times, C appears 2 times, O appears 4 times, H appears 2 times, and Ca appears 2 times. Choosing Na to start, multiply NaOH by 2 to balance it:
$$Na_2CO_3 + Ca(OH)_2 \rightarrow 2NaOH + CaCO_3$$
Upon checking it turns out that all other elements now are also balanced.

d) All elements appear twice in the initial equation
$$Na_2SO_4 + H_2 \rightarrow Na_2S + 4H_2O$$
Since Na and S are balanced initially, we can try balancing O; since the initial oxygen totals are 4 on left and 1 on right, we multiply H_2O by 4:
$$Na_2SO_4 + H_2 \rightarrow Na_2S + 4H_2O$$
Finally consider H which here has 2 on left and 8 on right; multiplying H_2 by 4 achieves balance.
$$Na_2SO_4 + 4H_2 \longrightarrow Na_2S + 4H_2O$$
Now all elements are balanced.

e) In the initial equation
$$Cu_2S + O_2 \rightarrow Cu_2O + SO_2$$
Cu and S appear twice, oxygen three times. Both Cu and S initially are balanced so we consider oxygen which initially has 2 on left, 3 on right. Multiplying O_2 by 3 and both Cu_2O and SO_2 by 2 gives
$$Cu_2S + 3O_2 \rightarrow 2Cu_2O + 2SO_2$$
Returning to Cu to balance it requires $2Cu_2S$:
$$2Cu_2S + 3O_2 \rightarrow 2Cu_2O + 2SO_2$$
Upon checking, we find that all elements now are balanced.

f) In the initial equation
$$Cu_2O + Cu_2S \rightarrow Cu + SO_2$$
the Cu appears 3 times, whereas S and O_2 appear twice. S already is balanced, so begin with O. Multiplying Cu_2O by 2 balances it:
$$2Cu_2O + Cu_2S \rightarrow Cu + SO_2$$
Since S still is balanced, we concentrate on copper which presently has 6 on left, 1 on right. Multiplying Cu by 6 gives an equation which, upon checking, is found to be balanced throughout:
$$2Cu_2O + Cu_2S \rightarrow 6Cu + SO_2$$

g) In the initial equation
$$Cu + H_2SO_4 \rightarrow CuSO_4 + H_2O + SO_2$$
copper and hydrogen appear twice, sulfur three times and oxygen four times. However Cu and H initially are balanced, so first we balance S by multiplying H_2SO_4 by 2:
$$Cu + 2H_2SO_4 \rightarrow CuSO_4 + H_2O + SO_2$$
This unbalances H, which easily is rectified by multiplying H_2O by 2:
$$Cu + 2H_2SO_4 \rightarrow CuSO_4 + 2H_2O + SO_2$$
The equation is now completely balanced.

h) Each element appears twice in the initial equation
$$B + SiO_2 \rightarrow Si + B_2O_3$$
Starting (arbitrarily) with B, balancing it yields
$$2B + SiO_2 \rightarrow Si + B_2O_3$$
Since Si is balanced, consider next the oxygen for which we have 2 on left, 3 on right and thus multiply SiO_2 by 3 and B_2O_3 by 2:
$$2B + 3SiO_2 \rightarrow Si + 2B_2O_3$$
Rebalancing B requires multiplication of (2B) by 2.

Finally, multiplying Si by 3 balances it:
$$4B + 3SiO_2 \rightarrow 3Si + 2B_2O_3$$

48. a) The "oxygen" here is O_2, since it is the stable form of the element. Thus the initial equation is
$$P_4 + O_2 \rightarrow P_4O_{10}$$
The P is balanced. Multiplying O_2 by 5 balances oxygen.
$$P_4 + 5O_2 \rightarrow P_4O_{10}$$

b) The initial equation is
$$Na + H_2O \rightarrow NaOH + H_2$$
Here Na and O appear twice each, H three times. However both Na and O initially are balanced.
The H can be balanced by multiplying H_2 by $\frac{1}{2}$; to obtain integer coefficients, multiply through by 2 to obtain
$$2Na + 2H_2O \rightarrow 2NaOH + H_2$$

c) Since water is H_2O, the initial equation is
$$NH_4NO_3 \rightarrow N_2O + H_2O$$
Hydrogen appears twice, oxygen and nitrogen three times so we begin with H. Multiplying H_2O by 2 balances it, since above there are 4 H on left and 2 on right:
$$NH_4NO_3 \rightarrow N_2O + 2H_2O$$
All elements now are balanced.

d) The initial equation is
$$Pb(NO_3)_2 \rightarrow PbO + NO_2 + O_2$$
Pb and N appear twice, O four times. Initially there are 2N on left (the subscript 2 applies to all elements within parentheses) and 1N on right, so we multiply NO_2 by 2:
$$Pb(NO_3)_2 \rightarrow PbO + 2NO_2 + O_2$$
There are 6 O on left now but 7 on right. Although we could multiply the left by 7 and the right by 6, this would ruin the balance for Pb and N. Since oxygen appears on its own as O_2 on the right, we can take advantage of this by multiplying everything except it by 2; this gives 12 oxygens on both sides and a completely balanced equation
$$2Pb(NO_3)_2 \rightarrow 2PbO + 4NO_2 + O_2$$

49. a) Each element appears twice in the initial equation
$$Na_2SO_4 + C \rightarrow Na_2S + CO_2$$
All but O are balanced initially; there are 4 O on

32

left and 2 O on right. Multiplying CO_2 by 2 balances O:

$$Na_2SO_4 + C \rightarrow Na_2S + 2CO_2$$

Only C now is unbalanced: 1 C on left, 2 C on right. Thus the balanced equation is

$$Na_2SO_4 + 2C \rightarrow Na_2S + 2CO_2$$

b) In the initial equation

$$Cl_2 + H_2O \rightarrow HCl + HOCl$$

both Cl and H appear three times and O twice. Upon inspection it turns out that not only is O already balanced, but so are Cl and H!

c) In the initial equation

$$PCl_3 + H_2O \rightarrow H_3PO_3 + HCl$$

we start with any element other than H (since it appears 3 times, the others twice). Balancing Cl gives

$$PCl_3 + H_2O \rightarrow H_3PO_3 + 3HCl$$

and then balancing oxygen yields

$$PCl_3 + 3H_2O \rightarrow H_3PO_3 + 3HCl$$

The equation now is completely balanced.

d) N appears 3 times, O four times, and H twice initially:

$$NO_2 + H_2O \rightarrow HNO_3 + NO$$

Balancing H by multiplying HNO_3 by 2 gives

$$NO_2 + H_2O \rightarrow 2HNO_3 + NO$$

We next try balancing N, since it appears the second smallest number of times:

$$3NO_2 + H_2O \rightarrow 2HNO_3 + NO$$

The entire equation now is balanced.

e) Mg, N, and O appear twice and H three times initially:

$$Mg_3N_2 + H_2O \rightarrow Mg(OH)_2 + NH_3$$

Balancing Mg gives

$$Mg_3N_2 + H_2O \rightarrow 3Mg(OH)_2 + NH_3$$

Balancing N gives

$$Mg_3N_2 + H_2O \rightarrow 3Mg(OH)_2 + 2NH_3$$

Balancing O gives

$$Mg_3N_2 + 6H_2O \rightarrow 3Mg(OH)_2 + 2NH_3$$

The entire equation is now balanced.

50. The balanced equation is

$$NH_3 + HCl \rightarrow NH_4Cl$$

To deduce mass of HCl, convert mass NH_3 to moles NH_3, and then to moles HO, and finally to mass HCl:

$$0.20 \text{ g } NH_3 \times \underbrace{\frac{1 \text{ mol } NH_3}{17.04 \text{g } NH_3}}_{\substack{\text{molar mass} \\ \text{converts mass} \\ NH_3 \text{ to moles} \\ NH_3}} \times \underbrace{\frac{1 \text{ mol } HCl}{1 \text{ mol } NH_3}}_{\substack{\text{based on balanced} \\ \text{equation; converts} \\ \text{moles } NH_3 \text{ to} \\ \text{to moles HCl}}} \times \underbrace{\frac{36.46 \text{g } HCl}{1 \text{ mol } HCl}}_{\substack{\text{molar mass HCl;} \\ \text{converts moles} \\ \text{to mass of} \\ HCl}}$$

= 0.43 g HCl

51. The balanced reaction is
   $$HCl(aq) + NaOH(aq) \rightarrow NaCl(aq) + H_2O$$
   To deduce what mass of chemicals react with each other or are produced, we first convert mass HCl to moles of it:
   $$3.00 \text{ g HCl} \times \frac{1 \text{ mole HCl}}{36.46\text{g HCl}} = 0.0823 \text{ moles HCl}$$
   Since according to the balanced equation 1 mole of HCl reacts with 1 mole NaOH to give 1 mole NaCl, we conclude that here 0.0823 moles NaOH will react with the HCl, and that 0.0823 moles NaCl will be produced. To transform these values into masses, we multiply by the molar masses:

   $$0.0823 \text{ moles NaOH} \times \frac{40.00\text{g NaOH}}{1 \text{ mole NaOH}} = 3.29 \text{ g NaOH}$$

   $$0.0823 \text{ moles NaCl} \times \frac{58.44\text{g NaCl}}{1 \text{ mole NaCl}} = 4.81 \text{ g NaCl}$$

52. The balanced equation is
   $$2H_3PO_4 + 3Ca(OH)_2 \rightarrow 6H_2O + Ca_3(PO_4)_2$$
   Using unit factors to transform from mass H_3PO_4 to moles of it, then to moles $Ca(OH)_2$ and finally to its mass, we have:
   $$30 \text{ g } H_3PO_4 \times \frac{1 \text{ mol } H_3PO_4}{98.00\text{g } H_3PO_4} \times \frac{3 \text{ mol } Ca(OH)_2}{2 \text{ mol } H_3PO_4} \times \frac{74.10\text{g } Ca(OH)_2}{1 \text{ mol } Ca(OH)_2}$$
   based on coefficients
   in the balanced equation

   $$= 34 \text{ g } Ca(OH)_2$$
   To compute the mass of the product $Ca_3(PO_4)_2$, we use a similar technique:

   $$30 \text{ g } H_3PO_4 \times \frac{1 \text{ mol } H_3PO_4}{98.00\text{g } H_3PO_4} \times \frac{1 \text{ mol } Ca_3(PO_4)_2}{2 \text{ mol } H_3PO_4} \times \frac{310.18\text{g } Ca_3(PO_4)_2}{1 \text{ mol } Ca_3(PO_4)_2}$$
   from balanced equation

   $$= 47 \text{ g } Ca_3(PO_4)_2$$

53. The unbalanced equation is
   $$P + Cl_2 \rightarrow PCl_3$$
   Balancing yields
   $$2P + 3Cl_2 \rightarrow 2PCl_3$$
   First convert 100.0 g of the product PCl_3 into moles:

   $$100.0 \text{ g } PCl_3 \times \frac{1 \text{ mol } PCl_3}{137.32\text{g } PCl_3} = 0.7282 \text{ mol } PCl_3$$

   Since 2 mol PCl_3 requires 2 mol P (see balanced equation), we require 0.7282 mol P. We can convert moles P to mass P using a unit factor based on the atomic mass of P:

   $$0.7282 \text{ mol P} \times \frac{30.97\text{g P}}{1 \text{ mol P}} = 22.55 \text{ g P}$$

54. Since carbon monoxide's formula is CO, and that of chlorine is Cl_2, the unbalanced reaction is

$$Cl_2 + SiO_2 + C \rightarrow SiCl_4 + CO$$

Balancing yields

$$2Cl_2 + SiO_2 + 2C \rightarrow SiCl_4 + 2CO$$

First convert the 15.0 g of reactant SiO_2 to moles:

$$15.0 \text{ g } SiO_2 \times \frac{1 \text{ mole } SiO_2}{60.09 \text{g } SiO_2} = 0.250 \text{ mol } SiO_2$$

Since 1 mol SiO_2 yields 1 mol $SiCl_4$, the yield of $SiCl_4$ also is 0.250 mol. Finally we convert 0.250 mol $SiCl_4$ to mass, using a factor based on the molar mass of $SiCl_4$:

$$0.250 \text{ mol } SiCl_4 \times \frac{169.89 \text{g } SiCl_4}{1 \text{ mol } SiCl_4} = 42.5 \text{ g } SiCl_4$$

55. The molar mass of BaO is

$$134.34 + 16.00 = 153.34 \text{ g}$$

To compute the formula of the original oxide, we can try first to obtain the masses of Ba and O. All the original compound's Ba is present in BaO; thus we can obtain the mass of Ba by use of the fact that one mole of BaO, i.e. 153.34 g, contains 137.34 g Ba:

$$5.00 \text{ g BaO} \times \frac{137.34 \text{g Ba}}{153.34 \text{g BaO}} = 4.48 \text{g Ba}$$

By difference, the mass of oxygen in the original oxide is $(5.53 - 4.48)$ g = 1.05 g.
Now we can proceed as usual to deduce the formula

	Barium	Oxygen
Mass of element in sample	4.48 g	1.05 g
Moles of element	$4.48\text{g}(\frac{1 \text{ mol}}{137.34\text{g}})$ = 0.0326	$1.05\text{g}(\frac{1 \text{ mol}}{16.00\text{g}})$ = 0.0656
Mole or Atomic ratio	$\frac{0.0326}{0.0326}$ = 1.00	$\frac{0.0656}{0.0326}$ = 2.01

The empirical formula of the unknown oxide of barium is, therefore, BaO_2.

56. First obtain moles SO_2 reacted:

$$0.32\text{g } SO_2 \times \frac{1 \text{ mole } SO_2}{64.06\text{g } SO_2} = 0.0050 \text{ mole } SO_2$$

To deduce the masses of O_2 and H_2O used and of H_2SO_4 produced, we first deduce the number of moles of each from the moles SO_2 and the coefficients in the balanced equation. Finally, the moles of O_2, H_2O and H_2SO_4 are converted to masses:

$$0.0050 \text{ mole } SO_2 \times \frac{1 \text{ mole } O_2}{2 \text{ moles } SO_2} \times \frac{32.00g \ O_2}{1 \text{ mole } O_2} = 0.080 \text{ g } O_2$$

$$0.0050 \text{ mole } SO_2 \times \frac{2 \text{ moles } H_2O}{2 \text{ moles } SO_2} \times \frac{18.02g \ H_2O}{1 \text{ mole } H_2O} = 0.090 \text{ g } H_2O$$

$$0.0050 \text{ mole } SO_2 \times \frac{2 \text{ moles } H_2SO_4}{2 \text{ moles } SO_2} \times \frac{98.08g \ H_2SO_4}{1 \text{ mole } H_2SO_4} = 0.49g \ H_2SO_4.$$

Notice that the mass of H_2SO_4 could have been deduced by adding the masses of all reactants: 0.32+0.08+0.09 = 0.49g.

57. Balancing gives
$$B_2O_3 + 6Mg \rightarrow 3MgO + Mg_3B_2$$
Presumably all the boron ends up as B_4H_{10}; thus
$$2 \text{ moles } Mg_3B_2 = 1 \text{ mole } B_4H_{10}$$
$$\text{Since } 1 \text{ mole } B_2O_3 = 1 \text{ mole } Mg_3B_2$$
we can relate the initial reactant, B_2O_3, to the final product, B_4H_{10}, by
$$2 \text{ moles } B_2O_3 = 1 \text{ mole } B_4H_{10}$$
Converting mass B_2O_3 to moles B_2O_3, then to moles B_4H_{10}, and finally to mass B_4H_{10} is achieved as follows:

$$10.00 \text{ g } B_2O_3 \times \frac{1 \text{ mol } B_2O_3}{69.62g \ B_2O_3} \times \frac{1 \text{ mol } B_4H_{10}}{2 \text{ mol } B_2O_3} \times \frac{53.34g \ B_4H_{10}}{1 \text{ mol } B_4H_{10}}$$

$$= 3.831 \text{ g } B_4H_{10}$$

58. From the information supplied, we can deduce the mass of $CaCO_3$ present initially:
$$1,000 \text{ g limestone} \times \frac{74.2g \ CaCO_3}{100g \text{ limestone}} = 742 \text{ g } CaCO_3$$
Now write the balanced equation for the reaction
$$CaCO_3 \rightarrow CaO + CO_2$$
From the mass of $CaCO_3$ we can compute moles $CaCO_3$, and by the balanced equation we obtain moles CO_2, which can be converted to mass CO_2:

$$742g \ CaCO_3 \times \frac{1 \text{ mole } CaCO_3}{100.09g \ CaCO_3} \times \frac{1 \text{ mole } CO_2}{1 \text{ mole } CaCO_3} \times \frac{44.01g \ CO_2}{1 \text{ mole } CO_2} = 326g \ CO_2$$

59. The balanced equation is
$$2AgNO_3(aq) + CaCl_2(aq) \rightarrow 2AgCl(s) + Ca(NO_3)_2(aq)$$
Since the moles of $AgNO_3$ and $CaCl_2$ available are equal but the reaction requires 2 moles $AgNO_3$ for each 1 mole of $CaCl_2$, clearly $AgNO_3$ is limiting. We deduce the yield of AgCl from the information for the limiting reactant:

$$0.010 \text{ moles } AgNO_3 \times \frac{2 \text{ moles } AgCl}{2 \text{ moles } AgNO_3} \times \frac{143.32g \ AgCl}{1 \text{ mole } AgCl} = 1.4 \text{ g } AgCl$$

60. The equation already is balanced. Since mass information is given for the two reactants, we must deduce which one is limiting by deducing the amount of one product, e.g. Cu, formed assuming each in turn is completely consumed.
If Zn is limiting:

$$2.0g \; Zn \times \frac{1 \; mole \; Zn}{65.37g \; Zn} \times \frac{1 \; mole \; Cu}{1 \; mole \; Zn} \times \frac{63.54g \; Cu}{1 \; mole \; Cu} = 1.9 \; g \; Cu$$

If $CuCl_2$ is limiting:

$$2.0g \; CuCl_2 \times \frac{1 \; mole \; CuCl_2}{134.44g \; CuCl_2} \times \frac{1 \; mole \; Cu}{1 \; mole \; CuCl_2} \times \frac{63.54g \; Cu}{1 \; mole \; Cu} = 0.95 \; g \; Cu$$

Thus $CuCl_2$ is limiting, and only 0.95 g Cu (not 1.9g) is produced.

61. The methodology is the same as for Q. 60, once we obtain a balanced equation:
$$2Sb + 3S \rightarrow Sb_2S_3$$
If Sb is limiting:
$$5.00g \; Sb \times \frac{1 \; mole \; Sb}{121.75g \; Sb} \times \frac{1 \; mole \; Sb_2S_3}{2 \; moles \; Sb} = 0.0205 \; moles \; Sb_2S_3$$

If S is limiting:
$$1.00g \; S \times \frac{1 \; mole \; S}{32.06g \; S} \cdot \times \frac{1 \; mole \; Sb_2S_3}{3 \; moles \; S} \cdot = 0.0104 \; moles \; Sb_2S_3$$

Thus S is limiting and we obtain 0.0104 moles Sb_2S_3, which in grams is
$$0.0104 \; moles \; Sb_2S_3 \times \frac{339.68g \; Sb_2S_3}{1 \; mole \; Sb_2S_3} = 3.53g \; Sb_2S_3$$

62. Since information is supplied about two reactants, we must decide which is limiting. Thus we calculate moles H_2SO_4 assuming in turn each of these reactants to limit the reaction:
$$5.6 \; moles \; SO_2 \times \frac{2 \; moles \; H_2SO_4}{2 \; moles \; SO_2} = 5.6 \; moles \; H_2SO_4$$

$$4.8 \; moles \; O_2 \times \frac{2 \; mole \; H_2SO_4}{1 \; mole \; O_2} \cdot = 9.6 \; moles \; H_2SO_4$$

Since SO_2 would produce the lesser amount of H_2SO_4, it will limit the reaction and only 5.6 moles H_2SO_4, not 9.6, actually will be produced.

63. The methodology is the same as for Q. 62, except that first we need to compute moles of reactants from their masses, and ultimately we need to compute mass $BaSO_4$:
If K_2SO_4 is limiting:

$$6.00g\ K_2SO_4\ \times\ \frac{1\ mole\ K_2SO_4}{174.26g\ K_2SO_4}\ \times\ \frac{1\ mole\ BaSO_4}{1\ mole\ K_2SO_4}\ \times\ \frac{233.40g\ BaSO_4}{1\ mole\ BaSO_4}$$

$$=\ 8.04g\ BaSO_4$$

If $Ba(NO_3)_2$ is limiting:

$$8.00g\ Ba(NO_3)_2\ \times\ \frac{1\ mole\ Ba(NO_3)_2}{261.36g\ Ba(NO_3)_2}\ \times\ \frac{1\ mole\ BaSO_4}{1\ mole\ Ba(NO_3)_2}$$

$$\times\ \frac{233.40g\ BaSO_4}{1\ mole\ BaSO_4}\ =\ 7.14g\ BaSO_4$$

Thus $Ba(NO_3)_2$ is limiting, and only 7.14g of $BaSO_4$ is produced.

64. The methodology is identical to that of Q. 63, except that the equation first must be balanced:

$$2Al\ +\ 6HCl\ \rightarrow\ 2AlCl_3\ +\ 3H_2$$

If Al is limiting:

$$2.70g\ Al\ \times\ \frac{1\ mole\ Al}{26.98g\ Al}\ \times\ \frac{2\ moles\ AlCl_3}{2\ moles\ Al}\ \times\ \frac{133.33g\ AlCl_3}{1\ mole\ AlCl_3}\ =13.3g\ AlCl_3$$

If HCl is limiting:

$$4.00g\ HCl\ \times\ \frac{1\ mole\ HCl}{36.46g\ HCl}\ \times\ \frac{2\ moles\ AlCl_3}{6\ moles\ HCl}\ \times\ \frac{133.33g\ AlCl_3}{1\ mole\ AlCl_3}$$
$$=\ 4.88g\ AlCl_3$$

Thus HCl is limiting, and only 4.88g $AlCl_3$ is produced.

65. The methodology is identical to that in Q. 63 and Q. 64. The balanced reaction is

$$3Mg(OH)_2\ +\ 2H_3PO_4\ \rightarrow\ Mg_3(PO_4)_2\ +\ 3H_2O$$

If $Mg(OH)_2$ is limiting:

$$7.00g\ Mg(OH)_2\ \times\ \frac{1\ mole\ Mg(OH)_2}{58.33g\ Mg(OH)_2}\ \times\ \frac{1\ mole\ Mg_3(PO_4)_2}{3\ moles\ Mg(OH)_2}$$

$$\times\ \frac{262.87g\ Mg_3(PO_4)_2}{1\ mole\ Mg_3(PO_4)_2}\ =\ 10.5g\ Mg_3(PO_4)_2$$

If H_3PO_4 is limiting:

$$9.00g\ H_3PO_4\ \times\ \frac{1\ mole\ H_3PO_4}{98.00g\ H_3PO_4}\ \times\ \frac{1\ mole\ Mg_3(PO_4)_2}{2\ moles\ H_3PO_4}$$

$$\times\ \frac{262.87g\ Mg_3(PO_4)_2}{1\ mole\ Mg_3(PO_4)_2}\ =\ 12.1g\ Mg_3(PO_4)_2$$

Thus $Mg(OH)_2$ is limiting, and only 10.5g of $Mg_3(PO_4)_2$ is produced.

66. a) 1 liter of a 1M solution will contain one mole of the compound in question. The mass required will, therefore, be the molar mass in each case:

$NaCl$: $(22.99 + 35.45)g = 58.44g$
H_2SO_4 : $[2(1.01) + 32.06 + 4(16.00)]g = 98.08g$
HCl : $(1.01 + 35.45)g = 36.46g$
Na_2SO_4 : $(2 \times 22.99 + 32.06 + 4 \times 16.00)g = 142.04g$

b) In 250 mL of a 0.025 molar solution, we have

$$0.250L \times \frac{0.025 \text{ mole}}{1 \text{ L}} = 0.00625 \text{ mole solute.}$$

Thus the mass in each case is 0.00625 times the molar mass from part a, i.e. 0.37g, 0.61g, 0.23g, and 0.89g respectively.

67. 12.00 g of potassium permanganate is equivalent to

$$12.00g \text{ } KMnO_4 \times \frac{1 \text{ mol } KMnO_4}{158.04g \text{ } KMnO_4} = 0.07593 \text{ mol } KMnO_4$$

The molarity of the $KMnO_4$ is given by the number of moles divided by the volume:

$$\frac{0.07593 \text{ mol } KMnO_4}{2.0 \text{ L solution}} = 0.03797 \text{ moles/L} = 0.03797 \text{ M}$$

68. a) From the volume and concentration, we find the quantity of glucose in terms of moles, which we then convert to grams:

$$0.25L \times \frac{0.10 \text{ moles glucose}}{1L} = 0.025 \text{ moles glucose} \times \frac{180.18g \text{ glucose}}{1 \text{ mole glucose}}$$
$$= 4.5g \text{ glucose}$$

b) To deduce volume, we can multiply moles by the volume per mole, i.e. by a conversion factor based upon the concentration

0.10 moles glucose $\equiv$ 1L solution

$$0.010 \text{ moles glucose} \times \frac{1L \text{ solution}}{0.10 \text{ moles glucose}} = 0.10L, \text{ i.e. 100 mL.}$$

69. From the volume and molarity of the solution to be prepared, we can deduce the moles H_2SO_4 required:

$$0.500L \times \frac{0.175 \text{ moles } H_2SO_4}{1L} = 0.0875 \text{ moles } H_2SO_4$$

Since the concentration of the concentrated solution is

39

quoted on a mass basis, we convert this quantity to mass of H_2SO_4:

$$0.0875 \text{ moles } H_2SO_4 \times \frac{98.08g \ H_2SO_4}{1 \text{ mole } H_2SO_4} = 8.58g \ H_2SO_4$$

Next we convert to the mass of solution, using a conversion factor based on the information that

$$100g \text{ solution} = 98g \ H_2SO_4$$

$$8.58g \ H_2SO_4 \times \frac{100g \text{ solution}}{98g \ H_2SO_4} = 8.8g \text{ solution}$$

Finally we convert to volume of concentrated solution by using the density:

$$8.8g \text{ solution} \times \frac{1 \text{ mL solution}}{1.842g \text{ solution}} = 4.8 \text{ mL solution}$$

70. a) The $0.10M$ $Ba(OH)_2$ solution must be diluted. We can arrive at the answer by using the appropriate conversion factors. We first calculate the number of moles of $Ba(OH)_2$ in $6.3L$ of the $0.0030M$ $Ba(OH)_2$ solution.

$$6.3L \ Ba(OH)_2 \times \frac{0.0030 \text{ mol } Ba(OH)_2}{1L \ Ba(OH)_2} = 0.019 \text{ mol}$$

The volume of the more concentrated solution containing 0.019 mole $Ba(OH)_2$ will be

$$0.019 \text{ mol } Ba(OH)_2 \ \frac{1L \ Ba(OH)_2}{0.10 \text{ mol } Ba(OH)_2} = 0.19L, \text{ or } 190 \text{ mL}$$

To prepare the required solution we must therefore take 190 mL of the $0.10M$ solution and dilute it with water to 6.3 litres.

b) In the final, $0.25M$ solution the number of moles of $Cr_2(SO_4)_3$ will be

$$0.75L \times \frac{0.25 \text{ moles } Cr_2(SO_4)_3}{1L} = 0.19 \text{ moles } Cr_2(SO_4)_3$$

Since we are given mass information about the originating solution, convert this requirement to mass:

$$0.19 \text{ moles } Cr_2(SO_4)_3 \times \frac{392.18g \ Cr_2(SO_4)_3}{1 \text{ mole } Cr_2(SO_4)_3} = 75g \ Cr_2(SO_4)_3$$

The mass of the originating solution then is obtained from

$$74g \ Cr_2(SO_4)_3 \ \times \ \frac{100g \ solution}{35g \ Cr_2(SO_4)_3} = 210g \ solution$$

We can determine the volume of the solution using a unit factor based upon the density:

$$210g \ solution \ \times \ \frac{1 \ cm^3 \ solution}{1.412g \ solution} = 150 \ cm^3 \ solution$$

Thus we take 150 mL of the 35% solution and dilute it with water to 750 mL.

71. a) To obtain moles KOH, we multiply volume by concentration; this is then converted to mass KOH using the molar mass:

$$1.5L \ \times \ \frac{0.532 \ moles \ KOH}{1L} \ \times \ \frac{56.11g \ KOH}{1 \ mole \ KOH} = 45g \ KOH$$

b) Deduce the moles and then mass of $HClO_4$ in the solution which is to be prepared, and then convert this to the mass of the solution:

$$0.600L \ \times \ \frac{0.10 \ moles \ HClO_4}{1L} \ \times \ \frac{100.46g \ HClO_4}{1 \ mole \ HClO_4} \ \times \ \frac{100g \ solution}{50g \ HClO_4}$$

= 12g (of the 50% solution)

c) Using the same logic as for part b,

$$2.5L \ \times \ \frac{1.5 \ moles \ H_3PO_4}{1L} \ \times \ \frac{98.00g \ H_3PO_4}{1 \ mole \ H_3PO_4} \ \times \ \frac{100g \ solution}{85g \ H_3PO_4}$$

= 430g H_3PO_4

72. First deduce the quantity of HNO_3 required for 250 mL of 0.100M nitric acid:

$$0.250L \ \times \ \frac{0.100 \ moles \ HNO_3}{1L} = 0.0250 \ moles \ HNO_3$$

Convert moles HNO_3 to mass HNO_3 and then to mass of the concentrated solution:

$$0.0250 \ moles \ HNO_3 \ \times \ \frac{63.02g \ HNO_3}{1 \ mole \ HNO_3} \ \times \ \frac{100g \ solution}{69g \ HNO_3} = 2.3g \ solution$$

Convert mass solution to volume solution via the density:

$$2.3g \ solution \ \times \ \frac{1 \ mL \ solution}{1.41g \ solution} = 1.6 \ mL \ solution$$

41

Thus 1.6 mL of concentrated nitric acid solution is
needed.

73.   Mass of $_1^2H$ = 2.01410 u

         Mass of $_2^3He$ = 3.01603 u

         Mass of neutron = 1.00866 u

a) The mass loss during the reaction.

   $2\ _1^2H\ \rightarrow\ _2^3He\ +\ 1$ neutron

   will be 2×2.01410 u $-$ (3.01603 u + 1.00866 u)
   = 0.00351 u. The loss will be 0.00351 g per
   2×2.01410 g of $_1^1H$. Thus the mass loss per 1 gram
   of deuterium =

   $$1g \times \frac{0.00351\ g}{2(2.01410)\ g}\ =\ 0.00087\ g$$

b) We compute the energy equivalent from $E = mc^2$
       $c = 3.00 \times 10^8$ m s^{-1}
   Now $m = 0.00087$ g
       $= 8.7 \times 10^{-7}$ kg
   Thus $E = 8.7 \times 10^{-7}$ kg $\times (3.00 \times 10^8$ m s$^{-1})^2$
       $= 7.8 \times 10^{10}$ kg m^2 s^{-2}
   In SI units, 1 Joule = 1 kg m^2 s^{-2} and thus
   $E = 7.8 \times 10^{10}$ Joules.

c) The conversion factor relating deuterium to hydrogen is
       0.015 g D = 100 g H
   The conversion factor relating mass H to mass H_2O is
       2.02 g H = 18.02 g H_2O
   Thus to convert mass D to mass H_2O we proceed as follows:

   $$1.00\ g\ D \times \frac{100g\ H}{0.015g\ D} \times \frac{18.02g\ H_2O}{2.02g\ H}\ =\ 5.95 \times 10^4\ g\ H_2O$$

CHAPTER 3

1. The species present in the different layers of the
    heterosphere are as follows:
    The lowest layer consists almost entirely of molecular
    nitrogen, N_2, and extends upwards to about 200 km. The
    next layer consists of atomic oxygen, O. As we proceed
    outwards we next encounter the helium layer which is composed
    mainly of helium atoms, He, and then, finally, the outermost
    layer which consists of atomic hydrogen, H, not hydrogen
    molecules.
    The upper boundaries of the atomic oxygen layer and the
    helium layer lie at about 1100 km and 3500 km above the
    earth's surface but no definite upper boundary can be set for
    the atomic hydrogen layer which extends into interstellar
    space.
    The separation of the upper atmosphere into layers has
    occurred due to slow diffusion over a long time period.
    Those species which have the smallest gravitational
    attraction are thus found in the outermost layers. Molecular
    oxygen is largely missing from the upper atmosphere due to
    dissociation brought about by the intense ultraviolet
    radiation from the sun.

2. The reactions are
    a) Photochemical decomposition of molecular oxygen followed
    by an equilibrium reaction between oxygen atoms and oxygen
    molecules to form ozone, which reaction is reversed by
    ultraviolet light

    $$O_2(g) \xrightarrow{\text{sunlight}} O(g) + O(g)$$

    $$O(g) + O_2(g) \underset{\text{u/v light}}{\overset{\longrightarrow}{\longleftarrow}} O_3(g)$$

    b) The ozone layer is extremely important in protecting
    life on earth from the harmful effects of ultraviolet
    radiation from the sun. Virtually no UV reaches the surface
    since it is efficiently absorbed in the stratosphere by the
    ozone layer.

3. a) oxygen and silicon
    b) aluminum
    c) hydrogen

4. a) $S + O_2 \rightarrow SO_2$
    b) $2Mg + O_2 \rightarrow 2MgO$ and in much smaller amount
       $3Mg + N_2 \rightarrow Mg_3N_2$
    c) $CH_4 + 2O_2 \rightarrow CO_2 + 2H_2O$

5. a) $Fe_2O_3 + 3CO \rightarrow 2Fe + 3CO_2$
    b) $Fe_2O_3 + 3H_2 \rightarrow 2Fe + 3H_2O$
    c) $CuO + CO \rightarrow Cu + CO_2$
    d) $Mg + H_2O \rightarrow MgO + H_2$

6. a) $3Fe + 4H_2O \rightarrow Fe_3O_4 + 4H_2$
    b) $Mg + H_2O \rightarrow MgO + H_2$
    c) $CH_4 + H_2O \rightarrow CO + 3H_2$

7. a) $N_2 + 3H_2 \rightarrow 2NH_3$
    b) $N_2 + O_2 \rightarrow 2NO$
    c) $3Mg + N_2 \rightarrow Mg_3N_2$

8. A catalyst is a substance which increases the rate of a
    reaction without changing the nature of the products.
    Examples are
    1. Manganese dioxide acts as a catalyst in the decomposition
    of hydrogen peroxide to water and oxygen gas

$$2H_2O_2 \xrightarrow{\quad MnO_2 \quad} 2H_2O + O_2$$

    2. In the production of hydrogen from water gas the carbon
    monoxide is oxidized to carbon dioxide in the presence of a
    catalyst at 500°C according to the reaction

$$(CO + H_2) + H_2O \xrightarrow[500°C]{catalyst} 2H_2 + CO_2$$
    WATER GAS

9. Carbon monoxide, CO, has a very low solubility in water
    whereas carbon dioxide, CO_2, is readily soluble, particularly
    under pressure. Hydrogen like carbon monoxide has a very
    low solubility in water and so the CO_2 formed may be readily
    removed from the mixture by "scrubbing" i.e. dissolving it
    in water.

10. a) Hydrogen: A glowing splint or lighted match brought to the
    mouth of the test-tube will cause a mild explosion.

    b) Oxygen: A glowing splint inserted into the mouth of the
    test-tube will be rekindled.

    c) $H_2(g) + \frac{1}{2}O_2(g) \longrightarrow H_2O(g)$
         $C(s) + O_2(g) \longrightarrow CO_2(g)$

11. a) $N_2 + 5/2\ O_2 + H_2O \longrightarrow 2HNO_3$
       or $2N_2 + 5O_2 + 2H_2O \longrightarrow 4HNO_3$

    b) 0.76g N_2 contains 0.76g x $\dfrac{1\ mol}{28.01g}$ = 0.027 mol N_2.

    This would produce 2 x 0.027 = 0.054 mol HNO_3.

    0.24g O_2 contains 0.24 x $\dfrac{1\ mol}{32.00g}$ = 0.0075 mol O_2.

This would produce $0.0075 \text{ mol } O_2 \times \dfrac{4 \text{ moles } HNO_3}{5 \text{ moles } O_2}$

$$= 0.0060 \text{ mol } HNO_3$$

Oxygen is, therefore, limiting and a maximum amount of

$0.0060 \text{ mol } HNO_3$ would be obtainable.

Therefore the maximum mass of HNO_3 produced will be

$$0.0060 \text{ mol } HNO_3 \times \dfrac{63.02\text{g } HNO_3}{1 \text{ mol } HNO_3} = 0.38 \text{ g } HNO_3.$$

12. (a) <u>Electrolysis</u>

$$H_2O(\ell) \xrightarrow{\text{electric current}} H_2(g) + \tfrac{1}{2}O_2(g).$$

(b) <u>Water gas reaction</u>

$$C(s) + H_2O(g) \longrightarrow CO(g) + H_2(g)$$

(c) <u>Synthesis gas reaction</u>

$$CH_4(g) + H_2O(g) \longrightarrow CO(g) + 3H_2(g).$$

In (b) and (c) $CO(g)$ is removed by catalytic conversion to $CO_2(g)$ and scrubbing with water. Consult Chapter 3 of the text for details.

Another reaction involves the oxidation of iron

$$Fe(s) + 4H_2O(g) \longrightarrow Fe_3O_4(s) + 4H_2(g)$$

13. Boyle's Law states that the volume of a fixed mass of gas varies inversely with pressure at constant temperature

$$V \alpha \frac{1}{P} \quad \text{or} \quad PV = \text{const.}$$

For two sets of conditions, therefore,

$$P_1V_1 = P_2V_2$$

Let the new pressure = P_2. Substituting we have

$$1.0 \text{ atm} \times 0.50 \text{ L} = P_2 \times 0.20 \text{ L}$$

$$\text{Therefore } P_2 = \frac{1.0 \times 0.50}{0.20} \text{ atm} = 2.5 \text{ atmospheres}$$

14. This is the same type of question as Q. 13.

$P_1V_1 = P_2V_2$. Let the new volume = V_2

Substituting

$$1.00 \text{ atm} \times 150 \text{ L} = 0.75 \text{ atm} \times V_2$$

$$\text{Therefore } V = \frac{1.00 \times 150}{0.75} \text{ L} = 200 \text{ L.}$$

15. The key relationship is once again

$$P_1V_1 = P_2V_2$$

Initial Conditions   Final Conditions

$P_1 = 0.98 \text{ atm}$ $P_2 = ?$

$V_1 = 2.00 \text{ L}$ $V_2 = 2.00 + 5.00 = 7.00$

Substituting

$$0.98 \text{ atm} \times 2.00 \text{ L} = P_2 \times 7.00 \text{ L}$$

$$\text{Therefore } P_2 = \frac{0.98 \times 2.00}{7.00} \text{ atm} = 0.28 \text{ atm.}$$

16. The next two questions are based upon Charles's Law which tells us that the volume of a fixed mass of gas varies directly with the temperature measured on the Kelvin scale at constant pressure or,

$$V \alpha T \qquad \text{or} \qquad \frac{V}{T} = constant.$$

For two sets of conditions, therefore,

$$\frac{V_1}{T_1} = \frac{V_2}{T_2} \qquad \text{Let } V_2 = \text{ new volume.}$$

Substituting,   (Note temperature conversions

$$\frac{1.60L}{298K} = \frac{V_2}{77\ K}$$

$$25°C = 298K$$
$$-196°C = 273-196 = 77K.)$$

Therefore $V_2 = \dfrac{1.60 \times 77}{298} L = 0.41\ L$

17. Again applying the equation

$$\frac{V_1}{T_1} = \frac{V_2}{T_2} \qquad \text{Let } T_2 \text{ be the new temperature}$$

Substituting directly

$$\frac{400\ mL}{373\ K} = \frac{200\ mL}{T_2}$$

(Note that it is permissible to use alternative volume units here as long as they are consistently applied. Temperatures must be stated in Kelvins.)

Therefore $T_2 = \dfrac{200 \times 373}{400} K = 186.5K$ or $-86.5°C.$

18. This question combines both Boyle's and Charles's Laws.

Since $V \alpha \dfrac{1}{P}$ (const T) for a fixed mass of gas and since $V \alpha T$ (constant P) for a fixed mass of gas then for the same mass of gas

$$V \alpha \frac{1}{P} \times T \qquad \text{or } \frac{PV}{T} = constant$$

For two sets of conditions, therefore

$$\frac{P_1 V_1}{T_1} = \frac{P_2 V_2}{T_2} \text{ for a fixed mass of gas.}$$

Initial Conditions	Final Conditions
$P_1 = 1.02$ atm	$P_2 = ?$
$V_1 = V_1$	$V_2 = 1.10\ V_1$ (10% increase)
$T_1 = 293K$ (20°C)	$T = 473K$ (200°C)

46

Substituting

$$\frac{1.02\text{atm} \times V_1}{293K} = \frac{P_2 \times 1.10 V_1}{473K}$$

$$P_2 = \frac{1.02 \times 473}{293 \times 1.10} \text{ atm} = 1.50 \text{ atmospheres.}$$

19. The following four questions may be solved by applying the equation developed in Q. 18 for a fixed mass of gas.

$$\frac{P_1 V_1}{T_1} = \frac{P_2 V_2}{T_2}$$

Initial Conditons
$V_1 = 10.0L$
$P_1 = 850 \text{ mm Hg}$
$T_1 = 298K \ (25°C)$
Substituting

Final Conditions
$V_2 = ?$
$P_2 = 760 \text{ mm Hg}$ STP conditions
$T_2 = 273K \ (0°C)$

$$\frac{850\text{mm} \times 10.0L}{298K} = \frac{760\text{mm} \times V_2}{273K}$$

Therefore $V_2 = \dfrac{850 \times 10.0 \times 273}{298 \times 760} L$

$= 10.2L.$

20. $$\frac{P_1 V_1}{T_1} = \frac{P_2 V_2}{T_2}$$

Initial Conditions
$V_1 = 150 \text{ L}$
$P_1 = 1.00 \text{ atm}$
$T_1 = 302K \ (29°C)$
Substituting

Final Conditions
$V_2 = ?$
$P_2 = 0.75 \text{ atm}$
$T_2 = 263K \ (-10°C)$

$$\frac{1.00 \times 150}{302} = \frac{0.75 \times V_2}{263}$$

Note: For clarity of type, units henceforth are not displayed in these problems.

Therefore $V_2 = \dfrac{1.00 \times 150 \times 263}{302 \times 0.75} L$

$= 174 \text{ L}$

21. $$\frac{P_1 V_1}{T_1} = \frac{P_2 V_2}{T_2}$$

Initial Conditions
$V_1 = 0.840 \text{ L}$
$P_1 = 0.450 \text{ atm}$
$T_1 = 310K \ (37°C)$
Substituting

Final Conditions
$V_2 = 0.150 \text{ L}$
$P_2 = ?$
$T_2 = 260K \ (-13°C)$

$$\frac{0.450 \times 0.840}{310} = \frac{P_2 \times 0.150}{260}$$

Therefore $P_2 = \dfrac{0.450 \times 0.840 \times 260}{310 \times 0.150}$ atm $= 2.11$ atm.

22. $$\frac{P_1 V_1}{T_1} = \frac{P_2 V_2}{T_2}$$

Initial Conditons
$P_1 = ?$
$V_1 = V$
$T_1 = 298K$ (25°C)

Final Conditions
$P_2 = 100$ atm.
$V_2 = V$
$T_2 = 573K$ (300°C)

Substituting
$$\frac{P_1 V}{298} = \frac{100 \times V}{573}$$

Therefore $P_1 = \dfrac{100 \times 298}{573} = 52.0$ atm.

The cylinder may be filled to a maximum pressure of 52.0 atm. at 25°C.

23. The dry ice is completely converted to gaseous CO_2 and therefore the ideal gas equation may be used directly in the form

$$m = \frac{PVM}{RT}$$ where m = mass of gas in g.
M = molar mass of gas in g mol^{-1}.

We convert pressure in mm Hg to atmospheres by dividing by 760.

Substituting

$$m = \frac{\dfrac{500}{760} \times 1.00 \times 44.01}{0.0821 \times 573}\ g = 0.615\ g\ of\ dry\ ice.$$

24. $$2BaO_2(s) \longrightarrow 2BaO(s) + O_2(g)$$

(a) First calculate the number of moles of oxygen required by applying the ideal gas equation in the form

$$n = \frac{PV}{RT}$$

Substituting: $n = \dfrac{1.00 \times 10,000}{0.0821 \times 298} = 409$ mol O_2

We may convert to the appropriate mass of $BaO_2(s)$ by the use of the appropriate conversion factors.

409 mol O_2 x $\dfrac{2\ mol\ BaO_2}{1\ mol\ O_2}$ x $\dfrac{169.34g\ BaO_2}{1\ mol\ BaO_2}$ x $\dfrac{1\ kg\ BaO_2}{1000g\ BaO_2}$
                    (from equation)
    = 138 kg BaO_2

48

(b) 409 mol O_2 would, at STP, occupy a total volume of

$$409 \text{ mol } O_2 \times \frac{22.41 \text{ L } O_2}{1 \text{ mol } O_2} = 9.17 \times 10^3 \text{ L } O_2 \text{ at STP.}$$

(standard molar volume)

At a rate of consumption of 1.00 L sec^{-1} the oxygen supply would last 9170 seconds.

25. The standard molar volume (Venus conditions) would be given by

$$V = \frac{nRT}{P}$$

Substituting,

$$V = \frac{1 \text{ mol } \times 0.0821 \text{ L atm mol}^{-1}\text{K}^{-1} \times 1073\text{K}}{75 \text{ atm}}$$

$$= 1.2 \text{ L}$$

26. For a gas being compared under two sets of conditions, the ideal gas law has the form

$$\frac{P_1 V_1}{n_1 T_1} = \frac{P_2 V_2}{n_2 T_2} \quad \text{or} \quad \frac{P_1 V_1 M_1}{m_1 T_1} = \frac{P_2 V_2 M_2}{m_2 T_2} \quad \text{is applicable}$$

where m = mass of gas in g

M = molar mass of gas in g mol^{-1}

In this case since the volumes are the same under both sets of conditions and since $M_1 = M_2$ we can write

$$\frac{P_1}{m_1 T_1} = \frac{P_2}{m_2 T_2}$$

Substituting

$$\frac{1.00}{1.89 \times 273} = \frac{1.25}{m_2 \times 473}$$

Therefore $m_2 = \frac{1.25 \times 1.89 \times 273}{1.00 \times 473}$ g = 1.36 g of gas

27. The form of the ideal gas law to be used in this example is

$$m = \frac{PVM}{RT} \quad \text{(see Q. 23)}$$

Substituting

$$m = \frac{0.240 \times 0.250 \times 36.46}{0.0821 \times 310}$$ g = 0.0860 g of HCl(g)

28. The water bed has a total volume of

$$(2.00 \times 1.50 \times 0.20)\text{m}^3 \times \frac{1000 \text{ L}}{1 \text{ m}^3} = 600 \text{ L}$$

Applying the ideal gas equation in the form

$$m = \frac{PVM}{RT} \quad \text{(see Q. 23)}$$

49

and substituting:

$$m = \frac{1.03 \times 600 \times 4.00}{0.0821 \times 296} \text{ g of Helium} = 102 \text{ g}.$$

29. The density of a gas may be compared under two sets of pressure and temperature conditions by employing the equation developed in Q. 26, namely

$$\frac{P_1}{m_1 T_1} = \frac{P_2}{m_2 T_2}$$

in which the volume term, 1.00 L in each case, has been eliminated.

Therefore $\frac{1.00}{1.62 \times 273} = \frac{0.950}{m_2 \times 575}$

Therefore $m_2 = \frac{0.950 \times 1.62 \times 273}{1.00 \times 575} = 0.731$ g of gas

Since the volume remained at 1.00 L throughout, the density of the gas will also be 0.731 g L^{-1}.

30. For convenience, consider 1 L of the gas mixture. The total mass of gas is 1.482 g, and thus we can write

$$m_{N_2O} + m_{O_2} = 1.482 \text{ g}$$

The PVT information can be used to deduce the moles of gas in 1 L:

$n = PV/RT = 0.980$ atm $\times$ 1 L$/(0.0821$ L atm mol^{-1}K$^{-1} \times 298$K$)$
    $= 0.0401$ mol

This value must be equal to the moles of N_2O plus those of O_2:

$$n_{N_2O} + n_{O_2} = 0.0401$$

The two equations involving the two components can be written in terms of the same variables if we recognize that

$n = m/M$

Thus $n_{N_2O} = m_{N_2O}/44.01$

and $n_{O_2} = m_{O_2}/32.00$

Thus the equation for moles becomes

$m_{N_2O}/44.01 + m_{O_2}/32.00 = 0.0401$

or, after multiplying through by 44.02 $\times$ 32.00,

$32.00\ m_{N_2O} + 44.01\ m_{O_2} = 56.49$

Substituting $m_{O_2} = 1.482 - m_{N_2O}$ into this equation, and

solving, we obtain

$m_{N_2O} = 0.728$ g

Thus the percent by mass of N_2O is $(0.728/1.482) \times 100\% = 49.1\%$.

31. We use the ideal gas equation in the form

$$\frac{P_1V_1}{n_1T_1} = \frac{P_2V_2}{n_2T_2}$$ and since n is 1 mole under both sets

of conditions we may simplify the equation to give V_2, the new molar volume, directly

$$V_2 = \frac{P_1V_1T_2}{P_2T_1}$$

Substituting

$$V_2 = \frac{1.00 \times 22.4 \times 203}{3.40 \times 273} \text{ L} = 4.90 \text{ L}$$

(Note: $-70°C = (273-70) = 203K$)

32. The gas can be identified by calculating its molar mass, which can be accomplished by applying the ideal gas equation in the form

$$PV = \frac{m}{M} RT \qquad \text{or} \qquad M = \frac{mRT}{PV}$$

Therefore $M = \dfrac{mRT}{PV} = \dfrac{0.20 \times 0.0821 \times 300}{0.48 \times 0.26}$ g mol^{-1}

$$= 39 \text{ g mol}^{-1}$$

The gas must, therefore, be argon, Ar.

33. From Q. 32, $M = \dfrac{mRT}{PV} = \dfrac{dRT}{P}$ where d the density of the

gas is given by $\dfrac{m}{V}$ or mass per unit volume.

Therefore, at constant temperature and pressure, $d \propto M$.
Let O_x be the molecular formula of ozone.

Therefore $\dfrac{d_{O_x}}{d_{O_2}} = \dfrac{M_{O_x}}{M_{O_2}}$, but $d_{O_x} = 1.50\, d_{O_2}$

Therefore $\dfrac{1.5d_{O_2}}{d_{O_2}} = \dfrac{M_{O_x}}{32.00}$, and therefore $M_{O_x} = 1.50 \times 32.00$

$$= 48.00 \text{g mol}^{-1}$$

The molar mass of O_x must therefore equal 48.00g mol^{-1} and so x = 3 and the molecular formula of ozone is O_3.

34. $M = \dfrac{mRT}{PV}$ see Q. 32.

Therefore $M = \dfrac{1.134 \times 0.0821 \times 293}{\frac{740}{760} \times 1.00}$ Note temperature and pressure conversions.

51

$$= 28.0 \text{ g mol}^{-1}$$

The empirical formula CH_2 has a mass of 14.0 g per mole of empirical formula units and so

$$(14.0)x = 28.0 \text{ or } x = 2$$

Therefore the molecular formula is $(CH_2)_2$ or C_2H_4.

35. Again $M = \dfrac{mRT}{PV}$

$$= \dfrac{2.57 \times 0.0821 \times 310}{\frac{785}{760} \times 2.00} \text{ g mol}^{-1} = 31.7 \text{ g mol}^{-1}$$

36. $M = \dfrac{dRT}{P}$ (see Q. 33).

a) $M = \dfrac{dRT}{P} = \dfrac{1.275 \times 0.0821 \times 291}{\frac{750}{760}} \text{ g mol}^{-1} = 30.9 \text{ g mol}^{-1}$

The molecular mass of the gas will, therefore, be 30.9 u.

b) To calculate the number of molecules, we must first calculate n, the number of moles of gas:

$$n = \dfrac{PV}{RT} = \dfrac{\frac{750}{760} \times \frac{0.010}{1000}}{0.0821 \times 291} \text{ moles}$$

$$= 4.1 \times 10^{-7} \text{ moles.}$$

Each mole contains 6.022×10^{23} molecules and so the total number of molecules present will be

$$4.1 \times 10^{-7} \times 6.022 \times 10^{23} = 2.5 \times 10^{17} \text{ molecules.}$$

37. $M = \dfrac{dRT}{P}$ (see Q. 36)

$$= \dfrac{1.402 \times 0.0821 \times 293}{\frac{740}{760}} \text{ g mol}^{-1} = 34.6 \text{ g mol}^{-1}$$

38. From the data given, the mass of the volatile liquid was 0.750 g and the atmospheric pressure was 0.980 atm. Applying the ideal gas equation in the form

$$M = \dfrac{mRT}{PV} \qquad \text{(see Q. 32.)}$$

$$= \dfrac{0.750 \times 0.0821 \times 373}{0.980 \times 0.350} \text{ g mol}^{-1} = 67.0 \text{ g mol}^{-1}$$

This is the Dumas method of molar mass determination in which a sample of a volatile liquid is completely vaporized and the mass of the vapour determined by difference.

39. a) The molar mass of the compound may be determined by applying the ideal gas equation in the form

$$M = \dfrac{mRT}{PV} \qquad \text{(see Q. 32)}$$

52

$$= \frac{1.673 \times 0.0821 \times 373}{1.00 \times 0.440} \text{ g mol}^{-1} = 116 \text{ g mol}^{-1}$$

b) We calculate the empirical formula from the composition (see Chapter 2 problems)

	C	H	O
Percentage	62.04%	10.41%	27.55%
Mass in 100 g sample	62.04g	10.41g	27.55g
Mole Ratios	$\frac{62.04}{12.01}$	$\frac{10.41}{1.01}$	$\frac{27.55}{16.00}$
=	5.166	10.3	1.72
Atomic Ratios	$\frac{5.166}{1.72}$	$\frac{10.3}{1.72}$	$\frac{1.72}{1.72}$
=	3.003	5.99	1.00

The empirical formula is, therefore, C_3H_6O, which has an empirical formula mass = 58.09, and the molar mass = 116 g mol^{-1} from (a).
Therefore $(58.09)x = 116$, or $x = 2.00$
Therefore the molecular formula is $(C_3H_6O)_2$ or $C_6H_{12}O_2$.

40. When one litre of each gas, originally at 1.00 atmosphere pressure, is placed in the 2.00 L volume, the partial pressure of each gas will be halved as a direct consequence of Boyle's Law which states that at constant temperature the pressure of a fixed amount of gas will vary inversely with volume.
Therefore the partial pressures of the oxygen, nitrogen and hydrogen will each be 0.500 atmospheres under the new conditions.
Dalton's Law tells us that the partial pressure of a gas in a mixture of non-reacting gases is the pressure that gas would exhibit if it alone occupied the container - as calculated above - and that the total pressure is the sum of the partial pressures of constituent gases
Therefore total pressure = 0.500 + 0.500 + 0.500 atmospheres
= 1.50 atmospheres.

41. The ideal gas equation PV = nRT may be written for each gas in the mixture in the form

$$P = \frac{mRT}{MV} \quad \text{where } m = \text{mass of gas in g}$$
$$M = \text{molar mass of gas}$$

a) $p_{He} = \dfrac{0.20 \times 0.0821 \times 300}{4.00 \times 0.225}$ atm = 5.5 atm.

and $p_{H_2} = \dfrac{0.20 \times 0.0821 \times 300}{2.02 \times 0.225}$ atm. = 11 atm.

b) The total pressure P is given by
$$P = p_{He} + p_{H_2} = (5.5 + 11) \text{ atm.}$$
$$= 16.5 \text{ atm or 17 atm to two significant figures.}$$

53

42. Atmospheric pollution of 0.94 ppm of NO means that there are 0.94 mL of NO in 1,000,000 mL or 1000 L of the atmosphere.
a) At constant temperature and pressure the volume of a gas is directly proportional to the number of molecules or moles of gas present (Avogadro's Principle). Therefore the ratio $\frac{0.94}{1.0 \times 10^6}$ = 9.4 x 10^{-7} represents the mole fraction of NO

in the atmosphere under the temperature and pressure conditions stated.

Therefore the partial pressure of NO = 750 x 9.4 x 10^{-7} mm Hg
(Dalton's Law)

$$= 7.1 \times 10^{-4} \text{ mm Hg} \quad (1)$$

$$= \frac{7.1 \times 10^{-4}}{760} \text{ atmospheres}$$

$$= 9.3 \times 10^{-7} \text{ atmospheres.}$$

b) 1 m^3 = 1000 L (refer to Chap. 1 of the text)
The number of moles of NO present in 1,000 L of the atmosphere can be calculated from the Ideal Gas Equation:

$$n = \frac{PV}{RT} = \frac{9.3 \times 10^{-7} \times 1000}{0.0821 \times 303} = 3.7 \times 10^{-5} \text{ mol NO}$$

in which equation P refers to the partial pressure of the NO.
Therefore the number of NO molecules = 3.7×10^{-5} mol

$$\times \frac{6.022 \times 10^{23} \text{ molecules}}{1 \text{ mol}}$$

$$= 2.2 \times 10^{19} \text{ molecules.}$$

43. Graham's Law states that the rate of diffusion or effusion of a gas is inversely proportional to the square root of its molecular (or molar) mass or, in other words, the lighter the gas the faster it will diffuse or effuse.
We construct the equation

$$\frac{\text{rate of effusion of } N_2}{\text{rate of effusion of } O_2} = \left(\frac{\text{Molar Mass of } O_2}{\text{Molar Mass of } N_2}\right)^{\frac{1}{2}}$$

$$= \left(\frac{32.00 \text{u or g mol}^{-1}}{28.01 \text{u or g mol}^{-1}}\right)^{\frac{1}{2}}$$

The effusion ratio = $1.07:1. N_2$, therefore, effuses faster than O_2.

44. $$\frac{\text{Rate of diffusion of } H_2}{\text{Rate of diffusion of } D_2} = \left(\frac{\text{Molar Mass of } D_2}{\text{Molar Mass of } H_2}\right)^{\frac{1}{2}} = \left(\frac{4.03}{1.01}\right)^{\frac{1}{2}}$$

(See text for isotopic masses.)
In this and subsequent problems of this type the units of molecular or molar mass are omitted.

molecular or molar mass are omitted.
The diffusion ratio = 2.00:1
H_2, therefore, diffuses faster than D_2.

45. $$\frac{\text{Rate of effusion of } ^{235}\text{UF}_6}{\text{Rate of effusion of } ^{238}\text{UF}_6} = \left(\frac{\text{Molar mass of } ^{238}\text{UF}_6}{\text{Molar mass of } ^{235}\text{UF}_6}\right)^{\frac{1}{2}}$$

$$= (352/349)^{\frac{1}{2}} = 1.004$$

The effusion ratio is 1.004:1

46. The average speed of a gas molecule will be proportional
to its rate of diffusion or effusion and so

$$\frac{\text{Average speed of He atoms}}{\text{Average speed of } N_2 \text{ molecules}} = \left(\frac{\text{molecular mass of } N_2}{\text{atomic mass of He}}\right)^{\frac{1}{2}}$$

Substituting $\dfrac{0.707 \text{ miles hr}^{-1}}{\text{Average speed of } N_2 \text{ molecules}} = \left(\dfrac{28.02}{4.00}\right)^{\frac{1}{2}} = 2.65$

Therefore average speed of N_2 molecules $= \dfrac{0.707}{2.65} = 0.267$ miles s^{-1}

47. The gases ammonia, NH_3, and hydrobromic acid, HBr, are
introduced into opposite ends of a tube. If the distance
travelled by the ammonia is d_{NH_3} and the distance travelled
by the HBr is d_{HBr} at the time they meet to form the white
cloud of NH_4Br, the ratio of these distances will be given by

$$\frac{d_{NH_3}}{d_{HBr}} = \frac{\text{rate of diffusion of } NH_3}{\text{rate of diffusion of HBr}} = \left(\frac{80.92}{17.04}\right)^{\frac{1}{2}} = 2.18$$

Thus $d_{NH_3} = 2.18\, d_{HBr}$. We know also that $d_{NH_3} + d_{HBr} = 1.00$m.

Substituting the former equation into the latter, we obtain
$d_{NH_3} = 0.686$ m. Thus the cloud will form 0.686 m from the

end at which the ammonia is entering.

48. First use the information to deduce the moles of NO to be
produced:
n = PV/RT = (740/760) x 500/(0.0821 x 773)
   = 7.67 moles of NO
Using the balanced equation, we can convert moles of NO to
moles of O_2 required:

7.67 moles NO x $\left(\dfrac{5 \text{ mol } O_2}{4 \text{ mol NO}}\right)$ = 9.59 mole O_2

From the ideal gas equation we can deduce the volume of O_2

$$V = nRT/P = 9.59 \times 0.0821 \times 298/0.896$$
$$= 262 \text{ L of } O_2$$

49. a)   In each case, we first obtain the balanced equation for the combustion reaction:
$$CH_4(g) + 2O_2(g) \longrightarrow CO_2(g) + 2H_2O(\ell)$$
At constant temperature and pressure the volume of a gas is directly proportional to the number of molecules and, therefore, to the number of moles of gas that volume contains. Therefore, from the balanced equation for the combustion of methane we can state that 2.00 L of oxygen are required to react with 1.00 L of methane.
Note that the above statement is a direct consequence of Avogadro's Hypothesis (or Law).

b) $C_6H_{14}(g) + 19/2 \ O_2 \longrightarrow 6CO_2 + 7H_2O(\ell)$
From the foregoing it will be clear that to burn 1.00 L of hexane, C_6H_{14}, in the gaseous state, 19/2 or 9.50 L of oxygen will be required.

50. $CaCO_3(s) \longrightarrow CaO(s) + CO_2(g)$
The standard molar volume of a gas is 22.4 L mol^{-1}.
Introducing the appropriate unit conversion factors, we convert mass $CaCO_3$ to moles $CaCO_3$ to moles CO_2 to volume CO_2:

$$1.00\text{kg } CaCO_3 \times \frac{1000g \ CaCO_3}{1 \ kg \ CaCO_3} \times \frac{1 \ mol \ CaCO_3}{100.09g \ CaCO_3} \times \frac{1 \ mol \ CO_2}{1 \ mol \ CaCO_3}$$

$$\times \frac{22.4L \ CO_2}{1 \ mol \ CO_2} = 224 \text{ L of } CO_2$$

Note that in this and other problems of this type which follow, we first convert mass to moles and then, using the chemical equation, we determine the mole relationships between reactants and products. Finally, we introduce molar volume at STP or apply the appropriate form of the ideal gas equation in order to complete our answer.

51. First we obtain the balanced equation for the process:
$$2Mg(s) + O_2(g) \longrightarrow 2MgO(s)$$
The standard molar volume of a gas is 22.4 L mol^{-1}.
Introducing the appropriate unit conversion factors
$$5.00 \text{ g Mg} \times \frac{1 \ mol \ Mg}{24.31 \ g \ Mg} \times \frac{1 \ mol \ O_2}{2 \ mol \ Mg} = 0.103 \text{ mol } O_2$$

Now $PV = nRT$ or $V = \dfrac{nRT}{P}$

Substituting values

$$V = \frac{0.103 \times 0.0821 \times 298}{\frac{740}{760}} = 2.59 \text{ L of } O_2$$

56

52. a) $CaH_2(s) + 2H_2O(\ell) \longrightarrow Ca(OH)_2(s) + 2H_2(g)$

   b) 1 mole of $H_2(g)$ occupies 22.4 L at STP. Introducing the appropriate unit conversion factors we have

$$10.0 \text{ L } H_2 \times \frac{1 \text{ mol } H_2}{22.4 \text{ L } H_2} \times \frac{1 \text{ mol } CaH_2}{2 \text{ mol } H_2} \times \frac{42.10 \text{ g } CaH_2}{1 \text{ mol } CaH_2}$$
$$= 9.40 \text{ g } CaH_2.$$

53. The reaction which occurs is

$$2KClO_3(s) \xrightarrow{\text{heat}} 2KCl(s) + 3O_2(g)$$

   One mole of $O_2(g)$ occupies 22.4 L at STP. Introducing the appropriate unit conversion factors,

$$5.00 \text{ L } O_2 \times \frac{1 \text{ mol } O_2}{22.4 \text{ L } O_2} \times \frac{2 \text{ mol } KClO_3}{3 \text{ mol } O_2} \times \frac{122.55 \text{ g } KClO_3}{1 \text{ mol } KClO_3}$$
$$= 18.2 \text{ g } KClO_3.$$

54. a) The balanced reaction is
$$ZnO(s) + H_2(g) \longrightarrow Zn(s) + H_2O(\ell)$$
   One mole of $H_2(g)$ occupies 22.4 L at STP. Introducing the appropriate unit conversion factors we have

$$1 \text{ kg } ZnO \times \frac{1000 \text{ g } ZnO}{1 \text{ kg } ZnO} \times \frac{1 \text{ mol } ZnO}{81.37 \text{ g } ZnO} \times \frac{1 \text{ mol } H_2}{1 \text{ mol } ZnO} \times \frac{22.4 \text{ L } H_2}{1 \text{ mol } H_2}$$
$$= 275 \text{ L of } H_2.$$

   b) $2H_2(g) + O_2(g) \longrightarrow 2H_2O(\ell)$
   The molar volume of $H_2(g)$ at STP is 22.4 L. Introducing the appropriate unit conversion factors as above we have

$$1 \text{ kg } H_2O \times \frac{1000 \text{ g } H_2O}{1 \text{ kg } H_2O} \times \frac{1 \text{ mol } H_2O}{18.02 \text{ g } H_2O} \times \frac{2 \text{ mol } H_2}{2 \text{ mol } H_2O} \times \frac{22.4 \text{ L } H_2}{1 \text{ mol } H_2}$$
$$= 1.24 \times 10^3 \text{ L of } H_2.$$

   c) $2Li(s) + H_2(g) \longrightarrow 2LiH(s)$
   Introducing the appropriate unit conversion factors as before we have

$$1 \text{ kg } LiH \times \frac{1000 \text{ g } LiH}{1 \text{ kg } LiH} \times \frac{1 \text{ mol } LiH}{7.95 \text{ g } LiH} \times \frac{1 \text{ mol } H_2}{2 \text{ mol } LiH} \times \frac{22.4 \text{ L } H_2}{1 \text{ mol } H_2}$$
$$= 1.41 \times 10^3 \text{ L of } H_2.$$

55. At constant temperature and pressure the volume of a gas is directly proportional to the amount of gas measured in moles. This follows from the ideal gas law in the form

$$V = \frac{nRT}{P} \quad \text{or } V \alpha n \text{ at constant T and P.}$$

Therefore $\dfrac{\text{Moles of cyclopropane}}{\text{Moles of } CO_2} = \dfrac{0.55}{1.65} = \dfrac{1}{3}$

But 1 mol of CO_2 contains 1 mole of carbon

Therefore $\dfrac{\text{Moles of cyclopropane}}{\text{Moles of carbon}} = \dfrac{1}{3}$

i.e. 1 mole of cyclopropane contains 3 moles of carbon atoms.

In addition $\dfrac{\text{Moles of } CO_2}{\text{Moles of } H_2O} = \dfrac{1.65}{1.65} = \dfrac{1}{1}$

But 1 mole of H_2O contains 2 moles of hydrogen atoms, and we know that moles of carbon equals the moles of carbon dioxide. Therefore moles of H = 2 x moles H_2O = 2 x moles C = 6 moles

1 mole of cyclopropane contains 6 moles of hydrogen atoms. The molecular formula of cyclopropane will, therefore, be C_3H_6.

56. For convenience, pick a sample of size 1.00 L to work with. The moles of gas in the sample is
n = PV/RT = 1 atm x 1.00 L/0.0821L atm mol^{-1} K^{-1} x 300 K
= 0.0406 mol
Given Avogadro's constant, the number of molecules present in 1 L then is

0.0406 mol x $\dfrac{6.022\times10^{23} \text{ molecules}}{1 \text{ mole}}$

i.e. 2.44 x 10^{22} molecules. Now 1 L = 1 dm^3 = 10^{-3} m^3; thus the average space available per molecule is
10^{-3} m^3/2.44x10^{22} molecules
= 4.10 x 10^{-26} m^3
Now consider the other information, i.e. that a molecule has a radius of about 100 pm = 100 x 10^{-12} m = 10^{-10} m. Thus its volume = 4/3 π r^3 = 4/3 x 3.14 x (10^{-10} m)^3 = 4.2 x 10^{-30} m^3. Thus the available volume is about 10,000 times larger than the actual molecular volume.

57. Consider 0.96 g of water. In the liquid state, it occupies 1.00 cm^3, i.e. 1.00 mL = 0.00100 L. By the ideal gas equation, we can deduce its volume as a gas:
V = nRT/P = (0.96/18.02) x 0.0821 x 373/1
= 1.63 L
Thus the ratio of volumes, gas to liquid, is 1.63/0.00100, i.e. 1630 to 1. This is the expansion factor.

58. Mass Xe in sample = 67.8883 - 67.6259 = 0.2624 g.
d = m/V = 0.2624 g/0.0500 mL = 5.25 g L^{-1}.
Mass of 65% of this sample = 0.1706 g Xe.
Now for the oxygen, the mass is the same as if it alone occupied a volume of 35% of 50 mL, i.e. 0.0175 L; thus

$m_{O_2} = 0.0175 \text{ L} \times 1.30 \text{ g L}^{-1} = 0.0228 \text{ g}.$

Thus the bulb's total mass is
$67.6259 + 0.1706 + 0.0228 = 67.8193 \text{ g}.$

CHAPTER 4

1.

	Symbol	Name	Class
a)	He	helium	non-metal
b)	P	phosphorus	non-metal
c)	K	potassium	metal
d)	Ca	calcium	metal
e)	Te	tellurium	semimetal
f)	Br	bromine	non-metal
g)	Al	aluminum	metal
h)	Sn	tin	metal

2. Ar and K since that for Ar (39.948) > K (39.102)
Co and Ni since that for Co (58.933) > Ni (58.71)
Te and I since that for Te (127.60) > I (126.904)
There also is an apparent reversal at Th (232.038) and Pa (231).

3. All properties quoted are characteristic of metals. From the Periodic Table we conclude that since the atomic number is 22, the element is Titanium.

4. a) From Figure 4.1 in the text, the element is In, i.e. indium.

b) The possible choices are selenium (Se) or tellurium (Te) since they are in the same group as sulfur. Oxygen is a poorer choice since often the second period element is rather different from others in the same group.

c) The most active group of metals is the alkali metals; thus the most reactive metal in the sixth period is cesium (Cs).

d) From Figure 4.1, since the halogens are Group VII, that in the fifth period is iodine, I.

e) The alkaline earth family is Group II; thus the answer is calcium, Ca.

5. a) $Mg(s) + 2H_2O(g) \rightarrow Mg(OH)_2(s) + H_2(g)$
b) $H_2(g) + S(s) \rightarrow H_2S(g)$
c) $2Na(s) + I_2(s) \rightarrow 2NaI(s)$
d) $2K(s) + 2H_2O(\ell) \rightarrow 2KOH(aq) + H_2(g)$
e) $H_2(g) + Cl_2(g) \rightarrow 2HCl(g)$
f) $Ne(g) + H_2O(\ell) \rightarrow$ NO REACTION

6. The valence trend with Group is 1, 2, 3, 4, 3, 2, 1, 0; thus since Ba is in Group II, its predicted valence is 2

    Cs − − − − − − I, − − − − − − − − − − − − − − 1
    Ga − − − − − −III, − − − − − − − − − − − − − − 3
    Te − − − − − − VI, − − − − − − − − − − − − − − 2
    Ar − − − − − VIII, − − − − − − − − − − − − − − 0
    Ge − − − − − − IV, − − − − − − − − − − − − − − 4
    Sb − − − − − − V, − − − − − − − − − − − − − − 3

    The formulas A_yB_z of the compounds can be deduced by using the formula from the text

    $$\frac{y}{z} = \frac{\text{valence of B}}{\text{valence of A}}$$

    and valences of 1, 2, and 1 for H, O, and F respectively. Thus the compounds with H and F will have identical formulas, with

    $$\frac{y}{z} = \frac{1}{\text{valence of A}}$$

    Thus we have

    a) BaH_2, CsH, GaH_2, TeH_2, Ar (no compound is formed), GeH_4, and SbH_3

    b) For the compounds with oxygen, $y/z = 2/\text{valence of A}$; if the valence of A is even, y and z can be 1 and 0.5 x valence of A respectively:

    BaO, Cs_2O, Ga_2O_3, TeO, (Ar), GeO_2, Sb_2O_3.

    c) BaF_2, CsF, GaF_3, TeF_2, (Ar), GeF_4, and SbF_3.

7. From valence trend with Group of 1, 2, 3, 4, 3, 2, 1, and 0, since alkali metals are Group I, the valence of Fr is 1 and the formulas for the hydride and chloride are FrH and FrCl. Since tin, Sn, is in Group 4, its expected valence of 4 will yield SnH_4 and $SnCl_4$. Since astatine is a halogen and therefore in Group VII, its expected valence is 1 and thus we have AtH and AtCl. Since radon is a noble gas, it probably will not form a hydride or chloride.

8. From the trend in valence with Group and the general formula (see Q. 6), then since the valence of chlorine is 1, the predicted formulas are:
BCl_3 $AlCl_3$ $GaCl_3$ $InCl_3$ $TlCl_3$

9. The valence of sulfur is 2 and that of nitrogen is 3 since they occur in Groups VI and V respectively. From this information, the trend in valence with group and the general formula (see Q. 6), we obtain:

Li_2S BeS B_2S_3 CS_2 N_2S_3 SO F_2S (Ne)
Li_3N Be_3N_2 BN C_3N_4 N_2 S_3N_2 NF_3 (Ne)

10. The trend of valence with Group number is 1, 2, 3, 4, 3, 2, 1, 0. Since element A forms AF_2, and since the valence of F is 1, the valence of A must be 2, and thus it is expected to be found in Group II or VI. Similarly, X is from Group III or V, Y is from Group IV and Z is from Group I or VII.

11.

Element:	C	Ca	He	B	Cl	Li	O
Class:	nm	m	nm	nm	nm	m	nm
Hydride:	CH_4	CaH_2	—	BH_3	HCl	LiH	H_2O

Element:	F	P	Mg
Class:	nm	nm	m
Hydride:	HF	PH_3	MgH_2

Here nm means nonmetal, m means metal. Formulas were deduced from expected valencies of 1 for H and by the usual correlation with Group number (see Q. 6) for the others.

12. For InO, write an expression for the percent by mass of O (or In);

$$\%O = \frac{\text{Mass O in 1 unit of InO}}{\text{Mass all atoms in 1 unit of InO}} \times 100\%$$

$$17.3 = \frac{16.00 \times 100}{16.00 + m}$$

where m is the mass of In. Solving for m, we obtain
$$m = 76.5$$
This mass would have placed In between As and Se in the fourth period, i.e. in Group VI. This would yield a predicted valence of 2 which would be appropriate to the InO formula of the oxide. However it would place Se in the halogen group and Br in the noble gases, etc. where they clearly do not belong since their properties are similar to other elements in Groups VI and VII respectively.
For the formula In_2O_3, we would obtain (see formula above)

$$17.3 = \frac{3 \times 16.00 \times 100}{3 \times 16.00 + 2m}$$

from which we obtain m = 115. Thus the atomic mass of indium is 115.

13. From the fact that element A has a high melting point and is silvery white and dissolves in water to give H_2, we can deduce that it is a metal. Since it forms ACl_2, its valence is 2 and it must therefore be an alkaline earth, i.e. it is from Group II. Its atomic mass can be deduced from the quantitative information concerning its reactions. From the mass of AgCl, we can deduce the mass of chlorine in ACl_2:

$$0.3760\text{g AgCl} \times \frac{1 \text{ mole AgCl}}{143.32\text{g AgCl}} \times \frac{1 \text{ mole Cl}}{1 \text{ mole Ag}} \times \frac{35.45\text{g Cl}}{1 \text{ mole Cl}} = 0.0930 \text{ g Cl}$$

Thus we know that the percent chlorine in the ACl_2 sample is $(0.0930/0.1456) \times 100\% = 63.9\%$. As in Q. 12, we can write an expression for the percent chlorine based upon the formula:

$$\%Cl = \frac{\text{Mass of 2 Cl}}{\text{Mass of A plus 2 Cl}} \times 100\%$$

$$63.9 = \frac{2 \times 35.45}{m + 2 \times 35.45} \times 100$$

Thus m = 40.0 and we deduce that element A is calcium.

14. a) We know that the first shell contains a maximum of 2 electrons, the second 8 electrons, and the third fills to 8 electrons. Since the number of electrons (in a neutral atom) equals the atomic number, the total number of electrons for P, C and K are 15, 6 and 19 respectively. Of the 15 for P, 2 are in the first shell, 8 in the second and the remaining 5 must be in the third. Similarly for carbon 2 are in the first shell and 4 in the second. For potassium, 2 are in the first shell, 8 in the second, 8 in the third, and the one remaining electron is placed in the fourth shell.

b) The core charge of an element is equal to the atomic number minus the number of inner shell electrons. Thus for P, since there are 2 + 8 = 10 electrons in inner shells (i.e. those below the last to be occupied), the core charge is 15 - 10 = 5. For carbon, only the first shell is an inner shell, and thus the core charge is 6 - 2 = 4. For potassium, all electrons except the one in the fourth shell are inner shell electrons, and thus the core charge is 1. Notice the same answers are obtained more easily by recalling that the core charge is equal to the Group Number!

15. The valence shell is the outermost shell of a neutral atom which contains electrons. The number of valence shell electrons in a neutral atom is equal to its core charge, which in turn equals the Group number (except for H and He). Thus the number of valence shell electrons is 3 for B, 7 for a halogen, 2 for He, 8 for Ne and 2 for Mg.

16. For a neutral atom, number of electrons = atomic number. A +1 ion is missing one of the electrons; a -1 ion has one electron in excess of neutrality. To deduce the shell arrangement, we place 2 in the first shell and 8 each in the second and third, as required:

Cl	17e	2,8,7
Cl^-	18e	2,8,8
Si	14e	2,8,4
Ne^+	9e	2,7

17. Since core charge = Group number, the answer is 4 for C, 2 for Mg and Mg^{2+}, 4 for Si, 6 for O and O^{2-} and S^{2-}.

18. The ionization energy of an element is the energy needed to remove an electron from a gaseous atom of that element. The ionization energy increases from left to right because the core charge increases in this direction, and the attraction of an electron to the atom increases with increasing core charge. The ionization energy decreases on going down a group since although the core charge remains constant, the shell number from which ionization occurs increases and thus the attraction of electrons to the nucleus decreases.

19. To deduce the order of ionization energies within a set of elements, we use the generalizations mentioned in Q. 18. Thus the ionization energy for Ne > F since both lie in the same period but Ne is further to the right. The values for F and Na can be compared by using as a reference the element which lies in the same group as Na and the same period as F, i.e. Li. From the trend within a period

$$F > Li$$

and from that within a group

$$Li > Na$$

Thus we can conclude that F > Na, and the overall ordering is

$$Ne > F > Na.$$

20. Using logic similar to that of Q. 19, we have for ionization energy values

$$Ba > Cs$$
$$F > Cl \quad \text{and } Cl > S \quad \text{so } F > S$$
$$S > Se \quad \text{and } Se > As \quad \text{so } S > As$$
$$As > Ca \quad \text{and } Ca > Ba \quad \text{so } As > Ba$$

Thus the order is Cs < Ba < As < S < F.

21. According to Table 4.3, the ionization energy of sodium is 0.50 MJ mol^{-1}; thus for 1.00g Na we obtain

$$1.00g \ Na \times \frac{1 \ mole \ Na}{22.99 \ g \ Na} \times \frac{0.50 \ MJ}{1 \ mole \ Na} = 0.022 \ MJ$$

22. The value for helium is greatest since ionization occurs from the first shell (i.e. that closest to the nucleus) and its core charge is the maximum possible for that period. In other directional trends (→ and ↑) in the Periodic Table for increasing ionization energy.

23. Core charge increases left to right across a Period, and thus so do the attraction of electrons to the core. For this reason the average radius of the valence electrons decreases from left to right and consequently so does the radius of the atom since its size is determined by the radius of the outermost electrons. The size increases from top to bottom in a Group since although the core charge is constant, the number of the shell and hence the distance of the shell from the nucleus, in which the valence electrons reside, increases.

24. Since the bond length in F$_2$ is 138 pm, the covalent radius of fluorine is 138 pm/2 = 69 pm. The length expected for the bonds in CF$_4$ is the sum of the covalent radii for C and F, i.e. 77 pm + 69 pm = 146 pm.

25. From the data for Cl$_2$, the covalent radius for Cl is 198/2 = 99 pm. Each CCl bond in CCl$_4$ has a length equal to the sum of the radii for C and Cl; thus the radius for C = 176 − 99 = 77 pm. From this value for C, the CBr and CI lengths of 194 and 215 can be used to deduce radii of 117 pm and 138 pm

64

respectively for Br and I. For Br_2, BrCl, and I_2 we sum the covalent radii of the two atoms in each molecule to obtain 234 pm, 216 pm and 276 pm respectively for the expected bond distances.

26. a) Cl>F   since size increases from top to bottom in a Group.
    b) B>C   since size increases from right to left in a Period.
    c) Si>C   for same reason as (a).
    d) Al>P   for same reason as (b).
    e) Choosing S as the "straw man" (see Q. 19), Si>S and S>O so Si>O.

27. The number of dots is equal to the number of valence-shell electrons, which for neutral atoms is the same as the Group number.

    K·   ·Ca·   .B.   ·Sn·   ·Sb·   ·Te: ·Br: :Xe:

    ·As·   ·Ge·

28. Mg, Rb, Al and Li are metals which therefore lose all their valence electrons (=their Group Number) upon ion formation. Thus we have

    Mg^{2+} Rb^+ Al^{3+} Li^+

    Br and S are nonmetals near the right side of the Periodic Table. Each will gain enough electrons to form an octet, i.e. gain (8-Group Number) electrons. Thus

    Br^- S^{2-}

29. In all cases, the metal ion has no valence electrons left and the non-metal has acquired an octet

    a) Li^+ :Cl:⁻   b) Na^+-:O:²⁻ Na^+ c) :F:⁻ Al^{3+}-:F:⁻
                                                               :F:⁻
    d) Ca^{2+} :S:²⁻   e) :Br:⁻ Mg^{2+}-:Br:⁻

30. a) Since Group Number = number of valence-shell electrons, i.e. number of dots, it follows that A is in Group 1, D in 4, E in 2, and G in 7.
    b) A and E are metals, and by the same logic as Q. 28, form A^+ and E^{2+} ions. G is a halogen and (Q. 28) will form G^-. D is from Group 4 and will usually participate in covalent bonding rather than in the formation of ions. If D did form ions, they could be D^{4+} or D^{4-}.

31. One way to approach this problem is to first deduce the charges on the ions and then to deduce the simplest formula which will yield a total charge of zero.
    If the formula is A_yB_z, with A the positive ion and B the negative ion, then for zero charge we must have
          y times charge on A = z times absolute of charge on B
    For example, in example (a), since the charge on Li is +1 and that on S is -2,
          Therefore y(1) = z(2)
    i.e. y/z = 2/1. Thus the simplest formula is Li_2S.

65

Similarly we obtain
b) CaO c) $MgBr_2$ d) NaH e) AlI_3

32. The methodology is identical to that for Q. 31. We obtain
    a) CaI_2 b) BeO c) Al_2S_3 d) $MgBr_2$ e) Rb_2Se f) BaO

33. By the same method as used in Q. 31, we obtain
    a) $(NH_4)_3PO_4$ b) Fe_2O_3 c) Cu_2O d) $Al_2(SO_4)_3$

34. In each case, we first deduce the charge on the two ions by
    the techniques in Q. 30, and then the formula from the
    technique used in Q. 31.
    a) BaI_2 b) $AlCl_3$ c) CaO d) Na_2S e) Al_2O_3

35. a) Given its position in Group II of the Periodic Table,
       it follows that Ca possesses two valence-shell electrons.
       $\cdot Ca \cdot$

    b) As the +2 ion, Ca has lost both its valence-shell
       electrons: Ca^{2+}

    c) Since it occurs in Group VIII, Ne has eight valence-shell
       electrons: $:\ddot{Ne}:$

    d) Since O occurs in Group VI, it has 6 valence-shell
       electrons. Thus O^{2-} has an octet: $:\ddot{O}:^{2-}$

    e) Similarly with d, we obtain $:\ddot{S}:^{2-}$

    f) Cl occurs in Group VII and thus has 7 valence-shell
       electrons: $\cdot \ddot{Cl}:$

    g) Similarly with (c), we obtain $:\ddot{Ar}:$

    The species Ca^{2+}, S^{2-} and Ar all have the same number of
    electrons and therefore are isoelectronic. Similarly O^{2-}
    and Ne are isoelectronic. (If we use a definition of
    isoelectronic which implies equality involving only
    valence-shell electrons, all five of these species are
    isoelectronic.)

36. All the examples other than Br^- and Na^+ contain non-metals
    bonded to nonmetals and therefore contain covalent bonds.
    Since hydrogen forms only one bond by the sharing of its
    only electron, the Lewis structures for the first five
    examples are easily constructed:
    a) $H-H$

    b) Since Cl is missing one electron from an octet, it
        contributes one electron to a shared pair with
        hydrogen $H-\ddot{Cl}:$

    c) Similarly, we obtain $H-\ddot{I}:$

d) Phosphorus is missing three electrons from an octet; thus it contributes three electrons to three shared pairs, i.e. one with each H atom:

$$H-:\overset{..}{P}:-H$$
$$\overset{..}{H}$$

e) Sulfur is missing two electrons from an octet; thus it forms two bonds:

$$H-:\overset{..}{\underset{..}{S}}:-H$$

f) Since Br is missing one electron from an octet, Br^- must possess an octet: $:\overset{..}{\underset{..}{Br}}:^-$

g) Na has but one valence shell electron; thus Na^+ has none

$$Na^+$$

h) Silicon is missing four electrons from an octet; each fluorine is missing one. Thus by using all four electrons, Si can acquire an octet. Each F shares only one of its seven electrons in achieving an octet:

$$\overset{..}{\underset{..}{:F:}}$$
$$:F: \overset{}{Si}:F:$$
$$\overset{..}{\underset{..}{:F:}}$$

i) Since the hydrogen atoms can form only one bond each, they cannot be used as internal parts of the carbon-hydrogen chain; thus the carbon atoms must be joined to each other. Since carbon is missing four electrons from an octet, we expect each C to form a total of four bonds. Try first assuming the carbons form a chain joined by single C-C bonds:

C-C-C

To fulfill the valence of four on the terminal carbons, three hydrogens must be bonded to each. Similarly the central carbon requires two hydrogens; thus all eight hydrogens are accounted for in a chain structure containing only single bonds:

$$\begin{array}{ccccc} & H & H & H & \\ H - & C & - C & - C & - H \\ & H & H & H & \end{array}$$

j) As discussed for SiF_4, each F will form a single bond. The oxygen requires two electrons to achieve an octet; thus the F atoms are each singly-bonded to the oxygen

$$:\overset{..}{\underset{..}{F}} - \overset{..}{\underset{..}{O}} - \overset{..}{\underset{..}{F}}:$$

37. Sulfur has six valence shell electrons; thus it needs two more electrons to acquire an octet. Its valence is therefore expected to be 2. As well, each S atom possesses four unshared electrons, since only 2 of its 6

original electrons are involved in bonding. These requirements are fulfilled by the structure

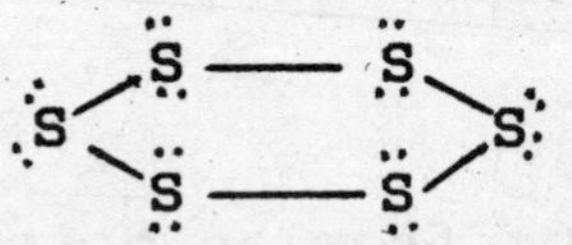

$$
\begin{array}{ccc}
 & \ddot{S} - \ddot{S} & \\
\ddot{S} & & \ddot{S} \\
 & \ddot{S} - \ddot{S} &
\end{array}
$$

38. a) Since neutral N has 5 electrons, N^+ has four and will form four single bonds to acquire an octet:

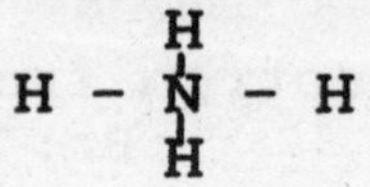

$$
H - \underset{\overset{|}{H}}{\overset{\overset{H}{|}}{N}} - H
$$

The average number of electrons associated with an atom is equal to one times the number of two-electron bonds it forms, plus the number of unshared electrons it possesses. Thus N has an average of 4 electrons here, compared to 5 for a neutral atom; thus its formal charge is +1. The hydrogens each have an average of 1 electron, and thus are neutral.

b) Since N^- has 6 valence-shell electrons, it forms two single bonds to acquire an octet.

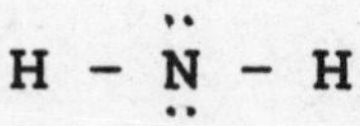

$$
H - \ddot{N} - H
$$

The average number of electrons on nitrogen is $1\times2+4=6$, so its formal charge is -1.

c) O^+ forms three bonds to obtain a octet about oxygen. The average number of electrons about O is $1\times3+2=5$, so the oxygen formal charge is +1:

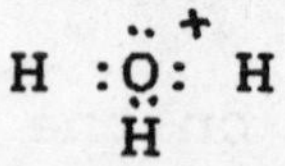

$$
H \overset{\cdot\cdot\,+}{\underset{\overset{|}{H}}{:O:}} H
$$

d) Similarly, we obtain $\quad H \; :\ddot{F}:^+ \; H$

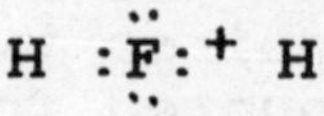

e) Similarly, we obtain
$$
H \; :\underset{\overset{}{\ddot{}}}{\ddot{P}}:^+ \; H \\
\overset{H}{\underset{H}{}}
$$

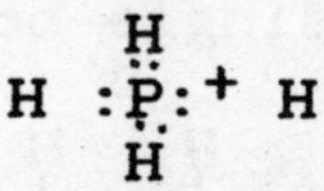

f) Similarly, we obtain
$$
H \; :\ddot{B}:^- \; H \\
\overset{H}{\underset{H}{}}
$$

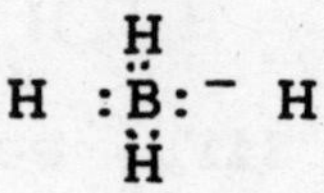

g) Each Cl here forms a single bond to the phosphorus which, since we have a +1 ion, has a valence of four:

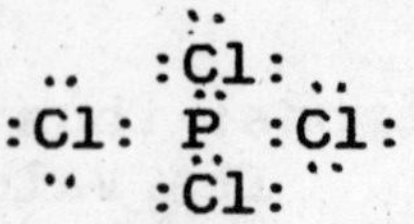

$$
\begin{array}{c}
\ddot{:Cl:} \\
:\ddot{Cl}: \; P \; :\ddot{Cl}: \\
:\ddot{Cl}:
\end{array}
$$

The average number of electrons associated with P is 1x4=4 so it is +1 in formal charge. The average number for Cl is 1x1+6=7, so each Cl is neutral.

39. a) The H atoms can form only single bonds, and there must be at least a single bond connecting carbon to oxygen, so we begin with the structure

$$\begin{array}{c} H \\ \diagdown \\ \diagup \\ H \end{array} C - O$$

The usual valence for C is 4 rather than the 3 associated with this structure; similarly oxygen usually forms 2 bonds rather than 1. We deduce therefore that there is another bond between C and O here.

$$\begin{array}{c} H \\ \diagdown \\ \diagup \\ H \end{array} C = O$$

As a tetravalent atom, C has no unshared electrons but as a divalent atom, O has four unshared electrons.

$$\begin{array}{c} H \\ \diagdown \\ \diagup \\ H \end{array} C = \overset{..}{O}:$$

b) Each P normally is trivalent; thus P_2 contains a triple phosphorus-phosphorus bond. When trivalent, each P has 2 unshared electrons. Thus the Lewis structure is

$$:P \equiv P:$$

c) Nitrogen normally is trivalent and has two unshared electrons. One bond from each nitrogen is used to bond a hydrogens; hence the NN bond is double:

$$H - \overset{..}{N} = \overset{..}{N} - H$$

d) Similarly with (c), if 2 of the 3 bonds of each nitrogen are used in bonding hydrogens, the NN bond here is single:

$$\begin{array}{ccc} & \overset{..}{N} - \overset{..}{N} & \\ H - & | \quad\quad | & - H \\ & H \quad H & \end{array}$$

40. If each Cl in PCl_5 achieves an octet by sharing one of its seven electrons, the P atom must use all five valence shell electrons to participate:

$$\begin{array}{ccc} & :\overset{..}{C}l: & \\ :\overset{..}{C}l \quad\quad \overset{..}{C}l: & & \\ & P & \\ :\overset{..}{C}l \quad\quad \overset{..}{C}l: & & \end{array} \quad \text{i.e.} \quad \begin{array}{ccc} & :\overset{..}{C}l: & \\ \cdot\overset{..}{C}l \diagdown \; | \diagup \overset{..}{C}l\cdot & & \\ & P & \\ :\overset{..}{C}l \diagup \quad \diagdown \overset{..}{C}l: & & \end{array}$$

Thus the phosphorus atom has 10 electrons about it and PCl_5 is an exception to the octet rule.

CHAPTER 5

1. a) unbalanced $\qquad$ $P + Cl_2 \longrightarrow PCl_3$

    balanced $\qquad$ $2P + 3Cl_2 \longrightarrow 2PCl_3$

    b) $\quad S + Cl_2 \longrightarrow SCl_2$

    $\quad 2S + Cl_2 \longrightarrow S_2Cl_2$

    c) $\quad C + 2F_2 \longrightarrow CF_4$

    d) $\quad 2As + 3Br_2 \longrightarrow 2AsBr_3$

2. In each case, the gas dissolves in water, followed by these additional reactions:

    a) $\quad HBr(aq) + H2O \longrightarrow Br^-(aq) + H_3O^+(aq)$

    b) $\quad CO_2(aq) + H_2O \rightleftharpoons H_2CO_3(aq)$

    and

    $\quad H_2CO_3(aq) + H_2O \rightleftharpoons HCO_3^-(aq) + H_3O^+(aq)$

    c) $\quad NH_3(aq) + H_2O \rightleftharpoons NH_4^+(aq) + OH^-(aq)$

    d) $\quad Cl_2(aq) + H_2O \rightleftharpoons HCl(aq) + HOCl(aq)$

    e) Fluorine oxidizes the water to O_2:

    $\quad 2F_2(aq) + 2H_2O \longrightarrow 4HF(aq) + O_2(g)$

3. a) $\quad Ca(s) + Cl_2(g) \longrightarrow CaCl_2(s)$
    b) $\quad 2Al(s) + 3Br_2(\ell) \longrightarrow 2AlBr_3(s)$
    c) $\quad Cl_2 + H_2O \longrightarrow HCl(aq) + HOCl(aq)$
    d) $\quad 2P(s) + 3Cl_2(g) \longrightarrow 2PCl_3(s)$
    (and, with excess chlorine, some PCl_5).
    e) $\quad 2P(s) + 3I_2(s) \longrightarrow 2PI_3(s)$

4. The electronegativity of an atom is determined principally by its core charge and by the distance of the valence shell from the core, i.e. by atomic size.

5. Electronegativity increases from left to right along each period since the core charge increases in that direction. Electronegativity decreases as we go down a group since although the core charge is constant, the distance of the valence shell from the nucleus increases.

6. a) F is higher, since it stands above Cl in Group 7 (see Q. 5 for trend within a Group).

b) F is higher, since it is to the right of O in their Period (see Q. 5).

c) S is higher, since it is to the right of S in their Period.

d) C is higher, since it stands above Si in Group 4.

e) O is higher, since it is higher than S (same Group) and S is higher than P (same Period). Here sulfur is a "straw man" which is used since it is in the same Group as O and the same Period as P.

f) Br is higher, since it lies to the right of Se in their Period.

g) P is higher, since it lies to the right of Al in their Period.

7.

Compounds	Bond Type	Explanation
Cl_2	covalent	atoms are identical
PCl_3, ClF	polar covalent	nonmetals but unequal in electronegativity
LiCl, $MgCl_2$	ionic	one atom a metal, the other a nonmetal

The structure for S_2Cl_2 is Cl-S-S-Cl. Its S-S bond is covalent since the two atoms are identical, but each S-Cl bond is polar covalent since nonidentical nonmetals are joined.

8.

Compounds	Bond Type	Explanation
Li_2O, MgO	ionic	metal + nonmetal
O_2	covalent	identical atoms joined
SO_2, Cl_2O, NO	polar covalent	nonequivalent nonmetals

9.

Compounds	Bond Type	Explanation
I_2, H_2	nonpolar	identical atoms joined
HBr, ClF	polar	nonequivalent atoms joined

72

10. Sodium chloride is a solid, ionic compound because when a large number of positive and negative ions are formed together, each positive ion tends to surround itself with as many negative ions as possible, and vice-versa. In other words, Na^+Cl^- molecules would combine together to give a giant molecule, in which the original molecules would no longer be distinguishable.

11. The ionization energy of an atom or ion increases as the positive charge already present on the ion increases; thus it requires more energy, for example, to form a +3 ion from a +2 than a +2 ion from a +1 ion. Presumably the energy cost to form ions of charge +4 and greater is prohibitively large.

12. Lithium fluoride is ionic, Li^+F^-, and for the same reasons as discussed in Q. 10 for NaCl, it exists as a crystalline solid. In contrast, F_2 contains no ions but rather nonpolar covalent bonds; since molecules containing covalent bonds attract each other only very weakly, and since these attractions are particularly weak for molecules such as F_2 which have relatively few electrons, F_2 is a gas.

13. a) K^+ and Ca^{2+} have the same number of electrons, but the nuclear charge for Ca^{2+} is greater and this pulls all electrons closer to the nucleus; thus $K^+ > Ca^{2+}$ in radius.

   b) $S^{2-} > Cl^-$ for the same reason as in (a).

   c) $Cl^- > K^+$ for the same reason as in (a).

   d) $Na^+ > Li^+$ since the outermost occupied shell for Na^+ is greater (and thus further out in space) than for Li^+.

   e) $I^- > Br^-$ for the same reason as in (d).

14. a) $Cl^- > Cl$ since addition of an electron to an atom increases the repulsions among the valence-shell electrons and forces it to expand.

   b) $Na > Na^+$ since in Na there is an electron in a shell beyond that in Na^+.

   c) $Na > Mg^{2+}$ since Na has an electron in a shell beyond that in Na^+ or Mg^{2+}; also Mg^{2+} will be smaller than Na^+ which itself is smaller than Na (see part b).

   d) $Cl^- > K^+$ for the same reason in Q. 13a.

15. To derive the formula, first deduce the charge on the ions. Group 1, 2, and 3 elements yield ions of +1, +2, and +3 charge respectively. Group 6 and 7 elements yield anions of charge -2 and -1 respectively, since this number of extra electrons gives them an octet.
   a) Since the ions are Ca^{2+} and I^- (see above), for

73

electrical neutrality (see Q. 16) the empirical formula must be CaI_2.

b) The ions are Be^{2+} and O^{2-}, and the formula is BeO.

c) The ions are Al^{3+} and S^{2-}, and the formula is Al_2S_3.

d) The ions are Mg^{2+} and Br^-, and the formula is $MgBr_2$.

e) The ions are Rb^+ and Se^{2-}, and the formula is Rb_2Se.

f) The ions are Be^{2+} and O^{2-}, and the formula is BaO.

16. The formula of an ionic compound is the simplest one which gives the net positive charge of the cations equal in magnitude to the net negative charge of the anions (since the compound is electrically neutral). Thus we obtain
a) $(NH_4)_3PO_4$ b) Fe_2O_3 c) Cu_2O d) $Al_2(SO_4)_3$

17. a) Iodide ion is I^-, and barium forms Ba^{2+} ions (since it is in Group 2). Using the same logic (i.e. electrical neutrality) as in Q. 16, the formula must therefore be BaI_2.

b) Aluminum is Al^{3+} and chloride is Cl^-; thus the formula is $AlCl_3$.

c) Perchlorate is ClO_4^- and ammonium is NH_4^+; thus the formula is NH_4ClO_4.

d) Nitrate is NO_3^- and calcium is Ca^{2+}; thus the formula is $Ca(NO_3)_2$.

18. The volume of the cube is $(0.1 \text{ cm})^3 = 0.001 \text{ cm}^3$; thus the mass of NaCl in the cube is

$$0.001 \text{ cm}^3 \times \frac{2.17 \text{ g}}{1 \text{ cm}^3} = 2.17 \times 10^{-3} \text{ g NaCl}$$

To obtain the number of ions, first convert mass NaCl to moles NaCl and then use Avogadro's constant:

$$2.17 \times 10^{-3} \text{ g NaCl} \times \frac{1 \text{ mole NaCl}}{58.44\text{g NaCl}} \times \frac{1 \text{ mole Na}^+}{1 \text{ mole NaCl}} \times \frac{6.022 \times 10^{23} \text{ Na}^+}{1 \text{ mole Na}^+}$$

$$= 2.24 \times 10^{19} \text{ ions of Na}^+$$

and similarly 2.24×10^{19} ions of Cl^-.

19.

74

20. Cl_2 is a stronger oxidizing agent than I_2; thus Cl_2 will react with I^- and oxidize it, rather than I_2 with Cl^-.
$$Cl_2 + 2I^- \longrightarrow 2Cl^- + I_2$$
Since Cl_2 acquires electrons, it is the oxidizing agent and Cl atoms are reduced. The I^- ions are oxidized, and thus it is the reducing agent.

21. a) $KI \longrightarrow K^+ + I^-$ in aqueous solution, and we expect the reaction is $Cl_2 + 2I^- \longrightarrow 2Cl^- + I_2$; thus the overall reaction is $Cl_2 + 2KI(aq) \longrightarrow I_2 + 2KCl(aq)$

b) N.R. since I_2 can't oxidize the Cl^- (produced from NaCl)

c) As in part (a), $Br_2 + I^- \longrightarrow 2Br^- + I_2$
so overall $Br_2 + 2NaI(aq) \longrightarrow I_2 + 2NaBr(aq)$

d) As the text states, $2F_2 + 2H_2O \longrightarrow 4HF + O_2$

22. Some brown I_2 is produced if any oxidizing agents are present as impurities; when present in tiny amounts it could be observed as yellow.

23. a) RbI exists as a salt, Rb^+I^-. Thus the reaction is
$$2Rb + I_2 \longrightarrow 2Rb^+I^-$$
Since Rb loses an electron, it is oxidized and therefore acts as the reducing agent. Since the I_2 gains electrons, it is reduced and therefore acts as the oxidizing agent.

b) Similarly with (a),
$$2Al + 3O_2 \longrightarrow 2(Al^{3+})_2(O^{2-})_3$$
reducing   oxidizing
agent; is   agent; is
oxidized   reduced

c) Clearly in the reaction
$$Cu^{2+} + 3I^- \longrightarrow Cu^+I^- + I_2$$
the Cu^{2+} gains an electron and therefore is reduced, i.e. acts as the oxidizing agent. Of the three I^- ions, one (that in Cu^+I^-) is neither oxidized nor reduced. The other two I^- ions lose electrons and therefore are oxidized, and act as the reducing agents.

d) Similarly with (a) and (b),
$$Zn + S \longrightarrow Zn^{2+}S^{2-}$$
reducing   oxidizing
agent; is   agent; is
oxidized   reduced

e) Since $MgCl_2$ is $Mg^{2+}(Cl^-)_2$, clearly Mg is the reducing agent and is oxidized. The hydrogen in HCl exists in solution as H^+ (or H_3O^+) and becomes H_2; thus it is reduced and acts as the oxidizing agent.

24. The reaction is $Mg + Cl_2 \longrightarrow MgCl_2$. Thus one mole Mg produces 1 mole of $MgCl_2$.

$$2.45g\ Mg \times \frac{1\ mole\ Mg}{24.31\ g\ Mg} \times \frac{1\ mole\ MgCl_2}{1\ mole\ Mg} \times \frac{95.21\ g\ MgCl_2}{1\ mole\ MgCl_2}$$

$$= 9.60\ g\ MgCl_2.$$

25. The easiest test to perform is that of adding a solution of silver nitrate to each solution. A precipitate of silver halide is obtained in each case, but the color of the solid varies from silver chloride (white) to silver bromide and silver iodide (pale yellow) - see experiment 5.9. There is some difficulty in distinguishing these precipitates on the basis of color.

$$Ag^+ + X^- \longrightarrow AgX(s) \quad \text{where } X = Cl^-, Br^- \text{ or } I^-.$$

A more clear-cut set of tests would be based on oxidation-reduction reactions. Addition of $Cl_2(aq)$ to the chloride solution would have no effect, but its addition to Br^- would result in Br_2 production with its characteristic color, and addition to I^- would result in I_2 production with its characteristic color:

$$Cl_2 + 2Br^- \longrightarrow 2Cl^- + Br_2$$
$$Cl_2 + 2I^- \longrightarrow 2Cl^- + I_2$$

26. After balancing, the equation for the reaction is

$$2AgNO_3 + BaCl_2 \longrightarrow 2AgCl(s) + Ba(NO_3)_2$$

To obtain mass AgCl, we convert mass $AgNO_3$ to moles $AgNO_3$, and the latter to moles AgCl, and finally the latter to mass AgCl:

$$2.50\ g\ AgNO_3 \times \frac{1\ mole\ AgNO_3}{169.88\ g\ AgNO_3} \times \frac{2\ moles\ AgCl}{2\ moles\ AgNO_3} \times \frac{143.32\ g\ AgCl}{1\ mole\ AgCl}$$

$$= 2.11\ g\ AgCl$$

27. The difficulty cannot be due to $AgNO_3$ solubility since it greatly exceeds 0.1 M. However Cl^- in the water would combine with Ag^+ to yield AgCl, an insoluble salt which would make the solution cloudy. Thus the $AgNO_3$ dissolves, but precipitates AgCl.

28. a) The most common bromine-containing acid is HBr; thus an example is

$$HBr + NaOH \longrightarrow NaBr + H_2O$$

b) A common oxidation-reduction reaction involving a compound of bromine is oxidation to the element, e.g. by chlorine:
$$Cl_2(aq) + 2KBr(aq) \longrightarrow Br_2(\ell) + 2KCl(aq)$$

c) To obtain a precipitation reaction, we must think of an insoluble salt containing bromine - AgBr is an example:
$$AgNO_3(aq) + NaBr(aq) \longrightarrow AgBr(s) + NaNO_3(aq)$$

29. The four properties are those listed as acid characteristics in section 5.6 of the text. In particular we would test Taste - since aqueous solutions of acids are sour.
a) Action on an Indicator - e.g. litmus, since acids turn it red.

b) Action on a Carbonate - since acids make it effervesce (CO_2).

c) Action on a Metal - e.g. Zn or Mg, since acids produce effervescence due to H_2 evolution.
We would not use taste, since the material could be harmful.

30. Of the acids listed only HNO_3 and H_2SO_4 are on the list of strong acids; hence H_3PO_4, $HOCl$ and HF are weak.

$$HNO_3 + H_2O \longrightarrow NO_3^- + H_3O^+$$

$$H_3PO_4 + H_2O \rightleftharpoons H_2PO_4^- + H_3O^+$$

and $$H_2PO_4^- + H_2O \rightleftharpoons HPO_4^{2-} + H_3O^+$$

and $$HPO_4^{2-} + H_2O \rightleftharpoons PO_4^{3-} + H_3O^+$$

$$HOCl + H_2O \rightleftharpoons OCl^- + H_3O^+$$

$$H_2SO_4 + H_2O \longrightarrow HSO_4^- + H_3O^+$$

$$HSO_4^- + H_2O \rightleftharpoons SO_4^{2-} + H_3O^+$$

$$HF + H_2O \rightleftharpoons F^- + H_3O^+$$

31. $$Na_2O + H_2O \longrightarrow 2Na^+ + 2OH^-$$

$$KOH \xrightarrow{\text{water}} K^+ + OH^-$$

$$NH_3 + H_2O \rightleftharpoons NH_4^+ + OH^-$$

$$KNH_2 \longrightarrow K^+ + NH_2^- \xrightarrow{H_2O} NH_3 + OH^-$$

All are strong except NH_3.

32. The simplest equation is
$$H_3O^+ + OH^- \longrightarrow 2H_2O$$
For the reaction discussed in the problem, we have
$$HCl + NaOH \longrightarrow NaCl + H_2O$$
From either the quantity of acid or base, we can deduce moles HCl (or NaOH) which must be equal to moles NaCl:
$$\frac{250 \text{ L}}{1000} \times \frac{1.0 \text{ moles HCl}}{1 \text{ L}} = 0.25 \text{ moles HCl}$$

Thus we will obtain 0.25 moles NaCl as product, and the concentration of NaCl will be

$$\frac{0.25 \text{ moles NaCl}}{0.75 \text{ L solution}} = 0.33 \text{ molar}$$

To deduce the mass of NaCl, we convert from moles to grams NaCl:

$$0.25 \text{ moles NaCl} \times \frac{58.44 \text{ g NaCl}}{1 \text{ mole NaCl}} = 15 \text{ g NaCl}$$

33. Since HZ is strong, its ionization is complete:

$$HZ + H_2O \longrightarrow Z^- + H_3O^+$$

Since HZ is a strong acid, its conjugate Z^- is of negligible strength as a base. Thus a solution of NaZ will contain only Na^+ and Z^- ions (plus any H_3O^+ and OH^- from water self-ionization). For HY, since it is a weak acid, its ionization is incomplete and its conjugate Y^- is a weak base:

$$HY + H_2O \rightleftharpoons Y^- + H_3O^+$$

An aqueous solution of NaY will contain not only Na^+ and Y^-, but also HY and OH^- due to the reaction of Y^- with H_2O:

$$Y^- + H_2O \rightleftharpoons HY + OH^-$$

34. The balanced reaction involves $CaCl_2$ as product:

$$2HCl + Ca(OH)_2 \longrightarrow CaCl_2 + 2H_2O$$

From mass of $Ca(OH)_2$ we can deduce moles $Ca(OH)_2$ and thus moles HCl, and then multiply by the inverse of the HCl solution concentration to obtain litres of acid:

$$5.00\text{g Ca(OH)}_2 \times \frac{1 \text{ mole Ca(OH)}_2}{74.10\text{g Ca(OH)}_2} \times \frac{2 \text{ moles HCl}}{1 \text{ mole Ca(OH)}_2} \times \frac{1 \text{ L HCl}}{0.100 \text{ moles HCl}}$$

$$= 1.35 \text{ L HCl solution}$$

35. The moles HCl can be obtained from its molarity and concentration; this can then be converted to moles of antacid, using the coefficients in the equation, and finally transformed to mass of antacid:

$$2.00\text{L} \times \frac{0.12 \text{ moles HCl}}{1 \text{ L}} \times \frac{1 \text{ mole NaAl(OH)}_2\text{CO}_3}{4 \text{ moles HCl}} \times \frac{144.00\text{g NaAl(OH)}_2\text{CO}_3}{1 \text{ mole NaAl(OH)}_2\text{CO}_3}$$

$$= 8.6 \text{ g of NaAl(OH)}_2\text{CO}_3.$$

36. Conjugate bases are acids minus H^+. Thus the answers are
   a) F^- b) NO_3^- c) ClO_4^- d) OH^- e) H_2O

37. Conjugate acids are bases plus one H^+. Thus the answers are
   a) NH_4^+ b) $CH_3NH_3^+$ c) H_2O e) H_3O^+

38. All species here obey the octet rule for the central atom, and all H atoms form one bond each to that atom:
   a) hydronium ion

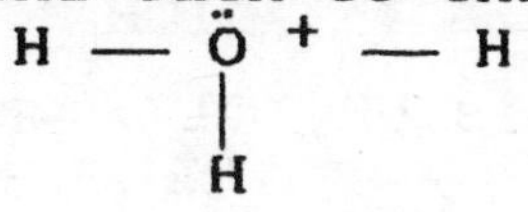

$$H - \overset{..}{O}{}^+ - H$$
$$|$$
$$H$$

   b) ammonium ion

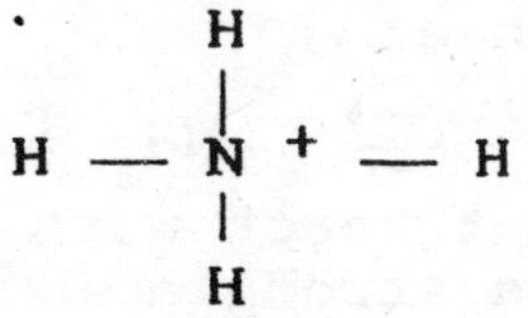

$$\overset{\cdot}{}\quad H$$
$$|$$
$$H - N^+ - H$$
$$|$$
$$H$$

   c) hydroxide ion

$$:\overset{..}{\underset{..}{O}}{}^- - H$$

39. In each case, the reaction involves donation to H_2O (the base) of a proton from the acid; the species missing its original proton is by definition the conjugate base and the H_3O^+ ion is an acid:

$$HCl + H_2O \longrightarrow Cl^- + H_3O^+$$
   acid   base   base   acid

$$CH_3CO_2H + H_2O \rightleftarrows CH_3CO_2^- + H_3O^+$$
   acid   base   base   acid

$$HClO_4 + H_2O \longrightarrow ClO_4^- + H_3O^+$$
   acid   base   base   acid

$$H_2SO_4 + H_2O \longrightarrow HSO_4^- + H_3O^+$$
   acid   base   base   acid

then $$HSO_4^- + H_2O \rightleftarrows SO_4^{2-} + H_3O^+$$
   acid   base   base   acid

$$HOCl + H_2O \rightleftarrows OCl^- + H_3O^+$$
   acid   base   base   acid

$$NH_4^+ + H_2O \rightleftarrows NH_3 + H_3O^+$$
   acid   base   base   acid

$$H_2O + H_2O \rightleftarrows OH^- + H_3O^+$$
   acid   base   base   acid

40. Sodium hypochloride is ClO^-Na^+, which in water yields the two ions:

$$ClONa \xrightarrow{\text{water}} ClO^- + Na^+$$

The hypochlorite ion is a weak base since it is the conjugate of a weak acid (hypochloric); thus it reacts with water:

$$ClO^- + H_2O \rightleftharpoons ClOH + OH^-$$

Ammonium chloride is $NH_4^+Cl^-$, which in water yields

$$NH_4Cl \longrightarrow NH_4^+ + Cl^-$$

The ammonium ion is a weak acid, since it is the conjugate of the weak base ammonia:

$$NH_4^+ + H_2O \rightleftharpoons NH_3 + H_3O^+$$

The ion Cl^- does not react with water, since it is the conjugate base of a strong acid (HCl).

41. The strongest acid that can exist in water is H_3O^+; the strongest base is OH^-. (All stronger acids or bases are levelled to those species.)

$$LiH \xrightarrow{\text{water}} Li^+ + H^-$$

$$\text{then} \quad H^- + H_2O \longrightarrow OH^- + H_2$$

$$CaH_2 \xrightarrow{\text{water}} Ca^{2+} + 2H^-$$

$$\text{then each} \quad H^- + H_2O \longrightarrow OH^- + H_2$$

$$Li_2O \xrightarrow{\text{water}} 2Li^+ + O^{2-}$$

$$\text{then} \quad O^{2-} + H_2O \longrightarrow 2OH^-$$

$$CaO \xrightarrow{\text{water}} Ca^{2+} + O^{2-}$$

$$\text{then} \quad O^{2-} + H_2O \longrightarrow 2OH^-$$

In terms of compounds, we could write the reactions as

$$LiH + H_2O \longrightarrow LiOH + H_2$$
$$CaH_2 + 2H_2O \longrightarrow Ca(OH)_2 + 2H_2$$
$$Li_2O + H_2O \longrightarrow 2LiOH$$
$$CaO + H_2O \longrightarrow Ca(OH)_2$$

42. The balanced reaction is

$$HBr + NaOH \longrightarrow NaBr + H_2O$$

From the volume and concentration of NaOH, we can obtain moles NaOH, which must be equal to moles HBr (see equation). Multiplying moles HBr times the inverse of the concentration, i.e. times L/moles, gives the volume of HBr solution required.

$$\frac{25.00 \text{ L}}{1000} \times \frac{0.107 \text{ moles NaOH}}{1 \text{ L}} \times \frac{1 \text{ mole HBr}}{1 \text{ mole NaOH}} \times \frac{1 \text{ L HBr solution}}{0.124 \text{ moles HBr}}$$

$$= 0.0216 \text{ L HBr solution, i.e. } 21.6 \text{ mL.}$$

43. This problem is very similar to Q. 42:

$$\frac{100.0 \text{ L}}{1000} \times \frac{0.211 \text{ moles HF}}{1 \text{ L}} \times \frac{1 \text{ mole KOH}}{1 \text{ mole HF}} \times \frac{1 \text{ L KOH solution}}{0.115 \text{ moles KOH}}$$

$$= 0.183 \text{ L KOH solutions, i.e. } 183 \text{ mL.}$$

44. It is clear from the high melting/boiling points and from
conductivity information that AB is an ionic compound. Since
reaction with $AgNO_3$ produces a precipitate, B must be a
halogen. If bubbling Cl_2 produced a brown colour, presumably
this is due to Br_2 obtained from the reaction
$$Cl_2 + Br^- \longrightarrow 2Cl^- + Br_2$$
This is confirmed by the fact that B is a liquid. To deduce
the nature of the metal A, we must use the stoichiometric
information supplied. In particular we know
$$\begin{array}{cc} ABr + AgNO_3 \longrightarrow & AgBr + ANO_3 \\ 0.543 \text{ g} & 0.857 \text{ g} \end{array}$$
We can deduce the mass of Br from that of AgBr, and by
subtracting it from that of ABr, obtain the mass of A.
$$0.857 \text{ g AgBr} \times \left(\frac{79.91 \text{ g Br}}{187.78 \text{ g AgBr}}\right) = 0.365 \text{ g Br}$$
where the unit factor is obtained from the mass of Br in 1
mole of AgBr. Thus
$$\text{Mass A} = 0.543 - 0.365 = 0.178 \text{ g}$$
Now in ABr, the ratio of masses of A to Br in the sample
must equal the ratio of their atomic masses; thus

$$\frac{\text{Atomic Mass A}}{\text{Atomic Mass Br}} = \frac{\text{Mass A in sample}}{\text{Mass Br in sample}}$$

$$\frac{\text{Atomic mass A}}{79.91} = \frac{0.178 \text{ g}}{0.365 \text{ g}}$$

Thus Atomic mass A = 39.0
From the periodic table, we deduce that the element A must
be potassium, K.

45. By analogy with the properties for the other halogens,
   a) solid
   b) ionization energy smaller, size larger (as these are the
   trends in descending any Group).
   c) AtBr
   d) Strong   e) pyramidal   f) ionic

g) $2Na + At_2 \longrightarrow 2NaAt$
    $Ca + At_2 \longrightarrow CaAt_2$
    $2P + 3At_2 \longrightarrow 2PAt_3$; with excess At_2,
    $\qquad\qquad\qquad 2P + 5At_2 \longrightarrow 2PAt_5$
    $H_2 + At_2 \longrightarrow 2HAt$

46. The unbalanced reaction must be
    $$Ca(OCl)_2 + CO_2 + H_2O \longrightarrow CaCO_3 + HOCl$$
    (We know H_2O is used as neither $Ca(OCl)_2$ nor CO_2 has any H,
    but H does appear in a product.) Upon balancing, we obtain
    $$Ca(OCl)_2 + CO_2 + H_2O \longrightarrow CaCO_3 + 2HOCl$$
    To obtain the concentration of HOCl we first need to deduce
    the number of moles of it; this can be obtained from the
    mass of $Ca(OCl)_2$:

    $$8.0 \text{ g } Ca(OCl_2) \times \frac{1 \text{ mole } Ca(OCl)_2}{142.98 \ Ca(OCl)_2} \times \frac{2 \text{ moles HOCl}}{1 \text{ mole } Ca(OCl)_2}$$

    $$= 0.11 \text{ mole HOCl}$$

    Thus HOCl concentration = 0.11 mole/0.200 L = 0.55 $\underline{M}$.

47. The unbalanced reaction is
    $$Cl_2 + NaOH \longrightarrow NaOCl + NaCl + H_2O$$
    Balancing the H requires 2NaOH, which balances all elements;
    thus the balanced reaction is
    $$Cl_2 + 2NaOH \longrightarrow NaOCl + NaCl + H_2O$$
    We can convert volume of Cl_2 to moles Cl_2, then to moles and
    then grams of sodium hypochlorite:

    $$1.00 \text{ L } Cl_2 \times \frac{1 \text{ mole } Cl_2}{22.4 \text{ L } Cl_2} \times \frac{1 \text{ mole NaOCl}}{1 \text{ mole } Cl_2} \times \frac{74.44 \text{ g NaOCl}}{1 \text{ mole NaOCl}}$$

    $$= 3.32 \text{ g NaOCl}$$

48. Since Radium is an element in Group 2, its chloride will
    have the formula $RaCl_2$. Let us express the information given
    concerning the composition of the salt in terms of one mole
    of $RaCl_2$:

    $$\% \text{ Ra} = \frac{\text{Mass Ra in 1 mole}}{\text{Mass } RaCl_2 \text{ in 1 mole}} \times 100\%$$

    i.e. $76.1 = \dfrac{X}{X + 2 \times 35.45} \times 100$

    Solving this equation, we obtain X = 226.

49. In an acid-base reaction, H^+ is transferred between reactants
    whereas in an oxidation-reduction reaction, one or more
    electrons is/are transferred. Using these criteria, we can

classify the reactions:

a) $Cl_2 + 2I^- \longrightarrow 2Cl^- + I_2$

An oxidation-reduction reaction since electrons are transferred from I to Cl atoms. Since I^- gives up electrons it is the reducing agent, whereas since Cl_2 takes electrons (from I^-) it is the oxidizing agent.

b) $HCl + H_2O \longrightarrow Cl^- + H_3O^+$

An acid-base reaction since H^+ is transferred from HCl, which therefore is the acid, to H_2O which acts here as the base.

c) $Zn + HCl \longrightarrow ZnCl_2 + H_2$

The compound $ZnCl_2$ is ionic, i.e. it is $Zn^{2+}(Cl^-)_2$ in the solid state. Clearly Zn has lost electrons to HCl and this process is an oxidation-reduction reaction with Zn as the reducing agent and HCl as the oxidizing agent.

d) The balanced equation is
$$HCO_3^- + H_3O^+ \longrightarrow CO_2 + 2H_2O$$
The H_3O^+ reactant loses H^+ to become one of the two water molecules - hence it acts as an acid. Upon acting as a base and receiving H^+, the HCO_3^- ion temporarily becomes H_2CO_3 which decomposes to $CO_2 + H_2O$. Thus the reaction is an acid-base process.

CHAPTER 6

1. We can rearrange the equation $c = \nu\lambda$ to give $\frac{c}{\nu} = \lambda$.
    Then by inserting the appropriate values and conversion factors we obtain

    <u>CBC, F.M.</u> $\lambda = \frac{c}{\nu} = \frac{3.00 \times 10^8 \text{m s}^{-1}}{94.1 \text{ MHz}} \times \frac{1 \text{ MHz}}{10^6 \text{ s}^{-1}}$

    Therefore $\lambda = 3.19$ m

    <u>CBC, AM</u> $\lambda = \frac{c}{\nu} = \frac{3.00 \times 10^8 \text{ m s}^{-1}}{740 \text{ kHz}} \times \frac{1 \text{ kHz}}{10^3 \text{ s}^{-1}}$

    Therefore $\lambda = 4.05 \times 10^2$ m $= 405$ m

2. This question calls for the selection of the appropriate unit conversion factors. From them, the wavelength of the mercury blue line may be expressed in various units. In each case, we first convert nm to m, and then m to the desired unit:

    a) <u>METERS</u>: 435.8 nm $\times \frac{10^{-9} \text{ m}}{1 \text{ nm}} = 4.358 \times 10^{-7}$ m

    b) μm: 435.8 nm $\times \frac{10^{-9} \text{ m}}{1 \text{ nm}} \times \frac{1 \mu\text{m}}{10^{-6} \text{ m}} = 4.358 \times 10^{-1}\ \mu$m

    c) Å: 435.8 nm $\times \frac{10^{-9} \text{ m}}{1 \text{ nm}} \times \frac{1\text{Å}}{10^{-10} \text{ m}} = 4.358 \times 10^3$ Å

    $= 4358$ Å

    and $\nu = \frac{c}{\lambda} = \frac{3.00 \times 10^8 \text{ m s}^{-1}}{4.358 \times 10^{-7} \text{ m}} = 6.884 \times 10^{14}$ Hz or s^{-1}

3. Applying the equation $\lambda = \frac{c}{\nu}$ we have

    $\lambda = \frac{3.00 \times 10^8 \text{ m s}^{-1}}{27.3 \times 10^6 \text{ s}^{-1}} = 11.0$ m

4. Each successive value of the frequency, ν, is calculated by applying the equation $\nu = c/\lambda$ (where $c = 3.0 \times 10^8$ m s^{-1}) and by expressing in the equation each wavelength λ in terms of meters, obtained using the conversion factors:

$$1 \text{ cm} = 10^{-2} \text{ m}, \quad 1 \text{ mm} = 10^{-3} \text{ m}, \quad 1 \mu\text{m} = 10^{-6} \text{ m},$$
$$1 \text{ nm} = 10^{-9} \text{ m}, \quad 1 \text{ pm} = 10^{-12} \text{ m} \quad 1 \text{ km} = 10^3 \text{ m}$$

Types of Radiation	Wavelength	Frequency(Hz)
radio frequency	1 km to 30 cm	3.0×10^5 to 1.0×10^9
microwave	30 cm to 2mm	1.0×10^9 to 1.5×10^{11}
far infra-red	2 mm to 30 μm	1.5×10^{11} to 1.0×10^{13}
near infra-red	30 μm to 710 nm	1.0×10^{13} to 4.2×10^{14}
visible	710 nm to 400 nm	4.2×10^{14} to 7.5×10^{14}
ultraviolet	400 nm to 4 nm	7.5×10^{14} to 7.5×10^{16}
x-rays	4 nm to 30 pm	7.5×10^{16} to 1.0×10^{19}
γ-rays	30 pm to 0.1 pm	1.0×10^{19} to 3.0×10^{21}

5.
$$\nu = \frac{c}{\lambda} = \frac{3.00 \times 10^8 \text{ m s}^{-1}}{633 \times 10^{-9} \text{ m}} = 4.74 \times 10^{14} \text{ Hz or s}^{-1}$$

   (Note $\lambda = 633$ nm or 633×10^{-9} m)

6. Similar to Q. 5

$$\nu = \frac{c}{\lambda} = \frac{3.00 \times 10^8 \text{ m s}^{-1}}{589.2 \times 10^{-9} \text{ m}} = 5.09 \times 10^{14} \text{ Hz or s}^{-1}$$

7. The energy of a photon is given by the equation
   $E = h\nu$ in which h = Planck's Constant
   $= 6.63 \times 10^{-34}$ J s.
   The frequency, ν, of the lithium red line is given by the equation

$$\nu = \frac{c}{\lambda} = \frac{3.00 \times 10^8 \text{ m s}^{-1}}{670.8 \times 10^{-9} \text{ m}} = 4.472 \times 10^{14} \text{ s}^{-1}$$

   Therefore $E = h\nu = 6.63 \times 10^{-34}$ J s x 4.47×10^{14} s^{-1}
   $= 2.97 \times 10^{-19}$ J.
   This is the energy of one photon of wavelength 670.8 mm.
   The energy of 1 mole of these photons (1 Einstein) will be
   $2.97 \times 10^{-19} \times 6.022 \times 10^{23} = 1.79 \times 10^5$ J $= 179$ kJ.

8. The energy, E, required to ionize one potassium atom will be
   given by

$$E = \frac{0.42 \text{ MJ}}{1 \text{ mol}} \times \frac{10^6 \text{ J}}{1 \text{ MJ}} \times \frac{1 \text{ mol}}{6.022 \times 10^{23} \text{ atoms}}$$

$$= 6.97 \times 10^{-19} \text{ J per atom.}$$

   To solve the remainder of the problem we may combine the
   equations

$$E = h\nu \text{ and } \nu = \frac{c}{\lambda} \text{ in the form } E = \frac{hc}{\lambda} \text{ or } \lambda = \frac{hc}{E}$$

   To bring about the ionization of the potassium atom,
   therefore, the energy of the photons must have a minimum

value of 6.97×10^{-19} J per atom and, therefore, a maximum wavelength given by

$$\lambda = \frac{hc}{E} = \frac{6.63 \times 10^{-34} \text{J s} \times 3.00 \times 10^{8} \text{ m s}^{-1}}{6.97 \times 10^{-19} \text{ J}}$$

$$= 2.85 \times 10^{-7} \text{ m}$$

Therefore $\lambda_{MAX} = 285$ nm

9. The energy range of the quanta of radiation equivalent to the wavelengths given in Q. 4 may be calculated by using the equation developed in Q. 8, viz.

$$E = \frac{hc}{\lambda} \text{ J}$$

In each case the wavelength of the radiation, λ, must be expressed in meters. One example will illustrate the method of calculation. For radiation with $\lambda = 710$ nm

$$E = \frac{hc}{\lambda} = \frac{6.63 \times 10^{-34} \text{J s} \times 3.00 \times 10^{8} \text{m s}^{-1}}{710 \times 10^{-9} \text{ m}}$$

$$= 2.80 \times 10^{-19} \text{ J (per quantum of radiation)}$$

Making similar calculations for each type of radiation we obtain

Types of Radiation	Wavelenth λ		Energy in Joules per Quantum
Radio frequency	1 km	– 30 cm	2.0×10^{-28} – 6.6×10^{-25}
Microwave	30 cm –	2 mm	6.6×10^{-25} – 1.0×10^{-22}
Far infra-red	2 mm –	30 μm	1.0×10^{-22} – 6.6×10^{-21}
Near infra-red	30 μm –	710 nm	6.6×10^{-21} – 2.8×10^{-19}
Visible	710 nm–	400 nm	2.8×10^{-19} – 5.0×10^{-19}
Ultraviolet	400 nm–	4 nm	5.0×10^{-19} – 5.0×10^{-17}
X-rays	4 nm –	30 pm	5.0×10^{-17} – 6.6×10^{-15}
γ-rays	30 pm –	0.1 pm	6.6×10^{-15} – 2.0×10^{-12}

The energy of radiation which will bring about the dissociation of a particular molecule must be at least equal to the dissociation energy of one molecule of the substance in question expressed in J.
The appropriate calculation in the case of the hydrogen molecule would be

$$\frac{434.0 \text{ kJ}}{1 \text{ mol}} \times \frac{1000 \text{ J}}{1 \text{ kJ}} \times \frac{1 \text{ mol}}{6.022 \times 10^{23} \text{ molecules}}$$

$$= 7.207 \times 10^{-19} \text{ J molecule}^{-1}$$

Consulting the table above we find that <u>ultraviolet radiation</u> would cause dissociation of the <u>hydrogen molecules</u>.
By making calculations of the same type for the other molecules we may construct the following table.

Molecule	Dissociation Energy kJ mol^{-1}	Dissociation Energy J molecule^{-1}	Dissociating Radiation
$H_2(g)$	434	7.21×10^{-19}	Ultraviolet
$O_2(g)$	498	8.27×10^{-19}	Ultraviolet
$Cl_2(g)$	243	4.04×10^{-19}	Visible
$F_2(g)$	159	2.64×10^{-19}	Near infra-red

10. The energy required to bring about he dissociation

$$NO_2(g) \rightarrow NO(g) + O(g)$$

is 305 kJ mol^{-1}. We may calculate the wavelength of light that can cause this dissociation by applying the equation

$$\lambda = \frac{hc}{E}$$

where E = the dissociation energy of one molecule of $NO_2(g)$

$$= \frac{305 \text{ kJ}}{1 \text{ mol}} \times \frac{1000 \text{ J}}{1 \text{ kJ}} \times \frac{1 \text{ mol}}{6.022 \times 10^{23} \text{ molecules}}$$

$$= 5.06 \times 10^{-19} \text{ J molecule}^{-1}$$

Therefore $\lambda = \dfrac{6.63 \times 10^{-34} \text{ J s} \times 3.00 \times 10^8 \text{ m s}^{-1}}{5.07 \times 10^{-19} \text{ J}}$

$$= 3.93 \times 10^{-7} \text{ m}$$
$$= 393 \text{ nm} = \text{maximum wavelength for dissociation.}$$

This wavelength corresponds to the ULTRAVIOLET region of the electromagnetic spectrum. The wavelength of 320 nm, being the minimum occurring at the earth's surface, is equivalent to radiation sufficiently energetic to bring about the dissociation of $NO_2(g)$ molecules.

11. The energy necessary to eject an electron from a lithium atom will be that of a photon with a wavelength of 520 nm or 520×10^{-9} m. This energy will be given by

$$E = \frac{hc}{\lambda} = \frac{6.63 \times 10^{-34} \text{ J s} \times 3.00 \times 10^8 \text{ m s}^{-1}}{520 \times 10^{-9} \text{ m}}$$

$$= 3.83 \times 10^{-19} \text{ J} = \phi \text{ in the equation}$$

$$E_{photon} = \phi + KE \text{ (refer to Q. 11)}$$

and $E_{photon} = \dfrac{hc}{\lambda} = \dfrac{6.63 \times 10^{-34} \text{ J s} \times 3.00 \times 10^8 \text{ m s}^{-1}}{360 \times 10^{-9} \text{ m}}$

$$= 5.53 \times 10^{-19} \text{ J}$$

Substituting in the equation

$$E_{photon} = \phi + KE$$

$$5.53 \times 10^{-19} = 3.83 \times 10^{-19} + KE$$

Therefore $KE = 5.53 \times 10^{-19} - 3.83 \times 10^{-19}$ J

$$= 1.70 \times 10^{-19} \text{ J} = \text{KE of emitted electrons}$$
$$= 102 \text{ kJ mol}^{-1}$$

12. A minimum energy of 496 kJ mol^{-1} is required to ionize sodium atoms, i.e. for

$$Na(g) + 496 \text{ kJ mol}^{-1} \rightarrow Na^+(g)$$

Therefore energy necessary to ionize one atom of Na(g) will be

$$\frac{496 \text{ kJ}}{1 \text{ mol}} \times \frac{1000 \text{ J}}{1 \text{ kJ}} \times \frac{1 \text{ mol}}{6.022 \times 10^{23} \text{ atoms}} = 8.24 \times 10^{-19} \text{ J per atom}$$

This energy is equivalent to a frequency given by

$$E = h\nu$$

Therefore $\nu = \dfrac{E}{h} = \dfrac{8.24 \times 10^{-19} \text{ J}}{6.63 \times 10^{-34} \text{ J s}} = 1.24 \times 10^{15} \text{ s}^{-1}$

This frequency is equivalent to electromagnetic radiation in the ultra-violet range, i.e. outside the visible range of the spectrum.
We apply the equation

$$E_{photon} = \phi + KE$$

in which $\phi = 8.24 \times 10^{-19}$ J (see above) and E_{photon} is given by

$$\frac{600 \text{ kJ}}{1 \text{ mol}} \times \frac{1000 \text{ J}}{1 \text{ kJ}} \times \frac{1 \text{ mol}}{6.022 \times 10^{23} \text{ atoms}} = 9.96 \times 10^{-19} \text{ J per atom}$$

Therefore $9.96 \times 10^{-19} = 8.24 \times 10^{-19} + KE$
Therefore $KE = 9.96 \times 10^{-19} - 8.24 \times 10^{-19} = 1.72 \times 10^{-19}$ J
= KE of the emitted electrons

13. a) The mass of an electron (see Chapter 2 or literature data tables) is 9.11×10^{-31} kg.
The kinetic energy of the emitted electrons will be given by

$$K.E = \frac{1}{2} mv^2 = \frac{1}{2} \times 9.11 \times 10^{-31} \text{ kg} \times (6.4 \times 10^4 \text{ m s}^{-1})^2 = 1.87 \times 10^{-21} \text{ J}$$

since 1 kg m^2 s^{-2} = 1 J.

Therefore K.E. = 1.9×10^{-21} J to two significant figures.

b) The energy of a 470.0 nm photon may be calculated by

combining the formulas $E = h\nu$ and $\nu = \dfrac{c}{\lambda}$

$$E = \frac{hc}{\lambda} = \frac{6.63 \times 10^{-34} \text{ J s} \times 3.00 \times 10^8 \text{ m s}^{-1}}{470.0 \times 10^{-9} \text{ m}} = 4.23 \times 10^{-19} \text{ J}$$

c) The minimum energy required to remove an electron from potassium metal will be given by the equation

Energy of Photon = Energy needed + Kinetic energy
for electron to of emitted
escape from metal

i.e. $E_{photon} = \phi + KE$

Therefore ϕ = E_{photon} - KE

ϕ = 4.23 x 10^{-19} - 1.9 x 10^{-21} = 4.21 x 10^{-19} J

14. The energy emitted when an electron moves from the n=6 to the n=2 level in the hydrogen atom may be calculated by using the equation

$$\Delta E = 1312 \left(\frac{1}{n_f^2} - \frac{1}{n_i^2}\right) \text{ kJ mol}^{-1}. \quad \text{(See Chapter 6.)}$$

Substituting n_i = 6 and n_f = 2 gives

$$\Delta E = 1312 \left(\frac{1}{(2)^2} - \frac{1}{(6)^2}\right) = 291.6 \text{ kJ mol}^{-1}$$

The energy emitted by one H atom is

$$E = \frac{291.6 \text{ kJ}}{1 \text{ mol}} \times \frac{1 \text{ mol}}{6.022 \times 10^{23} \text{ atoms}} \times \frac{1000 \text{ J}}{1 \text{ kJ}}$$

$$= 4.84 \times 10^{-19} \text{ J atom}^{-1}$$

Since one photon is emitted by one hydrogen atom this is also the energy of the photon. To find the wavelength of this photon we use the relationships

E_{photon} = $h\nu$ and $\lambda\nu$ = c

Thus E_{photon} = $\frac{hc}{\lambda}$ or λ = $\frac{hc}{E_{photon}}$

$$\lambda = \frac{6.63 \times 10^{-34} \text{ J s} \times 3.00 \times 10^{8} \text{ m s}^{-1}}{4.84 \times 10^{-19} \text{ J}}$$

$$= 4.11 \times 10^{-7} \text{ m}$$

= 410 nm. This wavelength corresponds to the visible spectrum.

15. $$\Delta E = 1312 \left(\frac{1}{n_f^2} - \frac{1}{n_i^2}\right) \text{ kJ mol}^{-1}$$

where n_f = 4 and n_i = 2.

Therefore ΔE = $1312 \left(\frac{1}{4^2} - \frac{1}{2^2}\right)$ kJ mol^{-1} = -246 kJ mol^{-1}

The negative sign indicates that energy is being absorbed. The energy absorbed by one hydrogen atom will be

$$E = \frac{246 \text{ kJ}}{1 \text{ mol}} \times \frac{1000 \text{ J}}{1 \text{ kJ}} \times \frac{1 \text{ mol}}{6.022 \times 10^{23} \text{ atoms}}$$

$$= 4.09 \times 10^{-19} \text{ J}$$

Since one photon is absorbed by one hydrogen atom this will also be the energy of the photon causing excitation. The wavelength of this photon will be given by

$$\lambda = \frac{hc}{E_{photon}}$$

$$= \frac{6.63 \times 10^{-34} \text{ J s} \times 3.00 \times 10^{8} \text{ m s}^{-1}}{4.09 \times 10^{-19} \text{ J}}$$

$$= 4.87 \times 10^{-7} \text{ m} = 487 \text{ nm}$$

This is the longest wavelength of light which will cause this excitation. Shorter wavelengths correspond to higher energies.

16.

$$\Delta E = 1312 \left(\frac{1}{n_f^2} - \frac{1}{n_i^2} \right) \text{ kJ mol}^{-1} \quad \ldots \ldots \quad (1)$$

The Lyman Series corresponds to electron transitions from higher energy levels to the n=1 level.
Therefore $n_f = 1$ and $n_i = n_i$, the required energy level.
A wavelength of 103 nm corresponds to an energy given by

$$E_{photon} = \frac{hc}{\lambda} \text{ J}$$

$$= \frac{6.63 \times 10^{-34} \text{ J s} \times 3.00 \times 10^{8} \text{ m s}^{-1}}{103 \times 10^{-9} \text{ m}}$$

$$= 1.93 \times 10^{-18} \text{ J per photon or atom.}$$

We now convert this energy into kJ mol^{-1} for substitution in equation (1)

$$\text{Therefore } \Delta E = \frac{1.93 \times 10^{-18} \text{ J}}{1 \text{ atom}} \times \frac{6.022 \times 10^{23} \text{ atoms}}{1 \text{ mol}} \times \frac{1 \text{ kJ}}{1000 \text{ J}}$$

$$= 1162 \text{ kJ mol}^{-1}$$

$$\text{Therefore } 1162 = 1312 \left(\frac{1}{1^2} - \frac{1}{n_i^2} \right)$$

$$\text{or} \quad 1162 = 1312 - \frac{1312}{n_i^2}$$

$$\text{or} \quad \frac{1312}{n_i^2} = 1312 - 1162 \quad \text{or} \quad n_i^2 = \frac{1312}{150}$$

Therefore $n_i = 3$

17.

$$\Delta E = 1312 \left(\frac{1}{n_f^2} - \frac{1}{n_i^2} \right) \text{ kJ mol}^{-1}$$

a) In this example the hydrogen atom is being ionized. This means that the electron is removed completely from the atom, equivalent to a value of $n_f = \infty$. $n_i = 1$

$$\text{Therefore } \Delta E = 1312 \left(\frac{1}{(\infty)^2} - \frac{1}{1^2} \right) \text{ kJ mol}^{-1}$$

$$= 1312 (0 - 1) = -1312 \text{ kJ mol}^{-1}$$

The negative sign indicates that energy is being absorbed by the atom.

The energy required to ionize one hydrogen atom will be given by

$$E = \frac{1312 \text{ kJ}}{1 \text{ mol}} \times \frac{1000 \text{ J}}{1 \text{ kJ}} \times \frac{1 \text{ mol}}{6.022 \times 10^{23} \text{ atoms}}$$

$$= 2.18 \times 10^{-18} \text{ J atom}^{-1}$$

Since one photon is absorbed by one hydrogen atom, this is also the energy of the photon which will just cause ionization of the hydrogen atom. To find the wavelength of this photon we employ the relationships

$$E_{photon} = h\nu \quad \text{and} \quad \lambda\nu = c$$

Therefore $E_{photon} = \frac{hc}{\lambda}$ or $\lambda = \frac{hc}{E_{photon}}$

$$\lambda = \frac{6.63 \times 10^{-34} \text{ J s} \times 3.00 \times 10^8 \text{ m s}^{-1}}{2.18 \times 10^{-18} \text{ J}} = 9.12 \times 10^{-8} \text{ m} = 91.2 \text{ nm}$$

b) In this part of the example $n_f = \infty$ as before but $n_i = 2$

Therefore $\Delta E = 1312 \times (\frac{1}{(\infty)^2} - \frac{1}{2^2}) \text{ kJ mol}^{-1}$

$$= -328.0 \text{ kJ mol}^{-1}$$

The energy required to ionize one hydrogen atom in this excited state will be given by

$$E = \frac{328.0 \text{ kJ}}{1 \text{ mol}} \times \frac{1000 \text{ J}}{1 \text{ kJ}} \times \frac{1 \text{ mol}}{6.022 \times 10^{23} \text{ atoms}}$$

$$= 5.45 \times 10^{-19} \text{ J atom}^{-1}$$

Since one photon is absorbed by one hydrogen atom, this is also the energy of the ionizing photon. To find the wavelength we use the equation from (a) above

$$\lambda = \frac{hc}{E_{photon}} = \frac{6.63 \times 10^{-34} \text{ J s} \times 3.00 \times 10^8 \text{ m s}^{-1}}{5.45 \times 10^{-19} \text{ J}}$$

$$= 3.65 \times 10^{-7} \text{ m} = 365 \text{ nm}$$

18. The de Broglie equation

$$\lambda = \frac{h}{mv}$$

permits us to calculate the wavelength associated with a minute particle provided that we know its momentum.
We must convert h to basic SI units to obtain the wavelength in meters. (1 Joule = 1 Newton meters = 1 kg m s^{-2}.)

$$\lambda = \frac{h}{mv} = \frac{6.63 \times 10^{-34} \text{ J s}}{1.67 \times 10^{-27} \text{ kg} \times 4.21 \times 10^3 \text{ m s}^{-1}} \times \frac{1 \text{ kg m}^2 \text{ s}^{-2}}{1 \text{ J}}$$

$$= 9.43 \times 10^{-11} \text{ m} = 94.3 \text{ pm}$$

Thus neutrons moving with a speed of 4.21×10^3 m s^{-1} have a wavelength of 94.3 pm.

19. In this problem, we employ the de Broglie equation in the re-arranged form

$$v = \frac{h}{m\lambda}$$

and the mass of the neutron is 1.67×10^{-27} kg (see Q. 18). Substituting and converting to basic SI units (see Q. 18)

$$v = \frac{6.63 \times 10^{-34} \text{ J s}}{1.67 \times 10^{-27} \text{ kg} \times 3.00 \times 10^{-10} \text{ m}} \times \frac{1 \text{ kg m}^2 \text{ s}^{-2}}{1 \text{ J}}$$

$$= 1.32 \times 10^3 \text{ m s}^{-1}$$

20. (a) The velocity of the neutron is 1.00×10^2 km s^{-1} or

$$\frac{1.00 \times 10^2 \text{ km}}{1 \text{s}} \times \frac{1000 \text{ m}}{1 \text{ km}} = 1.00 \times 10^5 \text{ m s}^{-1}$$

The mass of a neutron $= 1.67 \times 10^{-27}$ kg (Q. 18).

Substituting in the de Broglie equation

$$\lambda = \frac{h}{mv} \quad \text{and converting to basic SI units.}$$

$$\lambda = \frac{6.63 \times 10^{-34} \text{ J s}}{1.67 \times 10^{-27} \text{ kg} \times 1.00 \times 10^5 \text{ m s}^{-1}} \times \frac{1 \text{ kg m}^2 \text{ s}^{-2}}{1 \text{ J}}$$

$$= 3.97 \times 10^{-12} \text{ m} = 3.97 \text{ pm}$$

(b) The speed of the electron is 5.00×10^7 m s^{-1} and the mass of an electron is 9.11×10^{-31} kg.
Substituting in the de Broglie equation in the appropriate units

$$\lambda = \frac{6.63 \times 10^{-34} \text{ J s}}{9.11 \times 10^{-31} \text{ kg} \times 5.00 \times 10^7 \text{ m s}^{-1}} \times \frac{1 \text{ kg m}^2 \text{ s}^{-2}}{1 \text{ J}}$$

$$= 1.46 \times 10^{-11} \text{ m} = 14.6 \text{ pm}$$

21. First we make the appropriate unit conversions for speed and mass (see Chapter 1 for values).

$$\frac{95 \text{ miles}}{1 \text{ hour}} \times \frac{1 \text{ hour}}{3600 \text{ s}} \times \frac{1760 \text{ yards}}{1 \text{ mile}} \times \frac{1 \text{ m}}{1.094 \text{ yards}}$$
$$= 42.5 \text{ m s}^{-1} \quad \text{and}$$

$$5 \text{ oz} \times \frac{1 \text{ lb}}{16 \text{ oz}} \times \frac{1 \text{ kg}}{2.205 \text{ lbs}} = 1.42 \times 10^{-1} \text{ kg}$$

Applying the de Broglie equation as before,

$$\lambda = \frac{6.63 \times 10^{-34} \text{ J s}}{1.42 \times 10^{-1} \text{ kg} \times 42.5 \text{ m s}^{-1}} \times \frac{1 \text{ kg m}^2 \text{ s}^{-2}}{1 \text{ J}}$$
$$= 1.1 \times 10^{-34} \text{ m or } 1.1 \times 10^{-22} \text{ pm, a very short}$$
wavelength indeed!

22. Generally speaking, ionization energies increase from left to right, and decrease from top to bottom of the periodic table, and so the order of ionization energies of the noble gases may be predicted as He>Ne>Ar since they occur in the same group. In the cases of He, Li^+, and Be^{2+} a 1s electron is being removed from a $1s^2$ configuration, in the case of Li^+ against a nuclear charge of +3 and in the case of Be^{++} against a nuclear charge of +4. We predict then that the ionization energy of the Be^{++} ion is greater than that of the Li^+ ion, which in turn is greater than He (nuclear charge of +2). Thus the overall ordering is $Be^{2+}>Li^+>He>Ne>Ar$.

23. The energy required to remove an electron from a helium atom will be

$$\frac{2.37 \text{ MJ}}{1 \text{ mol}} \times \frac{1 \text{ mol}}{6.022 \times 10^{23} \text{ atoms}} \times \frac{10^6 \text{ J}}{1 \text{ MJ}} = 3.94 \times 10^{-18} \text{ J atom}^{-1}$$

The energy of a photon with a wavelength of 40.0 nm will be given by

$$E_{photon} = h\nu = \frac{hc}{\lambda}$$

$$= \frac{6.63 \times 10^{-34} \text{ J s} \times 3.00 \times 10^8 \text{ m s}^{-1}}{40.0 \times 10^{-9} \text{ m}}$$

$$= 4.97 \times 10^{-18} \text{ J}$$

and $E_{photon} = \phi + KE$
where $\phi =$ the ionization energy per atom
$= 3.94 \times 10^{-18}$ J

Therefore KE $= (4.97 \times 10^{-18} - 3.94 \times 10^{-18})$J
$= 1.03 \times 10^{-8}$ J per photoelectron.

24. The total number of orbitals associated with the n=3 level is 9:

             3s – 1 orbital
             3p – 3 orbitals
             3d – 5 orbitals
        Total – 9 orbitals

25. The 1p and 2d orbitals are not possible, since p orbitals first appear at the n=2 level and d orbitals first appear at the n=3 level.

26. The Pauli Exclusion Principle may be stated in general terms that 'no orbital can accommodate more than two electrons and these two electrons must have opposite spin.' Therefore beryllium cannot have the configuration $1s^4$.

27. (b) is not allowed. The 3s orbital may only accommodate a maximum of 2 electrons.

93

(d) is not allowed. The 3p orbitals have a maximum total
population of 6 electrons.

28. (a), (b) and (d) are not ground state configurations. The
    correct ground state configurations would be
    (a) $1s^2 2s^1$
    (b) $1s^2 2s^2 2p^2$
    (d) $1s^2 2s^2 2p^6 3s^2 3p^1$

29. (a) $_{19}$K: $1s^2 2s^2 2p^6 3s^2 3p^6 4s^1$
    (b) $_{13}$Al: $1s^2 2s^2 2p^6 3s^2 3p^1$
    (c) $_{17}$Cl: $1s^2 2s^2 2p^6 3s^2 3p^5$
    (d) $_{22}$Ti: $1s^2 2s^2 2p^6 3s^2 3p^6 4s^2 3d^2$
    (e) $_{30}$Zn: $1s^2 2s^2 2p^6 3s^2 3p^6 3d^{10} 4s^2$
    (f) $_{33}$As: $1s^2 2s^2 2p^6 3s^2 3p^6 3d^{10} 4s^2 4p^3$

30. (a) $_4$Be: $1s^2 2s^2$
    (b) $_7$N: $1s^2 2s^2 2p^3$
    (c) $_9$F: $1s^2 2s^2 2p^5$
    (d) $_{12}$Mg: $1s^2 2s^2 2p^6 3s^2$
    (e) $_{17}$Cl: $1s^2 2s^2 2p^6 3s^2 3p^5$
    (f) $_{10}$Ne$^+$: $1s^2 2s^2 2p^5$
    (g) $_{13}$Al^{3+}: $1s^2 2s^2 2p^6$

31.
(a) P:

1s	2s	2p			3s	3p		
↑↓	↑↓	↑↓	↑↓	↑↓	↑↓	↑	↑	↑

(b) Ca:

1s	2s	2p			3s	3p			4s
↑↓	↑↓	↑↓	↑↓	↑↓	↑↓	↑↓	↑↓	↑↓	↑↓

(c) V:

1s	2s	2p			3s	3p			4s	3d				
↑↓	↑↓	↑↓	↑↓	↑↓	↑↓	↑↓	↑↓	↑↓	↑↓	↑	↑	↑		

(d) Br:

1s	2s	2p			3s	3p			3d					4s	4p		
↑↓	↑↓	↑↓	↑↓	↑↓	↑↓	↑↓	↑↓	↑↓	↑↓	↑↓	↑↓	↑↓	↑↓	↑↓	↑↓	↑↓	↑

32. Referring to the Periodic Table, we find:
    (a) Li – 1st main group element, 2nd period
    (b) N – 5th main group element, 2nd period
    (c) Ca – 2nd main group element, 4th period
    (d) Ti – 2nd transition element, 4th period
    (e) As – 5th main group element, 4th period
    (f) I – 7th main group element, 5th period
    (g) Ba – 2nd main group element, 6th period

33. Hund's Rule tells us that, for atoms in their ground states,
    electrons enter orbitals (sublevels) of equal energy singly
    and with parallel spins until forced to pair spins. Of the
    examples given (b) and (e) are not in their ground states
    for the following reasons
    (b) – the 2p orbitals are not singly occupied with
            electrons having parallel spins

(e) — the 3p orbitals are incorrectly occupied. Only one pair of electrons will occupy one of the orbitals, the other two will have one electron each

Examples (a), (c) and (d) observe normal filling order and are, therefore, in their ground states. The two configurations (a) and (c) are identical.

34. Note that examples (a), (b) and (c) have identical numbers of electrons. All have atomic number 7 and therefore are nitrogen. Example (d) has eight electrons and is oxygen, and (e) has 16 electrons and is sulfur. Thus the answers are
(a) N   (b) N   (c) N   (d) O   (e) S

35. If two hydrogen atoms having electrons with opposite spins approach each other, a suitable environment for covalent bond formation is created. Each atom has a 1s orbital capable of accommodating a second electron of opposite spin. At first the nucleus of one hydrogen atom attracts the electron of the second until the electron densities of both atoms overlap. As a result, electron density increases in this region of overlap, and it is essentially this increased electron density which holds the nuclei together in a bond and so a stable H_2 molecule is created.

By contrast, when two helium atoms approach each other the electrons of one helium atom cannot be drawn into the region occupied by the electrons of the other because both orbitals, the 1s orbitals, are filled. Thus a bond cannot form. This is consistent with the Pauli Exclusion Principle which limits the number of electrons in any orbital to two.

36. Box diagram representation of the electronic configuration of Boron is

B: 1s[↑↓] 2s[↑↓] 2p[↑][ ][ ]

Boron, therefore, has only one unpaired electron and, for this reason, would be expected to form only one covalent bond. However, boron forms the molecule BF_3 and the ion BF_4^- with univalent fluorine. These species form because B and B^- are reacting in the promoted states, in which the number of singly-occupied orbitals and thus the valence is 3 and 4 respectively:

B(promoted): 1s[↑↓] 2s[↑] 2p[↑][↑][ ]

B^-(promoted): 1s[↑↓] 2s[↑] 2p[↑][↑][↑]

37. Box diagram representation of the ground state of the silicon atom is as follows.

Si: 1s[↑↓] 2s[↑↓] 2p[↑↓][↑↓][↑↓] 3s[↑↓] 3p[↑][↑][ ]

There are, therefore, two unpaired electrons and so a valence of 2 for silicon would be predicted. However, like boron in the previous question, silicon can react in the promoted state in which a 3s electron is raised to a 3p orbital

Si (promoted):

1s	2s	2p	3s	3p
↑↓	↑↓	↑↓ ↑↓ ↑↓	↑	↑ ↑ ↑

Thus the valence of silicon increases to four, since there are now four singly-occupied orbitals.

38. We can answer this question simply by finding the total number of electrons in each species by referring to the atomic numbers in the periodic table, and adding one electron to the totals in the case of each negative ion.

Molecule or ion	Total number of electrons
NO_2	23
O_3	24
SO_2	32
ClO_2	33
O_2^-	17
NO_2^-	24

Therefore NO_2, ClO_2 and O_2^- are odd electron species.

39. Any atom in its ground state which does not possess completely filled orbitals or sets of orbitals must have one or more unpaired electrons. This follows from Hund's rule which states that all available orbitals in a particular energy level are initially singly occupied. The appropriate electron configurations are

(a) Li: $1s^2 2s^1$
(b) Be: $1s^2 2s^2$
(c) O: $1s^2 2s^2 2p^4$
(d) Ne: $1s^2 2s^2 2p^6$
(e) Na: $1s^2 2s^2 2p^6 3s^1$
(f) Ca: $1s^2 2s^2 2p^6 3s^2 3p^6 4s^2$
(g) P: $1s^2 2s^2 2p^6 3s^2 3p^3$
(h) Zn: $1s^2 2s^2 2p^6 3s^2 3p^6 4s^2 3d^{10}$

Orbitals or orbital sets therefore remain unfilled in the following atoms.

(a) Li $(2s^1)$
(c) O $(2p^4)$
(e) Na $(3s^1)$
(g) P $(3p^3)$

CHAPTER 7

1. <u>Allotrope</u>   <u>Description</u>
    orthorhombic   brilliant yellow crystals, contain S_8
                                    molecules. The stablest form of S.

    monoclinic   long needle crystals; slowly reverts
                                    to orthorhombic form. Made by
                                    cooling molten sulfur.

    plastic   brown, rubbery solid; slowly reverts
                                    to orthorhombic form. Made by
                                    pouring molten S into cold water.
    See text section 7.2 for description and explanation of what
    is observed when sulfur is heated to boiling.

2. One test would be to add $BaCl_2$(aq) to the solution. If a
    precipitate forms, the anion present must be $SO_4{}^{2-}$ since
    $BaSO_4$ is insoluble whereas all metal sulfites are soluble.
    Another test would be to add acid to the solution, and
    observe whether this produces a detectable odor of sulfur
    dioxide; if it does the anion is $SO_3{}^{2-}$ since it reacts with
    H_3O^+ as
    $$SO_3{}^{2-} + 2H_3O^+ \longrightarrow SO_2(g) + 2H_2O$$
    whereas $SO_4{}^{2-}$ produces only $HSO_4{}^-$ only. Another test would
    be to add a drop of bromine water to the solution; if it is
    decoloured, the anion must be sulfite since only it acts as
    a reducing agent.

3. a) With concentrated sulfuric acid, even without heating
    $CaSO_4 \cdot 2H_2O \longrightarrow CaSO_4 + 2H_2O$ (absorbed by H_2SO_4).
    In addition, we expect
    $$CaSO_4 + H_2SO_4 \longrightarrow Ca(HSO_4)_2$$

    b) $H_2SO_4 + NaOH \longrightarrow NaHSO_4 + H_2O$
    $NaHSO_4 + NaOH \longrightarrow Na_2SO_4 + H_2O$
    These acid–base reactions ocur whether the acid is dilute or
    concentrated, hot or cold.

    c) $BaCl_2$(aq) $+ H_2SO_4 \longrightarrow BaSO_4(s) + 2HCl$
    This reaction should proceed regardless of the concentration
    and temperature of the acid.

    d) $H_2SO_4 + C_2H_5OH \longrightarrow C_2H_4 + H_3O^+ + HSO_4{}^-$
    This reaction proceeds at high temperature, and as
    experiment 7.5 indicates, it requires concentrated acid.

e) $NaF + H_2SO_4 \longrightarrow HF(g) + NaHSO_4$
This reaction should proceed, by analogy with that for HCl, only with concentrated acid.

f) $NaNO_3 + H_2SO_4 \longrightarrow HNO_3 + NaHSO_4$
This reaction proceeds only with hot, concentrated acid.
g) $C(s) + 2H_2SO_4 \longrightarrow CO_2(g) + 2H_2O + SO_2(g)$
This reaction proceeds only with concentrated acid and at high temperatures.

4. a) Reactions in which H_2SO_4 acts as an oxidizing agent are those which yield SO_2 and in which some material is oxidized. Examples given in the text include

$2Br^-(\text{or } 2I^-) + 2H_2SO_4(\text{conc}) \longrightarrow Br_2(\text{or } I_2) + SO_4^{2-} + SO_2 + 2H_2O$

$C(s) + 2H_2SO_4(\text{conc}) \longrightarrow CO_2 + 2SO_2 + 2H_2O$

$Cu + 2H_2SO_4(\text{conc}) \longrightarrow Cu^{2+} + SO_4^{2-} + SO_2 + 2H_2O$

$2Ag + 2H_2SO_4(\text{conc}) \longrightarrow 2Ag^+ + SO_4^{2-} + SO_2 + 2H_2O$

b) In acting as an acid, H_2SO_4 donates one or both H^+ ions to a base (often H_2O) and forms HSO_4^- and/or SO_4^{2-}.
Examples would include its reaction with water or any base MOH of an alkali metal M, or $M(OH)_2$ of an alkaline earth metal M.

e.g. $H_2SO_4 + H_2O \longrightarrow HSO_4^- + H_3O^+$

$HSO_4^- + H_2O \longrightarrow SO_4^{2-} + H_3O^+$

$H_2SO_4 + MOH \longrightarrow M^+ + HSO_4^- + H_2O$

$HSO_4^- + MOH \longrightarrow M^+ + SO_4^{2-} + H_2O$

c) In dehydration reactions, concentrated H_2SO_4 extracts hydrogen and oxygen from materials in the atom ratio 2:1, to form H_2O which then reacts with more H_2SO_4 to yield H_3O^+ and HSO_4^-. Examples from the text include

$CuSO_4 \cdot 5H_2O \longrightarrow CuSO_4 + 5H_2O(\longrightarrow 5H_3O^+ + 5HSO_4^-)$

$C_{12}H_{22}O_{11} + 11H_2SO_4 \longrightarrow 12C + 11H_3O^+ + 11HSO_4^-$

$HCO_2H + H_2SO_4 \longrightarrow CO + H_3O^+ + HSO_4^-$

$C_2H_5OH + H_2SO_4 \longrightarrow C_2H_4 + H_3O^+ + HSO_4^-$

5.
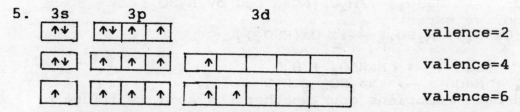

A valence of 8 cannot be achieved by sulfur since there are no further valence-shell lone pairs from which one electron can be promoted to the 3d level. Oxygen cannot achieve valences of 4 and 6 since it does not have low-lying d orbitals into which 2s or 2p electrons could be promoted to increase its valence.

6. $NaNO_3 + H_2SO_4 \rightleftharpoons HNO_3 + NaHSO_4$

98

$$NaCl + H_2SO_4 \; \underset{\longleftarrow}{\longrightarrow} \; HCl + NaHSO_4$$

Like HBr, HI cannot be prepared in this way since the H_2SO_4 would convert much of the I^- to I_2.

7. a) Sulfuric acid is used in the production of the phosphate fertilizers required in all modern agriculture, and in the manufacture of many products including paints and dyes, explosives, detergents, and synthetic fibers.

b) It is called the contact process since it involves the reaction of SO_2 and O_2, a process which occurs when these molecules came into contact on the surface of the V_2O_5 catalyst.

c) If water is added to concentrated sulfuric acid, the heat evolved by the reaction can be sufficient to boil some of the water, and cause drops of the acid to be thrown violently out of the container.

8. From the information supplied for SO_2 gas, we can use the Ideal Gas Law to deduce the moles of it, and thus the moles and mass of sulfur in the original sample of the compound:

$$P = 750 \text{ mm Hg} \times \frac{1 \text{ atm}}{760 \text{ mm Hg}} = 0.987 \text{ atm}$$

$$V = 173.6 \text{ mL} \times \frac{1L}{1000 \text{ mL}} = 0.1736 \text{ L}$$

$$T = 25 + 273 = 298 \text{ K}$$

Since $PV = nRT$

$$\text{then } n = PV/RT = \frac{0.987 \text{ atm} \times 0.1736 \text{ L}}{0.0821 \text{ L atm K}^{-1} \text{ mol}^{-1} \times 298 \text{ K}}$$
$$= 0.00700 \text{ mol } SO_2$$

Since 1 mole S gives 1 mole SO_2, we also must have 0.00700 moles S in the original sample. To deduce the moles Fe, we convert moles S to mass S and take the difference from the mass of the sample, which by definition is mass S + mass Fe:

$$0.00700 \text{ mol S} \times \frac{32.06 \text{ g S}}{1 \text{ mol S}} = 0.224 \text{ g S}$$

Mass Fe = Mass sample − mass S
     = 0.4203 − 0.224
     = 0.196 g Fe

We convert this mass of Fe to moles:

$$0.196 \text{ g Fe} \times \frac{1 \text{ mole Fe}}{55.85 \text{ g Fe}} = 0.00351 \text{ moles Fe}$$

Dividing both numbers of moles by the smallest,
Therefore Moles:Moles 1.99:1.00
Thus the empirical formula is FeS_2.

9. a) Since H_2SO_4 oxidizes Cu to Cu^{2+}, while being reduced to SO_2, it is its role as an oxidizing agent which is illustrated:
$$Cu(s) + 2H_2SO_4(conc) \longrightarrow Cu^{2+}(liq) + SO_4{}^{2-}(liq) + 2H_2O + SO_2$$

b) From the mass H_2SO_4, we can deduce moles H_2SO_4 and with the help of the equation in part (a) we can deduce the moles of SO_2.

$$50.0g\ H_2SO_4 \times \frac{1\ mole\ H_2SO_4}{98.08\ g\ H_2SO_4} \times \frac{1\ mole\ SO_2}{2\ moles\ H_2SO_4} = 0.255\ moles\ SO_2$$

We know that the molar volume at STP is 22.4 L; thus the volume of SO_2 is

$$0.255\ moles\ SO_2 \times \frac{22.4\ L}{1\ mole\ SO_2} = 5.71\ L\ SO_2$$

(Alternatively we could have deduced V from PV=nRT here.)

c) The moles of diluted acid can be obtained by multiplying the molarity times the volume in L

$$\frac{0.050\ mole}{1\ L} \times 50.0\ mL \times \frac{1\ L}{1000\ mL} = 0.0025\ moles$$

We convert this to mass H_2SO_4 using the molar mass:

$$0.0025\ moles\ H_2SO_4 \times \frac{98.08\ g\ H_2SO_4}{1\ mole\ H_2SO_4} = 0.25\ g\ H_2SO_4$$

This solution of H_2SO_4 would not dissolve copper, as only concentrated H_2SO_4 reacts with copper.

10. The oxidation half-reaction involving H_2S to S would be
$$H_2S \longrightarrow S + 2H^+ + 2e^-$$
Chlorine acts as an oxidizing agent by being reduced to chloride ion:
$$2e^- + Cl_2 \longrightarrow 2Cl^-$$
Adding these half-reactions, we obtain
$$Cl_2 + H_2S \longrightarrow 2Cl^- + S + 2H^+$$
Assuming that the ppm scale here refers to mass, and given that since the density of water and very dilute aqueous solutions is very close to one gram per mL, then the mass of H_2S in 5000 litres of water is

$$5000\ L\ water \times \frac{1000\ g\ water}{1\ L\ water} \times \frac{22\ g\ H_2S}{10^6\ g\ H_2O} = 110\ g\ H_2S$$

We convert this mass of H_2S to moles H_2S, and then to moles Cl_2 and finally to mass of Cl_2.

$$110\ g\ H_2S \times \frac{1\ mole\ H_2S}{34.08\ g\ H_2S} \times \frac{1\ mole\ Cl_2}{1\ mole\ H_2S} \times \frac{70.90\ g\ Cl_2}{1\ mole\ Cl_2} = 229\ g\ Cl_2$$

11. From the information given we can write
$$SO_2 + H_2S \longrightarrow S$$
Presumably the hydrogen and oxygen combine to form water:
$$SO_2 + H_2S \longrightarrow S + H_2O$$
Since H_2O appear twice but S appears three times, we balance

H or O first. H already is balanced so we try O:
$$SO_2 + H_2S \longrightarrow S + 2H_2O$$
The sulfur can now be balanced to yield a completely balanced equation:
$$SO_2 + 2H_2S \longrightarrow 3S + 2H_2O$$
We first deduce the moles SO_2 formed by 1 ton of coal:

$$10^6 \text{ g coal} \times \frac{4.00 \text{ g S}}{100 \text{ g coal}} \times \frac{1 \text{ mole S}}{32.06 \text{ g S}} \times \frac{1 \text{ mole } SO_2}{1 \text{ mole S}} = 1250 \text{ moles } SO_2$$

From the moles SO_2, we can deduce moles H_2S and also the moles and mass of sulfur; using coefficients in the balanced equation:

$$1250 \text{ moles } SO_2 \times \frac{2 \text{ moles } H_2S}{1 \text{ mole } SO_2} = 2500 \text{ moles } H_2S$$

$$1250 \text{ moles } SO_2 \times \frac{3 \text{ moles S}}{1 \text{ mole } SO_2} \times \frac{32.06 \text{ g S}}{1 \text{ mole S}} = 1.20 \times 10^5 \text{ g S}$$

We convert moles H_2S to volume H_2S using the Ideal Gas Law
$PV = nRT$

$$V = nRT/P = \frac{2500 \text{ moles} \times 0.0821 \text{ L atm mol}^{-1} \text{ K}^{-1} \times 298 \text{ K}}{(750 \text{ mm Hg}/760 \text{ mm Hg atm}^{-1})}$$

$$= 6.20 \times 10^4 \text{ L}$$

12. a) To melt white phosphorus, the individual P_4 molecules must be supplied with enough energy so they can move relative to each other. However they are held together only by weak forces. In contrast, to melt black phosphorus many of the covalent bonds in this giant molecule must be broken. Since the process in black phosphorus requires much more energy per P atom, it has a higher melting point.

b) White phosphorus dissolves in CS_2 since both are nonpolar small molecules. Red phosphorus does not dissolve since it is a giant molecule and to dissolve, some of its covalent bonds would have to be broken.

13. Presumably the other product in this combustion is water; thus
$$4PH_3 + 8O_2 \longrightarrow P_4O_{10} + 6H_2O$$

14. Phosphate rock is $Ca_3(PO_4)_2$; to convert it to phosphoric acid H_3PO_4 we need 3H per P atom; the most convenient source of acid is H_2SO_4:
$$Ca_3(PO_4)_2 + 3H_2SO_4 \longrightarrow 3CaSO_4 + 2H_3PO_4$$
(As indicated in the text, each mole of $CaSO_4$ will precipitate with two moles H_2O, and thus $6H_2O$ can be added as a reactant.)
Sodium phosphate, Na_3PO_4, could be obtained by adding 3NaOH

to each H_3PO_4 produced above:
$$H_3PO_4 + 3NaOH \longrightarrow Na_3PO_4 + 3H_2O$$
Superphosphate of lime is the mixture produced by reacting each mole of $Ca_3(PO_4)_2$ with only two moles of H_2SO_4:
$$Ca_3(PO_4)_2 + 2H_2SO_4 \longrightarrow CaSO_4 + Ca(H_2PO_4)_2$$
(As indicated in the text, each salt has some water of hydration.)
To produce white phosphorus, phosphate must be reduced - for example by carbon, as in the industrial process:
$$2Ca_3(PO_4)_2 + 6SiO_2 \longrightarrow P_4O_{10} + 6CaSiO_3$$
$$P_4O_{10} + 10C \longrightarrow P_4 + 10CO$$

15. The structure of P_4S_3 has the sulfur atoms bridging one of the phosphorus atoms of P_4 to the other three, which are still held to each other by P–P bonds.

16. NCl_5 has not been made presumably because nitrogen, unlike phosphorus, cannot achieve a valence of five since it has no low-lying d orbitals into which a valence-shell s electron could be promoted.
PH_5 has not been made since only very electronegative elements (of which hydrogen certainly is not one) are capable of stabilizing the 3d orbitals of phosphorus to an extent that makes 3s to 3d promotion energetically feasible.

17. The combustion presumably involves O_2 from air; thus the unbalanced equation is
$$P_4S_3 + O_2 \longrightarrow P_4O_{10} + SO_2$$
Since P and S appear twice and O three times, we balance them first. Phosphorus is already balanced, and sulfur can be by multiplying SO_2 by three:
$$P_4S_3 + O_2 \longrightarrow P_4O_{10} + 3SO_2$$
Finally, all 16 oxygen atoms on the right can be supplied by eight O_2; thus the balanced equation is
$$P_4S_3 + 8O_2 \longrightarrow P_4O_{10} + 3SO_2$$
To deduce the volume of SO_2, we convert mass P_4S_3 to moles P_4S_3 and then to moles SO_2:

$$0.157 \text{ g } P_4S_3 \times \frac{1 \text{ mole } P_4S_3}{220.06 \text{ g } P_4S_3} \times \frac{3 \text{ moles } SO_2}{1 \text{ mole } P_4S_3} = 0.00214 \text{ moles } SO_2$$

Since $PV = nRT$ and

$$P = 772 \text{ mm Hg} \times \frac{1 \text{ atm}}{760 \text{ mm Hg}} = 1.02 \text{ atm}$$
$$T = 20 + 273 = 293 \text{ K}$$

Therefore $V = nRT/P = \dfrac{0.00214 \text{ mol} \times 0.0821 \text{ L atm mol}^{-1} \text{ K}^{-1} \times 293 \text{ K}}{1.02 \text{ atm}}$

$$= 0.0505 \text{ L}$$

18. From the elemental composition, the empirical formula can be determined. From the gas density, the molar mass can be calculated. The molecular formula can then be obtained by combining these two pieces of information.

	P	F	O
% by mass	29.8	54.8	15.4
Mass in 100 g of compound	29.8 g	54.8 g	15.4 g
Moles of atoms in 100 g of compound	29.8/30.97 = 0.962	54.8/19.00 = 2.88	15.4/16.00 = 0.962
Divide by smallest	1.00	2.99	1.00

Thus the empirical formula is PF_3O.
Now at STP the molar volume is 22.4 L; thus 1 L contains 0.0446 moles of compound. Thus the molar mass of the compound is

$$\frac{4.46 \text{ g}}{0.0446 \text{ moles}} = 100 \text{ g mol}^{-1}$$

Now the empirical formula mass for PF_3O is (30.97 + 3 x 19.00 + 1 x 16.00) = 103.97. Thus the molecular formula must also be PF_3O.
The only possible Lewis structure has all other atoms bonded only to phosphorus. An octet about every atom is achieved in the structure

Since P can expand beyond an octet, and since there are adjacent opposite charges in this structure, we form another PO bond, to obtain

According to the rules for oxidation numbers, that for F must be -1 and that for oxygen -2; thus the sum of those for oxygen and three fluorines is -5. Since the molecule is neutral, the oxidation number for phosphorus must be +5.

19. Let us first try to rewrite the information in semi-symbolic form:
$AlP + H_2SO_4 \longrightarrow$ Al,S,O salt + gas (d=1.531)
    gas + HI $\longrightarrow$ P,H,I compound
From the latter equation, it follows that the unknown gas contains only P and H. From the density of the gas, we can deduce its molar mass. Since 1 L at STP contains 0.0446 moles (see Q. 18), the molar mass is

$$\frac{1.531 \text{ g}}{0.0446 \text{ moles}} = 34.3 \text{ g mol}^{-1}$$

The mass of phosphorus is 30.97; thus there can be only one P atom in the compound. Subtracting 30.97 from 34.3 gives 3.3, indicating that probably there are 3 H atoms in the compound and that its formula is PH_3. This is not absolutely certain, however, since gases do not behave completely ideally. We can check our conclusion using the information for the P,H,I compound by determining its formula:

	P	H	I
% by mass	19.1	2.5	78.4
Mass in 100 g of compound	19.1 g	2.5 g	78.4 g
Moles atoms in 100 g compound	19.1/30.97 = 0.617	2.5/1.01 = 2.5	78.4/126.90 = 0.618
Divide by smallest	1.00	4.05	1.00

Thus the empirical formula is PH_4I, i.e. in terms of the compounds used to prepare it, the formula is $PH_3 \cdot HI$. Thus the formula PH_3 for the gas is confirmed. The equations (unbalanced) must then be

$$AlP + H_2SO_4 \longrightarrow Al,S,O \text{ salt} + PH_3$$
$$PH_3 + HI \longrightarrow PH_4I$$

To balance the first equation, the ratio of AlP to H_2SO_4 must be 2 to 3; thus the Al,S,O salt must have the formula $Al_2(SO_4)_3$:

$$2AlP + 3H_2SO_4 \longrightarrow Al_2(SO_4)_3 + 2PH_3$$

The formula for aluminum sulfate could have been obtained from its elemental composition.

20. An element is oxidized in a reaction of its oxidation number is increased (in a positive sense); an element is reduced if its oxidation number is reduced.

21.

Oxidation State	Examples
+5	H_3PO_4, P_4O_{10}, PO_4^{3-} salts
+3	H_3PO_3, P_4O_6, HPO_3^{2-} salts
0	elemental P (all forms)
-3	PH_3, Ca_3P_2, AlP, PH_4^+

22. To assign oxidation numbers, we follow the rules that precede Example 7.1 of the text.
   a) PH_3: Since the oxidation number (O.N.) for H=+1, that for P=-3 if the sum is to be zero.
   b) AsH_3: Similarly with (a), H=+1 and As=-3.
   c) PF_3: Since O.N.=-1 for F, that for P=+3 since the sum=0.
   d) $K^+MnO_4^-$: The O.N.=+1 for K since it is an ion. The sum of the O.N. for Mn plus 4 times that of -2 for O must be -1, the ion charge. Thus the O.N. for Mn=+7.
   e) SiO_2: Since O.N.=-2 for O, thus O.N.=+4 for Si.
   f) TeF_6: Since O.N.=-1 for F, thus O.N.=+6 for Te.

   g) PH_4^+: Since O.N.=+1 for H, and the sum of the O.N. for P plus 4 times that for H must be the ion charge of +1, the O.N. for P=-3.

23. Similarly to Q. 22,
   a) Since O.N.=-2 for O, thus O.N.=+2 for C.
   b) Since O.N.=-2 for each O, thus O.N.=+4 for Si.

104

c) Since O.N.=+1 for H and -2 for each of the O's and +2 for each Ca, that for three P must add up to +15 if the sum is to be zero for the compound. Thus for each P, O.N.=+5.
d) Since O.N.=-1 for each F, thus O.N.=+6 for S.
e) Since sum is -2, each S is -1 here.
f) Since O.N.=-2 for each of the 3 oxygens and +1 for each of the two H atoms, then for the O.N.'s to sum up to the net charge of -1, then O.N.=+3 for P here.

24. The methodology is similar to that in Q.'s 22 and 23
a) Since H_2O_2 contains a peroxide bond and since O.N.=+1 for each hydrogen, therefore for each oxygen O.N.=-1.
b) Since the O.N.=+1 for lithium, that for oxygen is -2.
c) Since the O.N.=+1 for each H and -1 for I, the O.N. for P must be -3 if the sum over all atoms is to equal zero.
d) Since the O.N.=+1 for Na and -2 for each oxygen, the O.N. for Cl must be +7 if the sum is equal to zero.
e) Since the O.N.=-1 for F, that for oxygen must be +2.
f) Since the O.N.=+2 for Ca, it must be -1 for each sulfur.
g) Since the O.N.=+3 for Al, it must be -3 for P.
h) Since S_8 is an element rather than a compound, the sulfur O.N.=zero.
i) Since the O.N.=+2 for Ba and -2 for each oxygen, then for the sum to be zero that for each Cl must be +1.

25. The half-reaction for H_2SO_4 reduction to SO_2 is (unbalanced)

$$\overset{+6}{H_2SO_4} \longrightarrow \overset{+4}{SO_2}$$

After balancing, we have

$$2H^+ + H_2SO_4 + 2e^- \longrightarrow SO_2 + 2H_2O$$

The oxidation of Br^- to Br_2 is given by

$$2Br^- \longrightarrow Br_2 + 2e^-$$

Thus the balanced redox reaction is

$$2Br^- + H_2SO_4 + 2H^+ \longrightarrow Br_2 + SO_2 + 2H_2O$$

The other reaction is simply its reverse:

$$Br_2 + SO_2 + 2H_2O \longrightarrow 2Br^- + H_2SO_4 + 2H^+$$

The direction of the reaction under given circumstances can be predicted using Le Chatelier's Principle. When large concentrations of H_2SO_4 and Br^- are present, but little Br_2 or SO_2 is present, the direction of equilibrium is far to the right:

$$2Br^- + H_2SO_4 + 2H^+ \rightleftharpoons Br_2 + SO_2 + 2H_2O$$

Particularly if Br_2 and SO_2 escape from solution, the reaction will proceed from left to right. However if we start with a large concentration of Br_2 in solution and continuously bubble SO_2 through it, then since little Br^- or H_2SO_4 is present the equilibrium tries to shift to the left.

26. a) The unbalanced reaction is

$$\overset{-2}{H_2S} \longrightarrow \overset{0}{S}$$

Balancing with electrons for the change in oxidation number gives

$$H_2S \longrightarrow S + 2e^-$$

Balancing hydrogen using H^+ yields

$$H_2S \longrightarrow S + 2e^- + 2H^+$$

b)

$$\overset{+4}{S}O_2 \longrightarrow \overset{+6}{S}O_4{}^{2-}$$

Thus balancing for the change in oxidation number,

$$SO_2 \longrightarrow SO_4{}^{2-} + 2e^-$$

Balancing for oxygen by using H_2O yields

$$2H_2O + SO_2 \longrightarrow SO_4{}^{2-} + 2e^-$$

Balancing for hydrogen using H^+ yields

$$2H_2O + SO_2 \longrightarrow SO_4{}^{2-} + 2e^- + 4H^+$$

c) Following the usual steps,

$$\overset{+3}{H_3}PO_3 \longrightarrow \overset{+5}{H_3}PO_4$$
$$H_3PO_3 \longrightarrow H_3PO_4 + 2e^-$$
$$H_2O + H_3PO_3 \longrightarrow H_3PO_4 + 2e^-$$
$$H_2O + H_3PO_3 \longrightarrow H_3PO_4 + 2e^- + 2H^+$$

27. From the descriptions in the text, recall that for the first three species the sulfur atoms each have a valence of six, and for $HSO_3{}^-$ sulfur has a valence of four.
As a hexavalent species, S carries no lone pairs but when it is tetravalent it has one lone pair. Thus we have:

H_2SO_4:

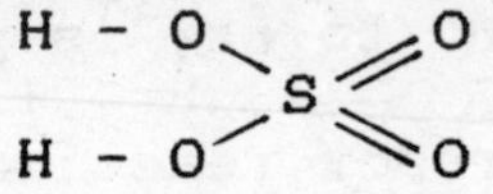

$H_2S_2O_7$:

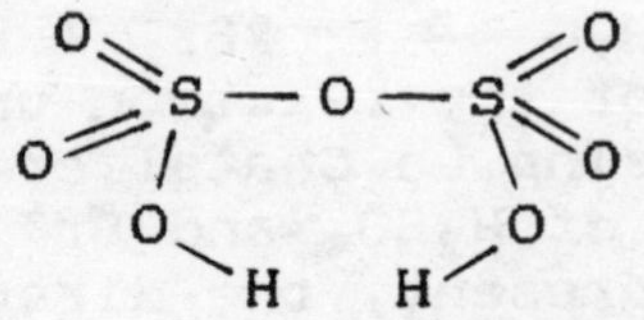

$SO_4{}^{2-}$:

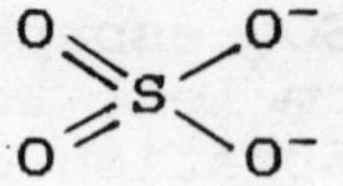

$HSO_3{}^-$:

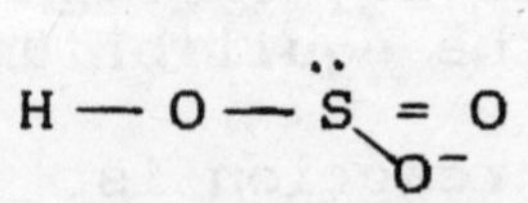

In the diagrams, each doubly-bonded oxygen carries two lone pairs, each O^- carries three and each - O - carries two; for simplicity these have been omitted.

28. a) Here sulfur is tetravalent and has one lone pair (see Q. 27)

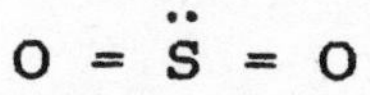

$$O = \overset{..}{S} = O$$

b) Here sulfur is hexavalent, and has no lone pairs.

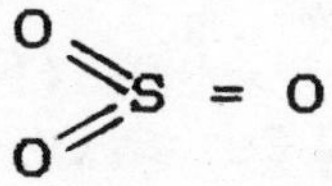

$$\overset{O}{\underset{O}{>}}\!\!S = O$$

c) Since two oxygens here are O^-, the sulfur is tetravalent and has a lone pair:

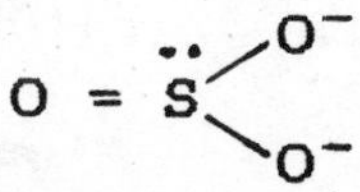

$$O = \overset{..}{S}\overset{O^-}{\underset{O^-}{<}}$$

d) The species $S_2O_3{}^{2-}$ is analogous to sulfate ions with one O^- replaced by S^-; thus the central sulfur is hexavalent.

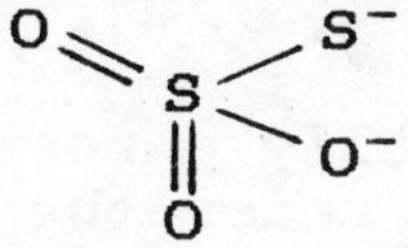

$$\overset{O}{\underset{O}{\overset{\|}{\diagdown}}}\!S\overset{S^-}{\underset{O^-}{\diagup}}$$

e) The structure is that of $H_2S_2O_7$, (Q. 27) but with the two hydrogen atoms ionized:

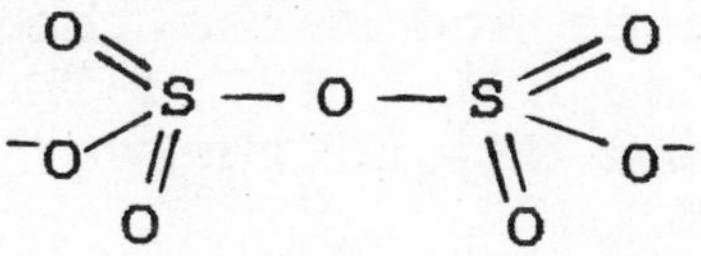

$$\overset{O}{\underset{O}{\overset{\diagdown}{\underset{\diagup}{}}}}\!S - O - S\overset{O}{\underset{O^-}{\diagup}}$$

29. a) Phosphoric acid is an example of a pentavalent phosphorus compound; in this state, the P atom has no lone pair.

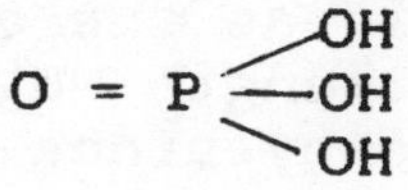

$$O = P\overset{OH}{\underset{OH}{-OH}}$$

b) In H_3PO_3, one H is bonded to P (rather than all H being bonded to O), so the phosphorus is pentavalent here also.

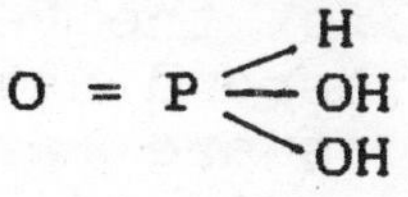

$$O = P\overset{H}{\underset{OH}{-OH}}$$

c)

$$\left[\overset{H}{\underset{H}{>}}\!P\overset{H}{\underset{H}{<}}\right]^{+}$$

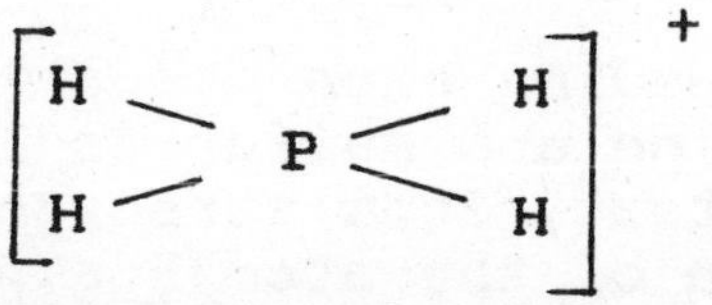

d) The hydrogen phosphate ion has the same structure as H_3PO_4 (see part a), except that two hydrogens have been ionized:

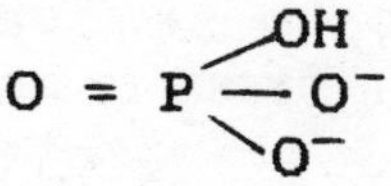

$$O = P\overset{OH}{\underset{O^-}{-O^-}}$$

107

e) In PCl_3, phosphorus is trivalent and carries a lone pair:

$$
\begin{array}{c}
\ddot{P} \\
Cl \diagup \mid \diagdown Cl \\
Cl
\end{array}
$$

30. In the text, acid strength is correlated with the value of m in the general formula $XO_m(OH)_n$. To solve this problem, we rewrite each formula in this form, and recall that if m=0 or 1 the acid is weak, but if m=2 or 3 it is strong.
    a) $B(OH)_3$, so m=0. Acid is weak.
    b) Phosphorous acid is H_3PO_3, i.e. $P(OH)_3$ so it also is weak.

    c) H_2SeO_3, i.e. $SeO_1(OH)_2$ so m=1 and the acid is weak.

    d) Nitric acid is HNO_3, i.e. $NO_2(OH)$. Since m=2, the acid is strong.

31. The answer to this question is essentially a restatement of the analysis presented in Section 7.5, under the heading "Nonmetal Hydrides". In general, acid strength of HX increases from left to right along each Period because the electronegativity of X increases and makes the bond increasingly polar in the sense $H^{\delta+} - X^{\delta-}$. Thus the acidity rises from near-zero in CH_4 and NH_3 to the very weak behavior in H_2O to weak in HF.
    The ability to act as a base is dependent upon the existence of at least one lone pair in the molecule. In addition, basicity decreases from left to right in general since the lone pairs become less accessible as the electronegativity of X increases. Thus in base strength $NH_3 > H_2O > HF$. Methane, CH_4, has no basic tendency since it has no lone pairs.

32. The answer here is identical to that for Q. 31. Within a given Group, the base strengths for the Period 3 hydrides are less than those for the corresponding Period 2 hydride since the atoms and the lone pairs are larger. Similarly the Period 3 hydrides are better acids since the atoms are larger and can therefore more readily lose H^+.

33. Atomic size increases on descending each group; thus chlorine is larger than fluorine and sulfur is larger than oxygen. As discussed in the text, acid strength for HX increases with increasing size of the atom X since it is easier to remove H^+ from a larger atom. Thus the acidity of HCl > HF and that for $H_2S > H_2O$.

34. It should be more difficult to remove H^+ from a negatively-charged ion than from a neutral molecule; thus H_mXO_n is the stronger acid.

35. Consider the oxoacids H_2CO_3 and HNO_2; they are derived from the (nonexistent) compounds $C(OH)_4$ and $N(OH)_3$ by loss of one H_2O molecule. Thus we expect the oxygen analog, $O(OH)_2$, to exist but it is not an oxoacid since all H atoms are lost. Nitric acid, HNO_3, can be considered as $N(OH)_5$ minus 2 water molecules. The corresponding system for oxygen would be $O(OH)_4$; after the expected loss of $2H_2O$, this system would yield O_3 which of course is also a stable molecule. We conclude that the analogs to the known oxoacids of carbon and nitrogen do exist, but since they contain no hydrogen they are not oxoacids.

36. $B(OH)_3$ and $Si(OH)_4$ both are the known oxoacids. Comparing the molecular formulas for $C(OH)_4$ and $P(OH)_3$ with the known oxoacids H_2CO_3 and H_3PO_4, we see that they differ by loss of H_2O in both cases. Similarly, $N(OH)_5$ and $S(OH)_6$ both lose $2H_2O$ to form HNO_3 and H_2SO_4 respectively.

37. The behavior of an $X(OH)_n$ compound as an acid or a base depends directly upon the electronegativity of X; in general the lower the electronegativity, the greater the behavior as a base since the XO bonds are polarized in the sense $X^{\delta+}O^{\delta-}$. Since the electronegativity of Si greatly exceeds that of the metals K and Ca, $Si(OH)_4$ is much less basic, i.e. more acidic, than are KOH and $Ca(OH)_2$.

38. a) Hydrofluoric acid is HF
    b) Phosphoric acid is H_3PO_4, i.e. $OP(OH)_3$
    c) Phosphorous acid is H_3PO_3
    d) Hypochlorous acid is HClO

39. a) Since Ca forms Ca^{2+} and sulfate is SO_4^{2-}, the formula is $CaSO_4$ for calcium sulfate.
    b) Since penta means five, phosphorus pentabromide is PBr_5.
    c) Since the valence of iodine is 1, the formula must be PI_3 since the valence for phosphorus is three.
    d) Ammonium ion is NH_4^+, and hydrogen phosphate is HPO_4^{2-}; thus for charge balance this compound must have the formula $(NH_4)_2HPO_4$.
    e) Since calcium is Ca^{2+} and nitride is N^{3-}, to have charge balance the formula for calcium nitride must be Ca_3N_2.
    f) Since tetra means four, sulfur tetrafluoride is SF_4.
    g) Since as an ion chloride is −1 in charge, the formula for chromium (III) chloride must be $CrCl_3$ to achieve charge balance.

40. a) Since PO_4 is phosphate, the compound is potassium phosphate.
    b) Carbon tetrafluoride.
    c) Since CO_3 is carbonate, the compound is zinc carbonate.

109

d) Since OCl is hypochlorite, the compound is calcium hypochlorite.
e) Since SO_3 is sulfite, the compound is calcium sulfite.

41. a) Since SeO_4, by analogy with SO_4, is called the selenate ion, the compound is potassium selenate.
b) Hydrogen telluride.
c) Disodium tetrasulfide. (Note that the number of each atom must be specified, as Na and S form other compounds.)
d) Iron (II) disulfide.
e) Since HSO_4 is the hydrogen sulfate ion, the name of the compound is rubidium hydrogen sulfate.
f) Tetraphosphorus hexaoxide.

42. a) H_2SO_4 is sulfuric acid
b) H_3PO_4 is phosphoric acid
c) H_3PO_3 is phosphorous acid
d) H_2CO_3 is carbonic acid
e) HNO_3 is nitric acid
f) H_3BO_3 is boric acid
g) H_4SiO_4 is silicic acid
h) HClO is hypochlorous acid
i) $HClO_4$ is perchloric acid

43. a) Since HNO_3 has only one hydrogen, the only reaction possible is

$$HNO_3 + NaOH \longrightarrow H_2O + NaNO_3$$
sodium nitrate
since NO_3^- is the nitrate ion

b) Since H_2SO_4 has two ionizable hydrogens, the possible reactions are
$$H_2SO_4 + NaOH \longrightarrow H_2O + NaHSO_4$$
sodium hydrogen sulfate

$$NaHSO_4 + NaOH \longrightarrow H_2O + Na_2SO_4$$
sodium sulfate

c) Since H_3PO_4 has three ionizable hydrogens, the possible reactions are
$$H_3PO_4 + NaOH \longrightarrow H_2O + NaH_2PO_4$$
sodium dihydrogenphosphate

$$NaH_2PO_4 + NaOH \longrightarrow H_2O + Na_2HPO_4$$
sodium hydrogenphosphate

$$Na_2HPO_4 + NaOH \longrightarrow H_2O + Na_3PO_4$$
sodium phosphate

d) Phosphorous acid has only two ionizable hydrogens, not three (see text). Thus the possible reactions are
$$H_3PO_3 + NaOH \longrightarrow H_2O + NaH_2PO_3$$
sodium dihydrogenphosphite

110

$$NaH_2PO_3 + NaOH \longrightarrow H_2O + Na_2HPO_3$$
$$\text{sodium hydrogenphosphite}$$

e) Diphosphoric acid has four ionizable hydrogens; thus the possible reactions are

$$H_4P_2O_7 + NaOH \longrightarrow H_2O + NaH_3P_2O_7$$
$$\text{sodium trihydrogendiphosphate}$$

$$NaH_3P_2O_7 + NaOH \longrightarrow H_2O + Na_2H_2P_2O_7$$
$$\text{(di)sodium dihydrogendiphosphate}$$

$$Na_2H_2P_2O_7 + NaOH \longrightarrow H_2O + Na_3HP_2O_7$$
$$\text{(tri)sodium hydrogendiphosphate}$$

$$Na_3HP_2O_7 + NaOH \longrightarrow H_2O + Na_4P_2O_7$$
$$\text{(tetra)sodium diphosphate}$$

The prefixes in parentheses are optional.

44. a) The reaction of sulfuric acid, H_2SO_4, with water is

$$H_2SO_4 + H_2O \longrightarrow HSO_4^- + H_3O^+$$
$$\text{hydrogensulfate} \qquad \text{hydronium}$$
$$\text{ion} \qquad \qquad \text{ion}$$

$$HSO_4^- + H_2O \rightleftharpoons SO_4^{2-} + H_3O^+$$
$$\text{sulfate ion}$$

Thus in solution we have HSO_4^-, SO_4^{2-}, H_3O^+, and of course H_2O and some OH^- (from self-ionization of H_2O). No H_2SO_4 is present, as it is a strong acid.

b) When SO_2 dissolves, the reactions are (see text)

$$SO_2(aq) + 2H_2O \rightleftharpoons H_3O^+ + HSO_3^-$$
$$\text{hydrogensulfite ion}$$

$$HSO_3^- + H_2O \rightleftharpoons H_3O^+ + SO_3^{2-}$$
$$\text{sulfite ion}$$

Thus a solution contains $SO_2(aq)$, HSO_3^-, SO_3^{2-}, H_3O^+ and H_2O and OH^- as well.

c) Phosphoric acid, H_3PO_4, is a triprotic acid and weak in all stages of ionization. Thus in solution there is H_3PO_4, $H_2PO_4^-$, HPO_4^{2-}, PO_4^{3-}, H_3O^+ and H_2O and OH^- as well. The names of the first four are respectively phosphoric acid, dihydrogenphosphate ion, hydrogenphosphate ion, and phosphate ion.

d) Carbonic acid is H_2CO_3 and is weak in both stages. Thus in solution we have H_2CO_3, HCO_3^- (hydrogencarbonate ion), CO_3^{2-} (carbonate ion), H_3O^+ as well as H_2O and OH^-. (It is also believed that $CO_2(aq)$ exists in such solutions.)

45. a) In the reaction, H^+ is transferred from H_2SO_4 to CO_3^{2-}. Thus it is an acid-base reaction, and by inspection it is seen already to be balanced. Since H_2SO_4 donates an electron to yield HSO_4^-, they are an acid-base conjugate pair (H_2SO_4 the acid, HSO_4^- the base). Similarly since CO_3^{2-}

accepts a proton to form HCO_3^-, they are respectively the base and acid of a conjugate pair.

b) Since the reaction involves H^+ transfer it is an acid-base process. In analogy with (a), HSO_4^- and SO_4^{2-} are the acid and base of one conjugate pair and H_2O and H_3O^+ are the base and acid of the other pair, respectively.

c) This is a redox reaction, since Cu is oxidized (since each Cu atom loses two electrons in forming Cu^{2+}), and some of the H_2SO_4 is reduced to SO_2. (The oxidation number of sulfur is +6 in H_2SO_4 but only +4 in SO_2; thus each sulfur that forms SO_2 loses two electrons.)

d) This is a redox reaction, since Br^- is oxidized to Br_2 and some of the H_2SO_4 is reduced to SO_2 (see (c) above).

e) This is an acid-base reaction, since H^+ is transferred from the base CO_3^{2-} ion in $CaCO_3$ and its conjugate acid HCO_3^- is produced. After loss of the proton, the acid H_3O^+ becomes its conjugate base H_2O.

f) This is a redox reaction, since Mg is oxidized to Mg^{2+} and H_3O^+ is reduced to H_2 (plus H_2O).

g) This is an acid-base reaction, since H^+ is transferred from the acid H_2O to the base P^{3-} (in the salt Ca_3P_2), forming the corresponding base OH^- (which combines with Ca^{2+} to form calcium hydroxide) and the acid PH_3 respectively.

46. a) In each case, there is a tetrahedral arrangement of phosphorus atoms.

b) Both $(HPO_3)_3$ and $(SO_3)_3$ have a six-membered ring structure, with alternating S (or P) and O atoms.

c) In all cases there is an approximately tetrahedral geometry around the central phosphorus or sulfur.

47. For the valence-shell electrons, the box diagrams are:

Since As has 3 and Se has 2 unpaired electrons in singly-occupied orbitals, the normal valencies will be 3 and 2 respectively and the hydride formulas AsH_3 and H_2Se. Arsenic can achieve a valence of 5, as it has in $AsCl_5$, by promoting one 4s electron into a 4d orbital:

As 4s [↑] 4p [↑][↑][↑] 4d [↑][ ][ ][ ][ ]

Selenium can achieve a valence of 4 by promotion of one 4p electron to 4d, and 6 by promotion of a 4s electron to 4d as well:

Se 4s [↑↓] 4p [↑][↑][↑] 4d [↑][ ][ ][ ][ ]
(valence=4)

Se 4s [↑] 4p [↑][↑][↑] 4d [↑][↑][ ][ ][ ]
(valence=6)

48. Nitric acid has a lower boiling point which is lower than that of HCl, and thus it would boil off in the process, whereas sulfuric and phosphoric acids are less volatile than HCl and will remain liquid at temperatures at which HCl is boiled off.

49. a) The acid has no Na atoms but an additional H; thus its formula is H_3PO_2.

b) Since H_3PO_3 is phosphorous acid, H_3PO_2 is named by adding a hypo prefix, yielding hypophosphorous acid.

c) If H_3PO_2 is monoprotic, then two H atoms are bonded to P and only one to an oxygen. Thus one oxygen is double-bonded to phosphorus:

$$
\begin{array}{c}
H \\
H \longrightarrow P = O \\
HO
\end{array}
$$

d) As an element, phosphorus in P_4 has a zero oxidation number. For PH_3, since the oxidation number for hydrogen is +1 that for phosphorus is −3. In NaH_2PO_2 since the O.N.=+1 for both Na and H, and −2 for each oxygen, then for neutrality phosphorus must be +1.

e) Since P oxidation number 0 produces some P with O.N.=−3 and some with O.N.=+1, phosphorus as P_4 is both oxidized and reduced.

f) For this reaction to work with N_2 rather than P_4, OH^- would have to react with it using vacant, valence-shell d orbitals of N as it does with P_4. Due to the lack of 2d orbitals, the reaction cannot occur, and no NH_3 can be obtained by this route.

g) The Ideal Gas Law PV=nRT can be used here to derive the number of moles of PH_3 gas from the P,V,T information:

n = PV/RT = 0.95 atm x 0.100 L/(0.0821 L atm mol^{-1} K^{-1} x 298 K)
        = 0.0039 mole PH_3

We transform moles PH_3 to moles P_4 and then to mass of P_4:

0.0039 moles PH_3 x $\dfrac{\text{1 mole } P_4}{\text{1 mole } PH_3}$ x $\dfrac{123.88 \text{ g } P_4}{\text{1 mole } P_4}$ = 0.48 g P_4

50. There is no "prescription" by which problems of this type can be solved. It is useful to rewrite the information in symbolic form:

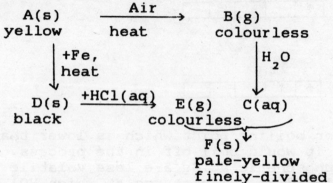

Both A and F could be elemental sulfur, one of the few solids which is yellow. The identification of A as sulfur is consistent with its reaction with iron to give a black solid, since iron sulfide is known to be black. Similarly, sulfur does combine upon heating with the oxygen in air to give a colorless gas, sulfur dioxide, which dissolves in water to give SO_2(aq). Iron sulfide (D) would react with hydrochloric acid to yield a colorless gas, hydrogen sulfide, which presumably is E. Finally, H_2S(E) and SO_2(C) are known to combine to give sulfur (F). Thus the equations are

$$S(s) + O_2(g) \xrightarrow{\text{heat}} SO_2(g)$$

$$SO_2(g) \xrightarrow{H_2O} SO_2(aq) \quad (\text{or } H_2SO_3)$$

$$S(s) + Fe(s) \longrightarrow FeS(s)$$

$$FeS(s) + 2HCl(aq) \longrightarrow H_2S(g) + FeCl_2(aq)$$

$$2H_2S(g) + SO_2(aq) \longrightarrow 3S(s) + 2H_2O$$

CHAPTER 8

General note on Lewis structures

The Lewis structures presented in these answers were derived in accordance with the rules which appear in the text. Formal charges are obtained by subtracting the number of electrons assigned to a particular atom (all non-bonding electron pairs and one half of the electrons in covalent bonds) from the core charge, which, for the main group elements, is given by the group number.

1. a) S_2^{2-}

    1. The basic structure of single bonds is S-S
    2. The total number of valence electrons

       Sulfur (Group VI):   2 x 6   = $12e^-$
                ion charge   = $2e^-$
                    Total   = $14e^-$

    3. Electrons localized in single bonds = $2e^-$
       Electrons available for completion of octets = (14-2) = $12e^-$
       Completing octets and assigning formal charges gives

$$:\overset{-}{\overset{..}{S}} - \overset{-}{\overset{..}{S}}:$$

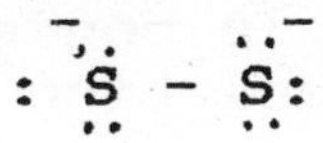

       which is the final Lewis structure.

  b) SO_3^{2-}

    1. The basic structure is

$$O - S - O$$
$$|$$
$$O$$

    2. The total number of valence electrons is 26.
    3. Electrons localized in single bonds = $6e^-$
       Electrons available for completion of octets = 26-6 = $20e^-$. Completing octets and assigning formal charges gives

$$:\overset{-}{\overset{..}{O}} - \overset{..}{S^+} - \overset{-}{\overset{..}{O}}:$$
$$|$$
$$:\overset{..}{O}:$$

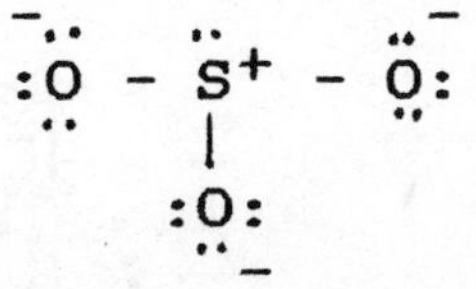

    4. Finally, since sulfur is in the third period of the periodic table it is not restricted to an octet of electrons and so we may remove one formal charge by forming a double bond:

$$\overset{\cdot\cdot}{\underset{\cdot\cdot}{O}} = \overset{\cdot\cdot}{\underset{|}{S}} - \overset{\cdot\cdot}{\underset{\cdot\cdot}{O}} \text{:}^{-}$$

$$\overset{\cdot\cdot}{\underset{\cdot\cdot}{O}} \text{:}_{-}$$

Note: We could have formed the double bond between sulfur and any of the oxygen atoms.

c) ClO^-
1. The basic structure is Cl - O
2. The total number of valence electrons is 14.
3. Localized in single bonds = $2e^-$
   Electrons available for octet formation = $(14-2) = 12e^-$
   Completing octets and assigning formal charges we have

$$\overset{\cdot\cdot}{\underset{\cdot\cdot}{:\!Cl}} - \overset{\cdot\cdot}{\underset{\cdot\cdot}{O}} \text{:}$$

This is the required Lewis structure.

d) $ClO_4{}^-$
1. The basic structure is

$$\begin{array}{c} O \\ | \\ O - Cl - O \\ | \\ O \end{array}$$

2. The total number of valence electrons is 32.
3. Electrons localized in single bonds = $8e^-$
   Electrons available for completion of octets = $(32-8)$
   = $24e^-$. Completing the octets around oxygen requires
   $24e^-$. We do this and assign formal charges

$$\begin{array}{c} \overset{\cdot\cdot}{:\!O}\text{:}^{-} \\ | \\ \overset{\cdot\cdot}{:\!O} - \overset{3+}{Cl} - \overset{\cdot\cdot}{O}\text{:}^{-} \\ {}_{-}^{} \quad | \\ \overset{\cdot\cdot}{:\!O}\text{:} \\ {}_{-} \end{array}$$

4. Since chlorine is in the third period it is not restricted to an octet of electrons. We may, therefore, complete the Lewis structure by eliminating three pairs of formal charges by completing double bonds

$$\begin{array}{c} :\!O\!: \\ \parallel \\ O = Cl - \overset{\cdot\cdot}{O}\text{:}^{-} \\ \parallel \\ :\!O\!: \end{array}$$

2. We may deduce the Lewis structures of the various species by following the methods illustrated in the answer to question 1 above.

   a) $:\!\overset{\cdot\cdot}{F} - \overset{\cdot\cdot}{O} - \overset{\cdot\cdot}{F}\!:$ b) $:\!\overset{\cdot\cdot}{F} - \overset{\cdot\cdot}{S} - \overset{\cdot\cdot}{F}\!:$ c) $:\!\overset{\cdot\cdot}{F} - \overset{\cdot\cdot}{S} - \overset{\cdot\cdot}{F}\!:$

   $:\!\overset{\cdot\cdot}{F}\!: \quad :\!\overset{\cdot\cdot}{F}\!:$

d) $\overset{\cdot\cdot}{\underset{\cdot\cdot}{O}} = \overset{\cdot\cdot}{S} = \overset{\cdot\cdot}{\underset{\cdot\cdot}{O}}$ e) $:\overset{\cdot\cdot}{\underset{\cdot\cdot}{Cl}} - \overset{\cdot\cdot}{P} - \overset{\cdot\cdot}{\underset{\cdot\cdot}{Cl}}:$ f) $:\overset{\cdot\cdot}{\underset{\cdot\cdot}{Cl}} - B - \overset{\cdot\cdot}{\underset{\cdot\cdot}{Cl}}:$

(e) has below P: $:\overset{}{\underset{\cdot\cdot}{Cl}}:$

(f) has below B: $:\overset{}{\underset{\cdot\cdot}{Cl}}:$

Thus the central atom does not obey the octet rule in the following molecules

SF_4 and SO_2 - expanded octets of $10e^-$

BCl_3 - incomplete octet of $6e^-$

3. a) $S_2O_3^{2-}$

1. The basic structure will be

$$\begin{array}{c} O \\ | \\ O - S - S \\ | \\ O \end{array}$$

2. The total number of valence electrons is 30.

3. Electrons localized in single bonds = $8e^-$
Electrons available for completion of octets = (30-8) = $24e^-$. Completing the octets requires $36e^-$. We do this and assign formal charges

$$\begin{array}{c} \overset{-}{:\overset{\cdot\cdot}{O}:} \\ | \ +2 \\ :\overset{-}{\underset{\cdot\cdot}{O}} - S - \overset{-}{\overset{\cdot\cdot}{\underset{\cdot\cdot}{S}}:} \\ | \\ :\overset{-}{\underset{\cdot\cdot}{O}}: \end{array}$$

4. Since sulfur is in the third period of the periodic table it will accept an expanded octet. We may, therefore, remove pairs of formal charges by completing double bonds. The final Lewis structure is, therefore

$$\begin{array}{c} :O: \\ \| \\ :\overset{-}{\overset{\cdot\cdot}{O}} - S - \overset{-}{\overset{\cdot\cdot}{\underset{\cdot\cdot}{S}}:} \\ \| \\ :O: \end{array} \quad \text{or} \quad \begin{array}{c} :O: \\ \| \\ :\overset{-}{\overset{\cdot\cdot}{O}} - S = \overset{\cdot\cdot}{S}: \\ | \\ :\overset{}{\underset{\cdot\cdot}{O}}:_- \end{array}$$

b) SO_3F^-

1. The basic structure is

$$\begin{array}{c} F \\ | \\ O - S - O \\ | \\ O \end{array}$$

2. The total number of valence electrons is 32.

3. Electrons localized in single bonds = $8e^-$
Electrons required for completion of octets = (32-8) = $24e^-$. Completion of octets around the atoms bonded to sulfur requires $24e^-$. We do this and assign formal charges.

119

$$
\begin{array}{c}
\ddot{\text{:F:}} \\
| \\
\text{:O} - \overset{2+}{\text{S}} - \text{O:} \\
| \\
\text{:O:}
\end{array}
$$

4. Since sulfur (3rd period element) may accept an expanded octet we may eliminate two pairs of formal charges by inserting double bonds. The final Lewis structure will, therefore, be

$$
\begin{array}{c}
\text{:F:} \\
| \\
\text{O} = \text{S} = \text{O} \\
| \\
\text{:O:}
\end{array}
$$

c) SOF_2
1. The basic structure is

$$
\begin{array}{c}
\text{F} - \text{S} - \text{F} \\
| \\
\text{O}
\end{array}
$$

2. The total number of valence electrons is 26.
3. Electrons localized in single bonds = $6e^-$
   Electrons available for the completion of octets = (26-6) = $20e^-$. Completing octets around oxygen, fluorine and sulfur requires $20e^-$. We do this and assign formal charges

$$
\begin{array}{c}
\text{:F} - \overset{+}{\text{S}} - \text{F:} \\
| \\
\text{:O:}
\end{array}
$$

4. Since sulfur is an element in the third period it can accommodate an expanded octet. We may, therefore, eliminate the formal charges by completing a double bond between sulfur and oxygen. The final Lewis structure will be

$$
\begin{array}{c}
\text{:F} - \text{S} - \text{F:} \\
\| \\
\text{:O:}
\end{array}
$$

d) SO_2F_2
1. The basic structure is

$$
\begin{array}{c}
\text{F} \\
| \\
\text{O} - \text{S} - \text{O} \\
| \\
\text{F}
\end{array}
$$

2. The total number of valence electrons is 32.
3. Electrons localized in single bonds = $8e^-$
   Electrons available for the completion of octets = (32-8) = $24e^-$. Completing all octets around

fluorine and oxygen requires 24e⁻. We do this and
assign formal charges.

$$\begin{array}{c} :\ddot{F}: \\ | \quad {}^{2+} \\ :\ddot{O} - S - \ddot{O}: \\ {}^{-} \qquad | \qquad {}^{-} \\ :\ddot{F}: \end{array}$$

4. Sulfur is an element in the third period and may,
therefore, accommodate an expanded octet. We may
eliminate the two pairs of formal charges by forming
double bonds. The final Lewis structure will be,

$$\begin{array}{c} :\ddot{F}: \\ | \\ \ddot{O} = S = \ddot{O} \\ | \\ :\ddot{F}: \end{array}$$

e) SNF_3
   1. The basic structure is

$$\begin{array}{c} F \\ | \\ F - S - F \\ | \\ N \end{array}$$

   2. The total number of valence electrons is 32.
   3. Electrons localized in single bonds = 8e⁻
      Electrons available for octet formation = 32-8 = 24e⁻
      Electrons required for octet completion = 24e⁻. We do
      this and assign formal charges.

$$\begin{array}{c} :\ddot{F}: \\ | \\ :\ddot{F} - S^{+2} - \ddot{F}: \\ | \\ :\ddot{N}:{}_{2-} \end{array}$$

   4. Sulphur is an atom in the third period and can,
   therefore, accommodate an expanded octet. We may
   eliminate the formal charges by converting two of the
   electron pairs assigned to nitrogen to double bonds.
   This retains the octet around nitrogen and gives us the
   final Lewis structure.

$$\begin{array}{c} :\ddot{F}: \\ | \\ :\ddot{F} - S - \ddot{F}: \\ ||| \\ N \end{array}$$

4. Utilizing the techniques developed in answering questions 1,
    2, and 3 we may complete the following table.

Molecule	Lewis Structure	AX_nE_m Type
CO_2	$:\overset{..}{O} = C = \overset{..}{O}:$	AX_2
CS_2	$:\overset{..}{S} = C = \overset{..}{S}:$	AX_2
SO_2	$\overset{..}{O} = \overset{..}{S} = \overset{..}{O}$	AX_2E
$PO_4{}^{3-}$	$^-:\overset{..}{O} - \overset{:\overset{..}{O}:^-}{\underset{:\overset{..}{O}:^-}{P}} = \overset{..}{O}$	AX_4
$SO_3{}^{2-}$	$^-:\overset{..}{O} - \overset{}{\underset{:\overset{..}{O}:}{S}} - \overset{..}{O}:^-$	AX_3E
$ClO_4{}^-$	$O = \overset{:\overset{..}{O}:^-}{\underset{:O:}{Cl}} = \overset{..}{O}$	AX_4
$BO_3{}^{3-}$	$^-:\overset{..}{O} - \overset{}{\underset{:\overset{..}{O}:^-}{B}} - \overset{..}{O}:^-$ or $^-:\overset{..}{O} - \overset{}{\underset{:\overset{..}{O}:^-}{\overset{-}{B}}} = \overset{..}{O}:$	AX_3

5. a) CN^-
   1. The basic structure is
                C - N
   2. The total number of valence electrons will be 10.
   3. Electrons localized in single bonds = 2e⁻
      Electrons available for completion of octets = 10-2
      = 8e⁻. Electrons required for completion of octets =
      12e⁻. There is, therefore, a deficiency of 12e⁻-8e⁻ =
      4e⁻. We assign the available electrons to the more
      electro-negative element first and assign formal
      charges.

               $:C^+ - \overset{..}{N}:^{2-}$

   4. Complete the octets using non bonding electron pairs
      and converting them to covalent bonds. We have

               $^-:C \equiv N:^-$

      Since no additonal formal charges have been created
      this is the final Lewis structure of the CN^- ion.
   b) $NO_2{}^-$
   1. The basic structure is
                O - N - O
   2. The total number of valence electrons is 18.

120

3. Electrons localized in single bonds = $4e^-$
   Electrons available for octet completion = $(18-4)$ = $14e^-$. Completing the octets about the more electronegative atoms first gives

$$^-:\ddot{O} - \overset{+}{\overset{\cdot\cdot}{N}} - \ddot{O}:^-$$

4. We form a double bond from N to one O using an oxygen nonbonding pair; the structure becomes

$$\ddot{O} = \overset{\cdot\cdot}{N} - \overset{-}{\underset{\cdot\cdot}{\ddot{O}:}}$$

c) O_3

1. The basic structure is
$$O - O - O$$

2. The total number of valence electrons is
   Oxygen (Group VI): $3 \times 6 = 18e^-$

3. Electrons localized in covalent bonds = $4e^-$
   Electrons available for octet completion = $(18-4)$ = $14e^-$. Electrons required for octet completion = 16e. There is, therefore, a deficit of two electrons or one electron pair. Complete octets as far as possible and assign formal charges.

$$^-:\ddot{O} - \overset{\cdot\cdot}{O}^{+2} - \ddot{O}:^-$$

4. Complete octets by taking a non-bonding electron pair from one of the oxygen atoms bearing a negative formal charge and converting it into a double bond. This has the effect of removing one pair of formal charges to give

$$^-:\ddot{O} - \ddot{O}^+ = \ddot{O}$$

Since no additional formal charges have been created this will be the final Lewis structure. Oxygen is an element in the second period and cannot, therefore, have an expanded octet. The remaining formal charges cannot be removed.

6. a) HNO_2

1. The basic structure is
$$H - O - N - O$$

2. The total number of valence electrons is 18.

3. Electrons localized in single bonds = $6e^-$
   Electrons available for completion of octets = $(18-6)$ = $12e^-$. Electrons required for completion of octets = $14e^-$. There is, therefore, a deficiency of $2e^-$. Complete octets as far as possible and assign formal charges

$$H - \ddot{O} - N^+ - \ddot{O}:^-$$

4. Complete octets by converting one electron pair from the oxygen atom carrying negative formal charge into a

covalent bond. This has the effect of removing the
formal charge and giving the final Lewis structure

$$H - \overset{\cdot\cdot}{\underset{\cdot\cdot}{O}} - \overset{\cdot\cdot}{N} = \overset{\cdot\cdot}{\underset{\cdot\cdot}{O}}$$

b) HNO_3

1. The basic structure is

$$O - N - O - H$$
$$\qquad\;\; |$$
$$\qquad\;\; O$$

2. The total number of valence electrons is 24.
3. Electrons localized in single bonds $= 8e^-$
   Electrons available for octet formation $= (24-8) = 16e^-$
   Electrons required for octet completion $= 18e^-$
   There is, therefore, a deficiency of $2e^-$. Complete
   octets as far as possible and assign formal charges.

$$\overset{-}{\underset{\cdot\cdot}{:}}\overset{\cdot\cdot}{O} - \overset{+2}{N} - \overset{\cdot\cdot}{\underset{\cdot\cdot}{O}} - H$$
$$\qquad\qquad |$$
$$\qquad\quad :\underset{-}{\overset{\cdot\cdot}{O}}:$$

4. Complete octets by converting one electron pair from an
   oxygen atom bearing a negative formal charge into a
   covalent bond. This has the effect of removing one
   pair of formal charges giving the final Lewis structure

$$\overset{-}{\underset{\cdot\cdot}{:}}\overset{\cdot\cdot}{O} - \overset{+}{N} - \overset{\cdot\cdot}{\underset{\cdot\cdot}{O}} - H$$
$$\qquad\qquad \|$$
$$\qquad\quad :O:$$

The remaining formal charges cannot be removed since
nitrogen cannot accommodate an expanded octet.

c) H_2SO_4

1. The basic structure is

$$\qquad\qquad\quad O$$
$$\qquad\qquad\quad |$$
$$H - O - S - O - H$$
$$\qquad\qquad\quad |$$
$$\qquad\qquad\quad O$$

2. The total number of valence electrons is 32.
3. Electrons localized in single bonds $= 12e^-$
   Electrons available for octet completion $= (32-12)$
   $= 20e^-$. Electrons required for octet completion $=$
   $= 20e^-$. Completing the octets and assigning formal
   charges gives

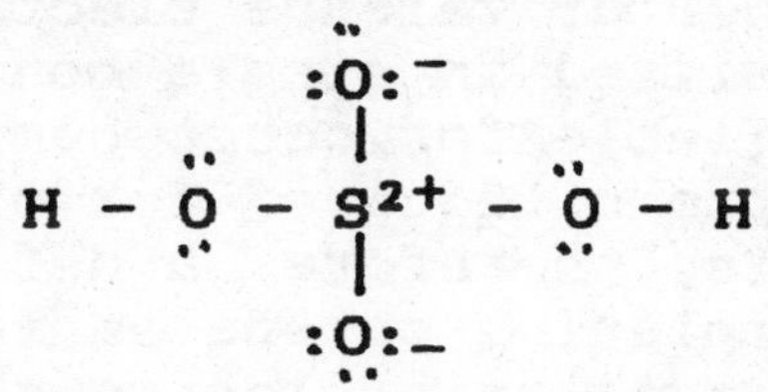

$$:\overset{..}{\underset{|}{O}}:^-$$
$$H - \overset{..}{\underset{..}{O}} - S^{2+} - \overset{..}{\underset{..}{O}} - H$$
$$:\overset{|}{\underset{..}{O}}:^-$$

4. Sulfur is an element in the third period and can accept an expanded octet. We may, therefore, remove formal charges by converting two non-bonding electron pairs on the oxygens carrying negative formal charges to covalent bonds giving the final Lewis structure

$$:O:$$
$$\parallel$$
$$H - \overset{..}{\underset{..}{O}} - S - \overset{..}{\underset{..}{O}} - H$$
$$\parallel$$
$$:O:$$

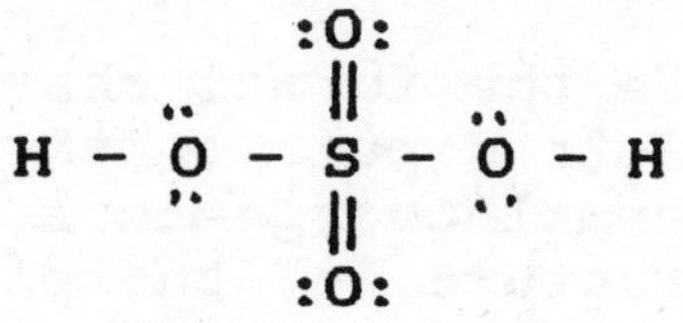

d) $HClO_3$

1. The basic structure is
$$O - Cl - O$$
$$\underset{H}{\overset{|}{O}}$$

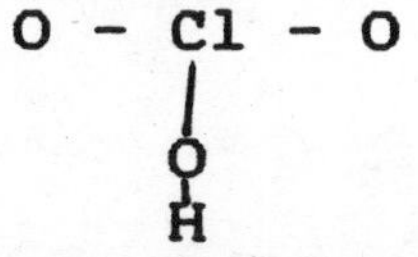

2. The total number of valence electrons is 26.

3. Electrons localized in single bonds = $8e^-$
Electrons available for octet completion = $(26-8)$ = $18e^-$. Electrons required for octet completion = $18e^-$. Completing octets and assigning formal charges we have

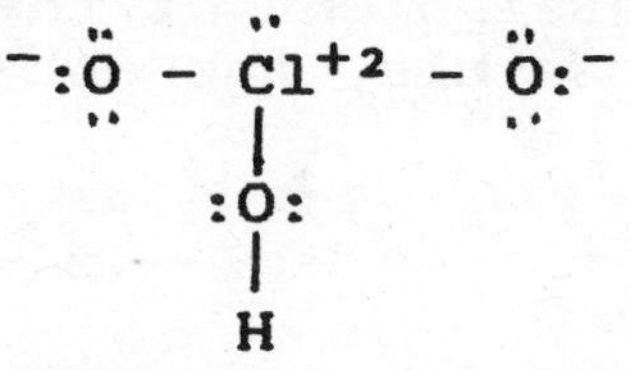

$$^-:\overset{..}{\underset{..}{O}} - \overset{..}{Cl}^{+2} - \overset{..}{\underset{..}{O}}:^-$$
$$:\overset{|}{\underset{|}{O}}:$$
$$H$$

4. Chlorine is an element in the third period of the periodic table and can, therefore, accept an expanded octet. We may, therefore, remove the formal charges by converting two pairs of non-bonding electrons on the oxygen atoms bearing the negative formal charges to covalent bonds giving the final Lewis structure

$$\overset{..}{\underset{..}{O}} = \overset{..}{Cl} = \overset{..}{\underset{..}{O}}$$
$$:\overset{|}{\underset{|}{O}}:$$
$$H$$

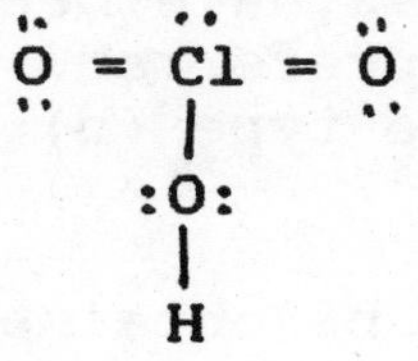

c) H_2CO_3

1. The basic structure is
$$H - O - C - O - H$$
$$\underset{O}{\overset{|}{}}$$

123

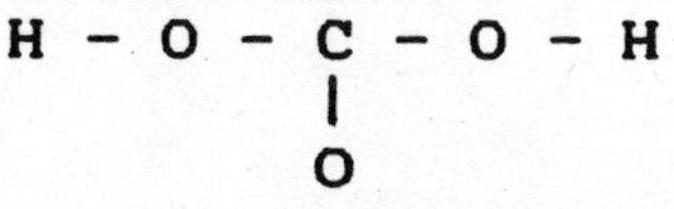

2. The total number of valence electrons is 24.
3. Electrons localized in single bonds = $10e^-$
   Electrons available for octet completion = $(24-10)$
   $= 14e^-$. Electrons required for octet completion =
   $16e^-$. There is, therefore, a deficiency of two
   electrons. Completing octets as far as possible by
   assigning the available electrons to the most
   electronegative elements first and assigning formal
   charges we have

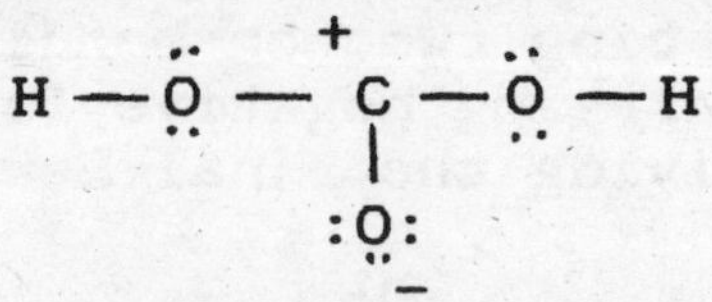

$$H - \overset{..}{\underset{..}{O}} - \overset{+}{\underset{\underset{\overset{|}{\underset{..}{\overset{..}{O}}}}{}}{C}} - \overset{..}{\underset{..}{O}} - H$$

4. We can eliminate the formal charges by converting a
   non-bonding electron pair on the oxygen atom bearing
   the negative formal charge to a covalent bond. The
   final Lewis structure is, therefore,

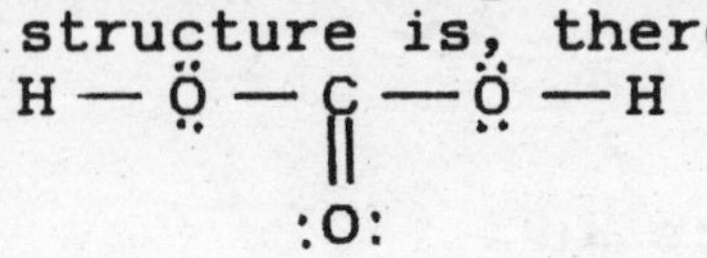

$$H - \overset{..}{\underset{..}{O}} - \overset{\|}{\underset{\|}{C}} - \overset{..}{\underset{..}{O}} - H$$
$$:O:$$

7. Each structure

   $$N - O - N \qquad\qquad \text{or} \qquad\qquad N - N - O$$
   $$\text{(a)} \qquad\qquad\qquad\qquad\qquad\qquad \text{(b)}$$

   possesses the same number of valence electrons, $16e^-$, and
   each has available to it a total of $12e^-$ for the completion
   of octets about each atom. This latter number is obtained by
   deducting from the total number of valence electrons the
   number of electrons, $4e^-$, in single bonds. Compare now the
   two structures after assignment of the available electrons to
   complete, as far as possible, the octets. Formal charges are
   also assigned.

   $$:\overset{..}{N} - \overset{..}{\underset{..}{O}} - \overset{..}{N}: \qquad\qquad\qquad :\overset{-2}{\overset{..}{N}} - \overset{+3}{N} - \overset{-}{\overset{..}{\underset{..}{O}}}:$$
   $$\text{(a)} \qquad\qquad\qquad\qquad\qquad\qquad \text{(b)}$$

   By converting non-bonding electron pairs to covalent bonds we
   obtain the following structures

   $$\overset{-}{\overset{..}{N}} = \overset{2+}{O} = \overset{-}{\overset{..}{N}} \qquad\qquad \overset{-}{\overset{..}{N}} = \overset{+}{N} = \overset{..}{O} \quad \text{or} \quad :N \equiv \overset{+}{N} - \overset{-}{\overset{..}{\underset{..}{O}}}:$$

   $$\text{(a)} \qquad\qquad\qquad\qquad\qquad\qquad \text{(b)}$$

   Since new formal charges have been created in (a), the
   previous structure is preferred. However it does not have
   complete octets, so the type (b) structure should be
   superior.

8. The Lewis diagrams may be obtained as follows.
   (a) N_2H_4 (b) N_2H_2

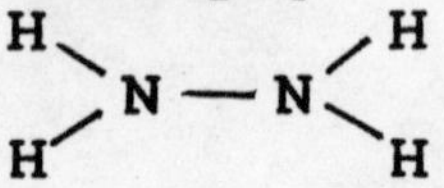

   $$\overset{H}{\underset{H}{>}}N - N\overset{H}{\underset{H}{<}} \qquad\qquad \text{Basic structure} \qquad\qquad H - N - N - H$$

124

$14e^-$	Total number of valence electrons	$12e^-$
$10e^-$	Total number of valence electrons localized in bonds	$6e^-$
$4e^-$	Electrons available for octet formation	$6e^-$
$4e^-$	Electrons required for octet completion	$8e^-$
0	Electrons deficient	$2e^-$
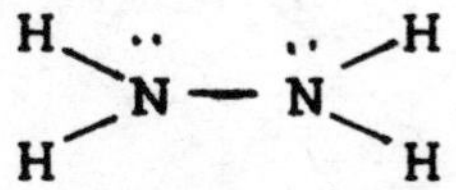	Preliminary structures with formal charges if any	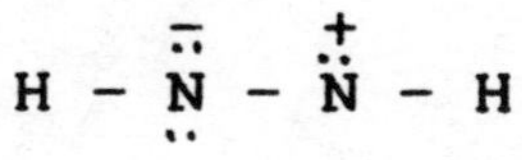
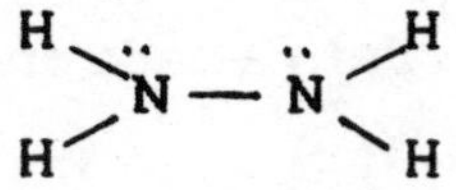	Final Lewis structures after reassigning non-bonding electron pairs and eliminating formal charges where necessary	

9. a) X —— A —— X Bond angles = 180°

b) 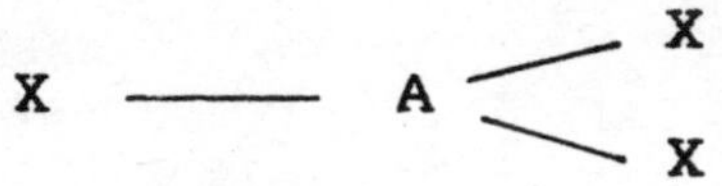 Bond angles = 120°

c) 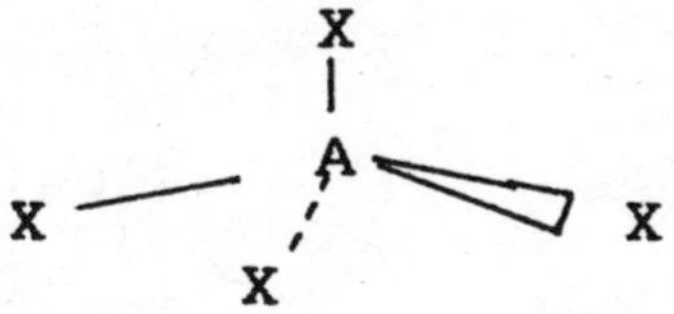 Bond angles = 109.5°

10.

Molecular Type	Geometry	Shape
AX_3E	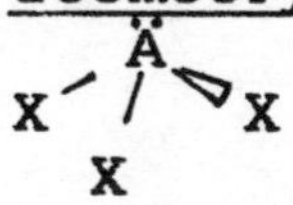	Triangular pyramid
AX_2E_2		Angular
AXE_3	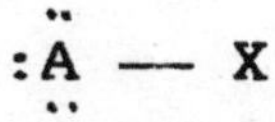	Linear
AX_2E	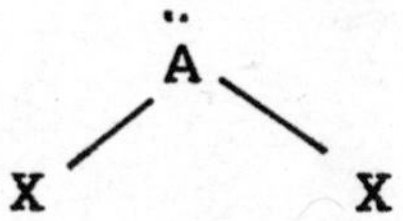	Angular
AXE_2		Linear
AX_2	X — A — X	Linear

11.

Molecule	Lewis Structure	Class of Molecule	Shape
H_2O	H — Ö — H	AX_2E_2	Angular
H_3O^+	H — Ö$^+$ — H (with H below)	AX_3E	Triangular pyramid
PCl_3	:Cl — P — Cl: (with :Cl: below)	AX_3E	Triangular pyramid
BCl_3	:Cl — B — Cl: (with :Cl: below)	AX_3	Triangular planar
SiH_4	H - Si - H (with H above and H below)	AX_4	Tetrahedron
BH_4^-	H - B$^-$ - H (with H above and H below)	AX_4	Tetrahedron
H_2S	H - S̈ - H	AX_2E_2	Angular
SCl_2	:Cl - S̈ - Cl:	AX_2E_2	Angular
NH_4^+	H - N$^+$ - H (with H above and H below)	AX_4	Tetrahedron
BeH_2	H - Be - H	AX_2	Linear
BeH_4^{2-}	H - Be^{2-} - H (with H above and H below)	AX_4	Tetrahedron

12.

Compound	Lewis Structure	Type of Molecule	Geometry	Shape
$BeCl_2$	:Cl – Be – Cl:	AX_2	Cl – Be – Cl	Linear
BCl_3	:Cl – B – Cl: (with :Cl: below)	AX_3	Cl — B with Cl, Cl	Triangular planar
CCl_4	:Cl – C – Cl: (with :Cl: above and :Cl: below)	AX_4	C bonded to Cl, Cl, Cl, Cl	Tetrahedron
NCl_3	:Cl – N – Cl: (with :Cl: below)	AX_3E	N bonded to Cl, Cl, Cl	Triangular pyramid
OCl_2	:Cl – O – Cl:	AX_2E_2	O bonded to Cl, Cl	Angular
FCl	:F – Cl:	AXE_3	F – Cl	Linear

13.

A represents the mid-point of the cube and tetrahedron. AZ is drawn perpendicular to the face diagonal.
We may calculate the angle ZAE = θ as follows.
Let the length of the side of the cube = a
The length of a face diagonal $= \sqrt{a^2 + a^2}$ (Pythagorus)
$= a\sqrt{2}$.

127

The length of the body diagonal EF will be $= \sqrt{a^2 + 2a^2} = a\sqrt{3}$ and so AE will equal one half of the body diagonal or $a\sqrt{3}/2$. units.

$$\text{Sin } \theta = \frac{ZE}{AE} = \frac{\frac{a\sqrt{2}}{2}}{a\frac{\sqrt{3}}{2}} = \frac{\sqrt{2}}{\sqrt{3}} = 0.816.$$

and so $\theta = 54.74°$. But $\theta =$ one half of the angle between two tetrahedrally orientated bonds. The tetrahedral angle, therefore, is equal to $2\theta = 2 \times 54.74 = 109.5°$.

14. a) CH_3OH
There is only one Lewis structure for CH_3OH.

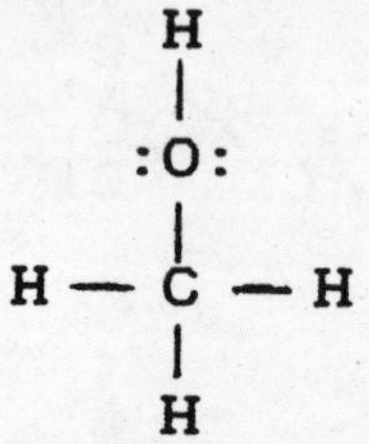

$$
\begin{array}{c}
H \\
| \\
:O: \\
| \\
H - C - H \\
| \\
H
\end{array}
$$

The CO bond order is one: The charge on oxygen is zero, since it has an average of 6 electrons, the same as in the free atom.

b) HCO_2^-
The resonance structures are

$$
\begin{array}{ccc}
:O: & & :\ddot{O}: \\
\parallel & & | \\
H - C - \ddot{O}: {}^- & \longleftrightarrow & H - C = \ddot{O}
\end{array}
$$

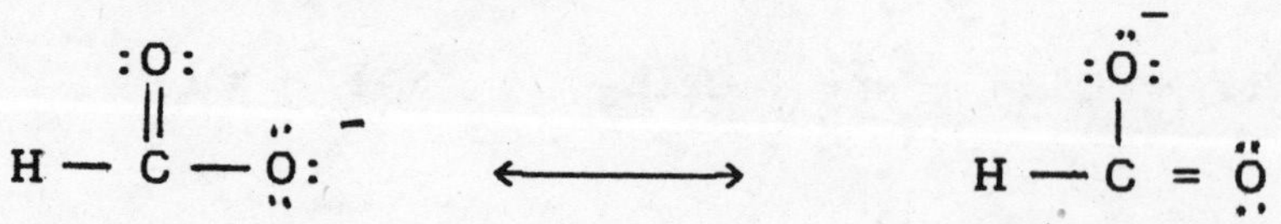

The CO bond order is $\frac{2+1}{2} = 1.5$: The charge on each oxygen atom is $\frac{0-1}{2} = -0.5$.

c) CO_3^{2-}
The resonance structures are as follows; they are generated by using each oxygen in turn as the positon for the double bond.

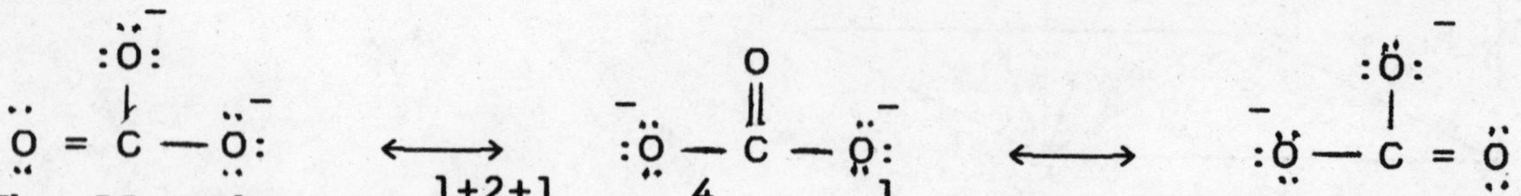

$$
\begin{array}{ccccc}
:\ddot{O}: {}^- & & O & & :\ddot{O}: {}^- \\
\downarrow & & \parallel & & | \\
O = C - \ddot{O}: {}^- & \longleftrightarrow & {}^-:\ddot{O} - C - \ddot{O}: {}^- & \longleftrightarrow & {}^-:\ddot{O} - C = \ddot{O}
\end{array}
$$

The CO order $= \frac{1+2+1}{3} = \frac{4}{3} = 1\frac{1}{3}$: The charge on each oxygen atom $= \frac{-1+0-1}{3} = -\frac{2}{3}$.

d) H_2CO

One Lewis structure describes this molecule. It is

$$\begin{array}{c} H \\ \end{array} \!\!\! \diagdown \!\! C = \ddot{O}\!:$$
$$\begin{array}{c} H \end{array} \!\!\! \diagup$$

The CO bond order is two and the charge on the oxygen atom is zero.

e) CO

One Lewis structure describes this molecule. It is

$$:\overset{-}{C} \equiv \overset{+}{O}:$$

The CO bond order is three. The formal charge on the oxygen is +1.

15. **a) NO_3^-**

The resonance structures are as follows; they are generated by using each oxygen in turn as the position for the double bond.

$$\ddot{O} = \overset{+}{N} - \ddot{O}: \quad\longleftrightarrow\quad :\ddot{\overset{-}{O}} - \overset{+}{N} = \ddot{O} \quad\longleftrightarrow\quad :\ddot{\overset{-}{O}} - N - \ddot{O}:$$
$$\quad\;\; | \qquad\qquad\qquad\qquad\;\; | \qquad\qquad\qquad\qquad\quad \|$$
$$\quad :\ddot{O}: \qquad\qquad\qquad\qquad :\ddot{O}: \qquad\qquad\qquad\qquad :O:$$

The bond order is $\dfrac{2+1+1}{3} = \dfrac{4}{3} = 1\frac{1}{3}$.

b) O_3

The resonance structures are

$$:\ddot{\overset{-}{O}} - \overset{+}{\ddot{O}} = \ddot{O} \quad\longleftrightarrow\quad \ddot{O} = \overset{+}{\ddot{O}} - \ddot{\overset{-}{O}}:$$

The bond order is $\dfrac{1+2}{2} = \dfrac{3}{2} = 1\frac{1}{2}$.

c) PO_4^{3-}

The resonance structures are

$$\begin{array}{ccccccc} :O: & & :\ddot{O}: & & :O: & & :\ddot{O}: \\ \| & & | & & | & & | \\ :\ddot{\overset{-}{O}} - P - \ddot{\overset{-}{O}}: & \longleftrightarrow & :\ddot{\overset{-}{O}} - P = \ddot{O} & \longleftrightarrow & :\ddot{\overset{-}{O}} - P - \ddot{O}: & \longleftrightarrow & \ddot{O} = P - \ddot{\overset{-}{O}}: \\ | & & | & & \| & & | \\ :\ddot{O}: & & :\ddot{O}: & & :O: & & :\ddot{O}: \end{array}$$

The bond order is $\dfrac{2+1+1+1}{4} = \dfrac{5}{4} = 1\frac{1}{4}$.

d) SO_4^{2-}. Here we have two double bonds, and the structures correspond to the six ways of assigning two double bonds to four O atoms.

$$:O - S = \overset{\displaystyle :O:}{\underset{\displaystyle :O:}{\overset{\|}{\underset{|}{S}}}} = \ddot{O} \longleftrightarrow \quad :\ddot{O} - \overset{\displaystyle :O:}{\underset{\displaystyle :O:}{\overset{\|}{\underset{\|}{S}}}} - \ddot{O}: \longleftrightarrow \quad :\ddot{O} - \overset{\displaystyle :\overset{-}{\ddot{O}}:}{\underset{\displaystyle :O:}{\overset{|}{\underset{\|}{S}}}} = \ddot{O} \longleftrightarrow$$

$$\ddot{O} = \overset{\displaystyle :\overset{-}{\ddot{O}}:}{\underset{\displaystyle :\ddot{O}:}{\overset{|}{\underset{|}{S}}}} = \ddot{O} \longleftrightarrow \quad O = \overset{\displaystyle :O:}{\underset{\displaystyle :\ddot{O}:}{\overset{\|}{\underset{|}{S}}}} - \ddot{O}: \longleftrightarrow \quad \ddot{O} = \overset{\displaystyle :\overset{-}{\ddot{O}}:}{\underset{\displaystyle :O:}{\overset{|}{\underset{\|}{S}}}} - \ddot{O}:$$

The bond order is $\dfrac{2+2+1+1+1+2}{6} = \dfrac{9}{6} = 1\frac{1}{2}$.

e) ClO_4^-
The resonance structures are

$$:\overset{-}{\ddot{O}} - \overset{\displaystyle :O:}{\underset{\displaystyle :O:}{\overset{\|}{\underset{\|}{Cl}}}} = \ddot{O} \longleftrightarrow \quad \ddot{O} = \overset{\displaystyle :\overset{-}{\ddot{O}}:}{\underset{\displaystyle :O:}{\overset{|}{\underset{\|}{Cl}}}} = \ddot{O} \longleftrightarrow \quad \ddot{O} = \overset{\displaystyle :O:}{\underset{\displaystyle :O:}{\overset{\|}{\underset{\|}{Cl}}}} - \overset{-}{\ddot{O}}: \longleftrightarrow \quad \ddot{O} = \overset{\displaystyle :O:}{\underset{\displaystyle :\overset{-}{\ddot{O}}:}{\overset{\|}{\underset{\|}{Cl}}}} = \ddot{O}$$

The bond order is $\dfrac{2+1+2+2}{4} = \dfrac{7}{4} = 1\frac{3}{4}$.

16. The Lewis structure for ClO^- is

$$:\ddot{Cl} - \ddot{\overset{-}{O}}:$$

The bond order is, therefore, one.
There are four possible resonance structures for the ClO_4^- ion and the bond order is 1 3/4 - see answer to question 15 above. Since multiple bonds are   shorter than single bonds due to the increased electron density between the atoms forming the bond, the Cl-O bond in ClO^- will be longer than that in ClO_4^-.

17. The Lewis structures for HNO_3 and NO_3^- are

$$:\overset{-}{\ddot{O}} - \overset{+}{\underset{\displaystyle :O:}{\underset{\|}{N}}} - \ddot{O} - H \qquad\qquad \text{and} \qquad\qquad :\overset{-}{\ddot{O}} - \overset{+}{\underset{\displaystyle :O:}{\underset{\|}{N}}} - \ddot{O}:$$

HNO_3 NO_3^-
Writing the resonance forms for HNO_3 we have:

130

$$\overset{-}{:\ddot{O}} - \overset{+}{N} - \ddot{O} - H \quad\longleftrightarrow\quad \ddot{O} = \overset{+}{N} - \ddot{O} - H$$
$$\underset{:\ddot{O}:}{\overset{\parallel}{}} \qquad\qquad \underset{:\ddot{O}:}{\overset{\mid}{}}$$

Thus the bond order of the N-O bond which does not have a hydrogen atom bonded to oxygen will be $\frac{2+1}{2} = 1\frac{1}{2}$, whereas the

N-O bond which also has the hydrogen atom bonded to oxygen will have a bond order of 1.
On the other hand the NO_3^- ion has three resonance forms.

$$\ddot{O} = \overset{+}{N} - \overset{-}{\ddot{O}:} \quad\longleftrightarrow\quad \overset{-}{:\ddot{O}} - \overset{+}{N} - \overset{-}{\ddot{O}:} \quad\longleftrightarrow\quad \overset{-}{:\ddot{O}} - \overset{+}{N} = \ddot{O}$$
$$\underset{:\ddot{O}:}{\overset{\mid}{}} \qquad\qquad \underset{:\ddot{O}:}{\overset{\parallel}{}} \qquad\qquad \underset{:\ddot{O}:}{\overset{\mid}{}}$$

The bond order of the NO bond in the ion will, therefore, be $\frac{2+1+1}{3} = \frac{4}{3} = 1\frac{1}{3}$.

These calculations are consistent with the information that the HNO_3 molecule has two different NO bond lengths since there are two values of bond order while the NO bond length in NO_3^- has one value which is intermediate since its bond order is intermediate between the values for HNO_3.

18. The P_4O_{10} molecule has two different types of P-O bond. This is evident from its Lewis structure

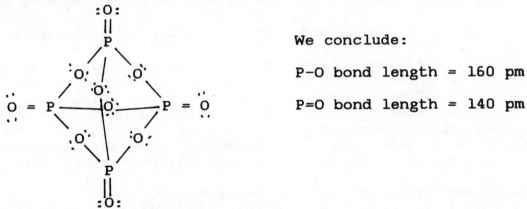

We conclude:

P-O bond length = 160 pm

P=O bond length = 140 pm

Consider first the PO_4^{3-} ion. From Q. 15, the bond order is $1\frac{1}{4}$. Since the P-O bond length is 160 pm, and the P=O bond length is 140 pm, therefore by linear extrapolation a bond order of 1.25 would correspond to a bond length of of $160-(160-140) \times 0.25 = 155$ pm which is in good agreement with the observed value.

HPO_3^{2-}
HPO_3^{2-} has the Lewis structure

$$
\begin{array}{c}
\text{H} \\
| \\
{}^{-}\!\!:\!\overset{..}{\text{O}} - \text{P} = \overset{..}{\text{O}} \\
| \\
{}_{-}\!\!:\!\overset{..}{\text{O}}:
\end{array}
$$

and the resonance forms are

$$
\begin{array}{ccccc}
\quad\quad\text{H} & & \quad\quad\text{H} & & \quad\quad\text{H} \\
{}^{-}\quad| & & {}^{-}\quad| & & \quad\quad| \quad\quad {}^{-} \\
:\overset{..}{\text{O}} - \text{P} = \overset{..}{\text{O}} & \longleftrightarrow & :\overset{..}{\text{O}} - \text{P} - \overset{..}{\text{O}}: & \longleftrightarrow & \overset{..}{\text{O}} = \text{P} - \overset{..}{\text{O}}: \\
\quad| & & \quad|| & & \quad| \\
:\overset{..}{\text{O}}: & & :\overset{..}{\text{O}}: & & :\overset{..}{\text{O}}: \\
{}_{-} & & & & {}_{-}
\end{array}
$$

and the PO bond order is given by $\dfrac{2+1+1}{3} = \dfrac{4}{3} = 1\frac{1}{3}$.

A bond order of 1 1/3 for the PO bond would correspond to a bond length of 160-(160-140)x0.333 = 153 pm in reasonable agreement with the observed value.

$P_2O_7{}^{4-}$

The Lewis structure for the pyrophosphate ion is

$$
\begin{array}{ccccc}
:\overset{..}{\text{O}}:{}^{-} & & :\overset{..}{\text{O}}:{}^{-} & & \\
| & & | & & \\
\overset{..}{\text{O}} = \text{P} - \overset{..}{\text{O}} - \text{P} = \overset{..}{\text{O}} \\
| & & | & & \\
:\overset{..}{\text{O}}: & & :\overset{..}{\text{O}}: & & \\
{}_{-} & & {}_{-} & &
\end{array}
$$

There are nine possible resonance forms of the ion; each

structure contains a P-O-P bridge in which the P-O bond order

is one. The bond order of the remaining PO bonds is 1 1/3.

The $P_2O_7{}^{4-}$ ion, therefore, contains two types of PO bond. One of these with a bond order of one should exhibit a bond length of about 160 pm. The other type of PO bond which has a bond order of 1 1/3 should exhibit a bond length of about 153 pm as demonstrated in the case of the $HPO_3{}^{2-}$ ion. These values are in good agreement with the experimentally determined values of 161 pm and 152 pm respectively.

19. We may construct the following table.

Molecule	Lewis structure	Molecular Type	Dipole (D) or Zero-Dipole(ZD)
BF_3	:F: (top), :F̈ - B - F̈:	AX_3	ZD
NF_3	:F: (top), :F̈ - N - F̈:	AX_3E	D
$BeCl_2$	:Cl - Be - Cl:	AX_2	ZD

Molecule	Lewis structure	Type	
SCl_2	$:\ddot{C}l - \ddot{S} - \ddot{C}l:$	AX_2E_2	D
I_2	$:\ddot{I} - \ddot{I}:$	AXE_3	ZD
ICl	$:\ddot{I} - \ddot{C}l:$	AXE_3	D

$$:\ddot{C}l - \underset{\underset{\displaystyle :\ddot{C}l:}{|}}{\overset{\overset{\displaystyle :\ddot{C}l:}{|}}{C}} - \ddot{C}l:$$

CCl_4 AX_4 ZD

$$:\ddot{C}l - \underset{\underset{\displaystyle :\ddot{C}l:}{|}}{\overset{\overset{\displaystyle H}{|}}{C}} - \ddot{C}l:$$

$CHCl_3$ AX_3Y D

$$:\ddot{C}l - \underset{\underset{\displaystyle H}{|}}{\overset{\overset{\displaystyle H}{|}}{C}} - \ddot{C}l:$$

CH_2Cl_2 AX_2Y_2 D

Note: in the cases of $CHCl_3$ and CH_2Cl_2 the vector sum of the dipole moments will not equate to zero despite the fact that both molecules are tetrahedra. This is because of the two different types of bond, C–Cl and C–H, involved.

20. In order that the central atom A in the molecule ACl_3 may be surrounded by an integral number of electron pairs and since each chlorine atom brings one electron to the covalent bond it forms with A, A can only belong to groups III, V or VII. However, if A belonged to group III there would be a total of six electrons in the valence shell of A and the molecule would be of the type AX_3, or equilateral triangle, and would have no dipole moment.
Consider now the other two cases.

Group V
The Lewis structure would be

$$:\ddot{C}l - \underset{\underset{\displaystyle :\ddot{C}l:}{|}}{A} - \ddot{C}l:$$

type AX_3E – Polar molecule

shape: triangular pyramid

Group VII
The Lewis structure would be

$$:\ddot{C}l - \underset{\underset{\displaystyle :\ddot{C}l:}{|}}{\ddot{A}} - \ddot{C}l:$$

type AX_3E_2 – Polar molecule

shape: T–shaped

Thus if ACl_3 has a dipole moment, A is from Groups V or VII, whereas if it does not have a dipole moment, A is from Group III.

21. We may present the solution in tabular form.

Molecule	Lewis structure, bond polarity and shape		Dipole(D) or Zero Dipole (ZD)
SO_2	O $\overset{=}{\longleftarrow}$ S $\overset{=}{\longrightarrow}$ O	angular	D
CO_2	O $\overset{=}{\longleftarrow}$ C $\overset{=}{\longrightarrow}$ O	linear	ZD
H_2O	H $\overset{-}{\longrightarrow}$ O $\overset{-}{\longleftarrow}$ H	angular	D
NH_3	H $\overset{-}{\longrightarrow}$ N $\overset{-}{\longleftarrow}$ H with H below (↑)	triangular pyramid	D
SO_3	O $\overset{=}{\longleftarrow}$ S $\overset{=}{\longrightarrow}$ O with O below (↓‖)	triangular planar	ZD
BeH_2	H $\overset{-}{\longrightarrow}$ Be $\overset{-}{\longleftarrow}$ H	linear	ZD

22. The Lewis structures of the two possible forms of ozone are

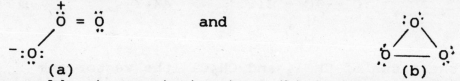

and

We would not expect structure (b) to have a net dipole
moment since the atoms all are equivalent and therefore the
bonds are nonpolar; even if the bonds were polar, the vector
sum is zero. The bonds in (a) can be polar, however, and
their vector sums do not cancel; thus the structure must be
angular, as in (a).

23. The charge distributions may be depicted thus,

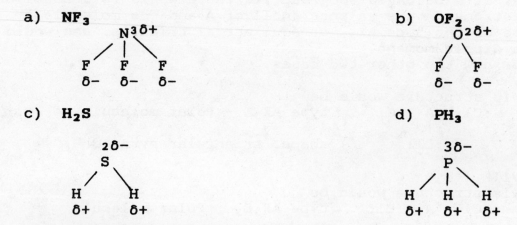

24. The arrangements should be
a) HI < HBr < HCl < HF since the electronegativity differences
increase from I to F.

b) $AsH_3 < PH_3 <$ NH_3

134

c) Cl_2O, F_2O, H_2O since the electronegativity differences
     increase in this order.

d) H_2Te, H_2Se, H_2S, H_2O

25. Both F_2O and H_2O are angular molecules. However, the
    magnitudes of the individual O-F and O-H dipoles are related
    to the electronegativity differences between the atoms making
    up the bonds. The electronegativity difference between
    oxygen and hydrogen is approximately twice that between
    oxygen and fluorine. It is to be expected, therefore, that
    the dipole moment of the H_2O molecule will exceed that of the
    F_2O molecule.

    b) The CS_2 molecule is a linear molecule consisting of two
    identical polar C=S bonds
             S $=$ C $=$ S
             $\longleftarrow$ $\longrightarrow$

    The vector sum of the dipoles will therefore be zero.
    However, in the case of COS, which is also a linear molecule
             S $=$ C $=$ O
    the bonds and therefore the dipoles are not equivalent.
    Their vector sum will not be zero and so COS will have a
    measurable dipole moment.

CHAPTER 9

1. Four reducing agents that may be used to prepare metals from their compounds are,
   i) carbon   ii) carbon monoxide   iii) aluminum
   iv) free electrons
   Balanced equations are
   a) Copper: $Cu_2O + CO \longrightarrow 2Cu + CO_2$

   b) Iron: $Fe_2O_3 + 2Al \xrightarrow{\text{heat}} 2Fe + Al_2O_3$

   c) Aluminum: $Al_2O_3 \xrightarrow{\text{melt}} 2Al^{3+} + 3O^{2-}$

   (Electrolysis) $2Al^{3+} + 6e^- \longrightarrow 2Al$
   $$3O^{2-} \longrightarrow 3/2\ O_2 + 6e^-$$
   $$\overline{Al_2O_3 \longrightarrow 2Al + 3/2\ O_2}$$

   d) Lead: $PbO + C \longrightarrow Pb + CO$

2. 1 metric ton $= 10^6$ g and so 10^6 g of copper are contains
   $$10^6\ g \times \frac{1.60\ g\ Cu}{100\ g} = 1.60 \times 10^4\ g\ Cu$$
   From the equation $Cu_2S + O_2 \longrightarrow 2Cu + SO_2$, the roasting of copper sulfide in air, we deduce that one mole of SO_2 gas is obtained for every two moles of copper contained in one ton of ore. By choosing the appropriate unit conversion factors we can calculate the number of moles of SO_2 obtained
   $$1.60 \times 10^4\ g\ Cu \times \frac{1\ mol\ Cu}{63.54\ g\ Cu} \times \frac{1\ mol\ SO_2}{2\ mol\ Cu} = 126\ mol\ SO_2$$
   Now substitute in the ideal gas equation in the form
   $$V_{SO_2} = \frac{n_{SO_2} \times R \times T}{P_{SO_2}}$$

   $$= \frac{126 \times 0.0821 \times 293}{1.00}\ L \quad (760\ mm\ Hg = 1\ atm)$$
   $$= 3.03 \times 10^3\ L$$

3. The appropriate reaction is
   $$CaCO_3 + SiO_2 \longrightarrow CaSiO_3 + CO_2$$
   Iron ore contains 12.2% SiO_2. Thus
   2.00 metric tons iron ore contain $2.00 \times \frac{12.2}{100} = 0.244$ tons SiO_2

This will require a mass of $CaCO_3$ equivalent to the same number of moles of $CaCO_3$ as there are moles of SiO_2 in 0.244 tons of SiO_2 – see equation above – and this will be given by

$$0.244 \text{ tons } SiO_2 \quad \times \quad \frac{10^6 \text{ g } SiO_2}{1 \text{ ton } SiO_2} \quad \times \quad \frac{1 \text{ mol } SiO_2}{60.09 \text{ g } SiO_2} \quad \times$$

$$\frac{1 \text{ mol } CaCO_3}{1 \text{ mol } SiO_2} \quad \times \quad \frac{100.09 \text{ g } CaCO_3}{1 \text{ mol } CaCO_3}$$

$$= \quad 4.06 \times 10^5 \text{ g } CaCO_3$$

The limestone is impure, however, and so the minimum mass of 96% $CaCO_3$ required will be

$$4.06 \times 10^5 \text{ g } CaCO_3 \quad \times \quad \frac{100 \text{ g limestone}}{96 \text{ g } CaCO_3} \quad = \quad 4.23 \times 10^5 \text{ g limestone}$$

4. a) A mineral is a naturally occurring substance with a characteristic range of chemical composition. An ore is a mineral deposit which may profitably treated for the extraction of one or more metals. The common ores are oxides, sulfides and carbonates due to the abundance of oxygen and sulfur and the fact that most metals occur in the earth's crust as positive ions, that is in their oxidized form. Extraction of a metal from one of these ores is by reduction.

 b) <u>Oxide ore</u>: Cuprite, Cu_2O (copper(I) oxide)
     $Cu_2O + C \longrightarrow 2Cu + CO$ – Reduction with coke
 <u>Sulfide ore</u>: Galena, PbS_2 (lead(II) sulfide)
     $2PbS + 3O_2 \longrightarrow 2PbO + 2SO_2$ – Roasting to
     remove S
     $PbO + C \longrightarrow 2Pb + CO_2$ –Reduction with coke
 <u>Carbonate ore</u>: Malachite, $Cu_2(CO_3)(OH)_2$, Copper(II)
     carbonate hydroxide.
     $Cu_2(CO_3)(OH)_2 + C \longrightarrow 2Cu + 2CO_2 + H_2O$
     – Reduction with coke

 c) The following equations illustrate
 The reduction of iron(III) oxide by the metal aluminum:
  $Fe_2O_3 + 2Al \longrightarrow Al_2O_3 + 2Fe$
 The reduction of lead(II) oxide by the non-metal carbon:
  $2PbO + C \longrightarrow 2Pb + CO_2$

5. a) 100 g ore contain 30 g Fe_2O_3
  30 g Fe_2O_3 contains

$$30 \text{ g } Fe_2O_3 \times \frac{1 \text{ mol } Fe_2O_3}{159.70 \text{ g } Fe_2O_3} \times \frac{2 \text{ mol Fe}}{1 \text{ mol } Fe_2O_3} \times \frac{55.85 \text{ g Fe}}{1 \text{ mol Fe}}$$

$$= \quad 21 \text{ g Fe}$$

The theoretical yield of steel from 100 g of ore would, therefore, be 21 g, or 0.21 kg of steel per kg of ore. To produce 10^6 metric tons of steel would, therefore, require

$$10^6 \text{ tons steel} \times \frac{1000 \text{ kg steel}}{1 \text{ ton steel}} \times \frac{1 \text{ kg ore}}{0.21 \text{ kg steel}}$$

$$= 4.8 \times 10^9 \text{ kg of ore}$$

$$= 4.8 \times 10^6 \text{ tons}$$

(b) 1 kg ore contains 0.21 kg of iron - see (a) above - and so the mass of iron in one ton of ore will be

$$\frac{0.21 \text{ kg iron}}{1 \text{ kg ore}} \times \frac{1000 \text{ kg ore}}{1 \text{ ton ore}} = 210 \text{ kg iron/ton ore}$$

(c) $Fe_2O_3 + 3C \longrightarrow 2Fe + 3CO$

1 ton of ore would produce 210 kg of iron - see (b) above. Combining this information with that derived from the equation for the reduction of the iron oxide with coke, we can calculate the mass of coke required:

$$210 \text{ kg Fe} \times \frac{1000 \text{ g Fe}}{1 \text{ kg Fe}} \times \frac{1 \text{ mol Fe}}{55.85 \text{ g Fe}} \times \frac{3 \text{ mol C}}{2 \text{ mol Fe}} \times$$

$$\frac{12.01 \text{ g C}}{1 \text{ mol C}} \times \frac{1 \text{ kg C}}{1000 \text{ g C}}$$

$$= 68 \text{ kg of coke.}$$

6. i) Fe_3O_4: is a component of iron ore which is an impure mixture of Fe_2O_3 and Fe_3O_4. Fe_3O_4 is, therefore, a component of the feedstock for the blast furnace.

   ii) Coke: consists of carbon which, at high temperature, is converted in the blast furnace to carbon monoxide according to the reaction

$$2C + O_2 \longrightarrow 2CO$$

   iii) CO: The carbon monoxide produced in (ii) above is the reducing agent which reduces the $Fe_2O_3:Fe_3O_4$ mixture to iron and carbon dioxide

$$Fe_2O_3 + 3CO \longrightarrow 2Fe + 3CO_2$$
$$Fe_3O_4 + 4CO \longrightarrow 3Fe + 4CO_2$$

   iv) CaO: Calcium oxide, formed by the decomposition of calcium carbonate (limestone), $CaCO_3$, which is part of the blast furnace charge, combines with silica impurities in the iron ore to form a layer of molten slag, $CaSiO_3$. The slag forms a layer on top of the molten iron and prevents its reoxidation.

7. In general, those elements displaying metallic character are the most numerous in the periodic table and occupy all but the top and right of the table where the non-metals are found. The metals and non-metals are separated by a diagonal band of elements which exhibit both metallic and non-metallic properties, the so-called metalloids.
The third period elements consist of three elements, sodium, magnesium and aluminium, which display well defined metallic

properties, one of the most important being the ability to conduct electricity. Silicon, although displaying the properties of a non-metal, is a semi-conductor of electricity and may be described as a metalloid. The remaining elements phosphorus, sulfur, chlorine and argon are non-metals. The elements in group IV of the periodic table display a transition from non-metallic to metallic properties. Carbon is clearly a non-metal; however, both silicon and germanium are metalloids. Tin and lead are clearly defined metals.

8. (a) Closest packing of spheres
    See Box 9.2 of the text for the diagram. A single, two dimensional, layer of spheres with closest packing. Each sphere has six immediate neighbors within the layers.

    (b) Square packing of spheres
    See Box 9.2 of the text for the diagram. A single layer of spheres with square packing. Each sphere has four immediate neighbors within the layer.

9. Bonding in the Na_2 molecule, which exists only in the gaseous phase, occurs due to the overlap of the 3s orbitals of two sodium atoms. Thus a covalent bond is formed. In sodium metal, metallic bonding is exhibited. In the solid state the 3s orbital of a particular sodium atom can overlap with the 3s orbitals of neighboring sodium atoms. This results in a spreading out of the electron density to encompass all the sodium atoms. As a result the process resembles ionization giving, essentially, sodium ions, Na^+, and free electrons which may migrate throughout the metal. The electrostatic attraction between the mobile electron cloud and the positive ions provides the 'glue' which holds them together. The essential difference between the Na_2 molecule and the metal is that in the former the electrons are localized between specific atoms whereas in the metal they are not.

10. The electrical conductivity exhibited by a metal is due to the ability of the valence electrons in the metal to move between the positively charged metal ions. Thus when an electric potential is applied across a metal the electrons can migrate and carry the current. This is called metallic conduction. As the temperature is decreased the conductivity of a metal increases due to a decrease in the number of collisions between metal ions and electrons. This decrease occurs because, at lower temperatures, the amplitude of the vibrations of the ions decrease, thus reducing their tendency to collide with electrons and impede their flow. The excellent heat conduction exhibited by metals is also a function of the rapid and easy electron flow within the metal. Thus heat applied to one part of the metal results in a rapid increase in the kinetic energies of the electrons in that region which results in

rapid conduction to other parts of the metal by means of electron flow.

11. <u>Body-centered cubic structure</u>

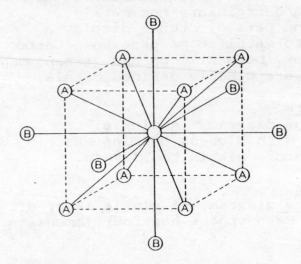

The eight nearest neighbors to the body centered atom or ion are those atoms and ions at the corners of the cube. They touch along the body diagonals. They are designated by A on the above diagram. The six next nearest atoms or ions to the body centered atom or ion are those which are, themselves, body centered atoms or ions of cubes sharing faces with the first. These atoms and ions are designated by B on the above diagram.

12. The metals gold, silver, copper, tin, lead and iron are all found either in the free state or in ores which are readily reduced to yield the free metal. They are also relatively unreactive, particularly gold, which renders them suitable for the manufacture of artifacts.
On the other hand, lithium, sodium, potassium and aluminium are all highly reactive and occur in nature only in the combined state. Once extracted the alkali metals lithium, sodium and potassium must be stored in an inert liquid because they react rapidly with the oxygen in the air and violently with water.

13. Aluminum is the best choice for space vehicle constructions. The main advantages are lightness and the fact that it readily forms alloys, such as duralumin (an alloy with magnesium, copper and manganese) which have high tensile strengths. Aluminum is also abundant in nature. Its main disadvantages are that despite its widespread nature it is still relatively expensive. It is also very reactive.
Copper is the metal of choice for the town square statue. It has the advantages that it is relatively non-reactive and is easily worked. It is particularly suitable in the form of its alloy bronze which has been known since ancient times and

which consists of a mixture copper and tin. Bronze is harder than copper but is readily cast into shapes. The principal disadvantage of copper is one of increasing cost. Copper, and its alloy bronze, also become tarnished due to weathering over long periods although this is sometimes considered to be aesthetically pleasing. The green patina acquired by copper clad roofs is a case in point.

14. a) Copper was one of the earliest known metals because, not only does it occur in the metallic state in nature, but many of its ores are readily reduced. Copper artifacts have been found which date back to about 4000 B.C.

b) Copper covered roofs acquire a green colour due to the formation of copper carbonate or copper sulfate hydroxides on the surface of the copper due to prolonged weathering. The process can take many years to occur.

c) Copper is one of the so-called coinage metals due to its resistance to corrosion. It is alloyed with silver in 'silver' coins because it not only reduces the overall cost of producing the coinage but also improves its durability. Pure silver is too soft for satisfactory coinage manufacture.

d) The ability of aqueous ammonia to dissolve slightly soluble copper salts is due to the formation of the soluble cation $Cu(NH_3)_4^{2+}$.

e) Although aluminum is a rather reactive metal, it is covered by a thin, hard layer of aluminum oxide, and does not react further. Thus it can be usd for cooking utensils.

f) Aluminum is very difficult and costly to remove from its ores. Although the metal was known in the mid 18th century, it was not until the late 19th century that a satisfactory electrolytic process for the production of aluminum was developed and the price of the metal came within an acceptable range.

15. Both iron, Fe, and zinc, Zn, react with dilute hydrochloric acid solution. The reaction equations are
$$Fe(s) + 2HCl(aq) \longrightarrow FeCl_2(aq) + H_2(g)$$
$$\text{iron(II)chloride}$$
$$Zn(s) + 2HCl(aq) \longrightarrow ZnCl_2(aq) + H_2(g)$$
$$\text{zinc(II)chloride}$$
In both cases hydrogen gas is evolved. Neither copper, Cu, nor lead, Pb, will react with dilute hydrochloric acid solution.

16. a) Aluminum reacts with dilute aqueous sulfuric acid according to the equation
$$2Al(s) + 3H_2SO_4(aq) \longrightarrow Al_2(SO_4)_3(aq) + 3H_2(g)$$

141

b) Silver reacts with hot concentrated sulfuric acid according to the equation

$$2Ag + 2H_2SO_4 \longrightarrow Ag_2SO_4(s) + SO_2(g) + 2H_2O(\ell)$$

In this reaction silver sulfate is formed and sulphur dioxide gas is obtained by the reduction of sulfuric acid.

17. (a) $SO_3^{2-}(aq) + MnO_4^-(aq) \longrightarrow SO_4^{2-}(aq) + Mn^{2+}(aq)$

We have

Oxidation $\qquad \overset{+4}{SO_3^{2-}}(aq) \longrightarrow \overset{+6}{SO_4^{2-}}(aq)$

Reduction $\qquad \overset{+7}{MnO_4^-}(aq) \longrightarrow \overset{+2}{Mn^{2+}}(aq)$

Adding electrons we have

Oxidation $\qquad \overset{+4}{SO_3^{2-}}(aq) \longrightarrow \overset{+6}{SO_4}(aq) + 2e^-$

Reduction $\qquad \overset{+7}{MnO_4^-}(aq) + 5e^- \longrightarrow Mn^{2+}(aq)$

Now balance charges by adding hydrogen ions and balance oxygen atoms by adding H_2O.

$$SO_3^{2-}(aq) + H_2O \longrightarrow SO_4^{2-}(aq) + 2H^+ + 2e^-$$
$$MnO_4^-(aq) + 8H^+ + 5e^- \longrightarrow Mn^{2+}(aq) + 4H_2O$$

Eliminate the electrons by multiplying the first equation by five and the second equation by two, adding and also eliminating redundancies in H^+ and H_2O.

$$5SO_3^{2-}(aq) + 5H_2O \longrightarrow 5SO_4^{2-}(aq) + 10H^+ + 10e^-$$
$$2MnO_4^-(aq) + 16H^+ + 10e^- \longrightarrow 2Mn^{2+}(aq) + 8H_2O$$

$$5SO_3^{2-}(aq) + 2MnO_4^-(aq) + 6H^+ \longrightarrow 5SO_4^{2-}(aq) + 2Mn^{2+}(aq) + 3H_2O$$

(b) $H_2O_2(aq) + MnO_4^-(aq) \longrightarrow Mn^{2+}(aq) + O_2(g)$

We have

Oxidation $\qquad \overset{-1}{H_2O_2}(aq) \longrightarrow \overset{0}{O_2}(g)$

Since each O is -1, the net change is from -2 to 0.

Reduction $\qquad \overset{+7}{MnO_4}(aq) \longrightarrow \overset{+2}{Mn^{2+}}(aq)$

See part (a) for balancing this half-reaction.
Adding electrons we have

Oxidation $\qquad \overset{-1}{H_2O_2}(aq) \longrightarrow \overset{0}{O_2}(g) + 2e^-$

Now balance charges by adding hydrogen ions and balance oxygen atoms by adding H_2O

$$H_2O_2(aq) \longrightarrow O_2(g) + 2H^+ + 2e^-$$
$$MnO_4^-(aq) + 8H^+ + 5e^- \longrightarrow Mn^{2+}(aq) + 4H_2O$$

Eliminate the electrons by multiplying the first equation by five and the second equation by two, adding and also eliminating redundancies in H^+.

$$5H_2O_2(aq) \longrightarrow 5O_2(g) + 10H^+ + 10e^-$$
$$2MnO_4^-(aq) + 16H^+ + 10e^- \longrightarrow 2Mn^{2+} + 8H_2O$$

$$5H_2O_2(aq) + 2MnO_4^-(aq) + 6H^+ \longrightarrow 2Mn^{2+} + 5O_2(g) + 8H_2O$$

142

(c) $Zn(s) + NO_3^-(aq) \longrightarrow Zn^{2+}(aq) + N_2O(g)$
We have

$$\underset{Oxidation}{\text{Oxidation}} \qquad \overset{0}{Zn(s)} \qquad \longrightarrow \qquad \overset{+2}{Zn^{2+}(aq)}$$

$$\underset{Reduction}{\text{Reduction}} \qquad \overset{+5}{2NO_3^-(aq)} \longrightarrow \overset{+1}{N_2O(g)}$$

Note: Atoms other than hydrogen and oxygen are balanced at this stage. Since each N changes by 4e, the net change is 8e.
Adding electrons we have

$$\underset{Oxidation}{\text{Oxidation}} \qquad \overset{0}{Zn(s)} \longrightarrow \overset{+2}{Zn^{2+}}(aq) + 2e^-$$

$$\underset{Reduction}{\text{Reduction}} \qquad \overset{+5}{2NO_3^-}(aq) + 8e^- \longrightarrow \overset{+1}{N_2O(g)}$$

Now balance charges by adding hydrogen ions and balance oxygen atoms by adding H_2O.

$$Zn(s) \longrightarrow Zn^{2+}(aq) + 2e^-$$
$$2NO_3^-(aq) + 8e^- + 10H^+ \longrightarrow N_2O(g) + 5H_2O$$

Eliminate the electrons by multiplying the first equation by four and adding.

$$4Zn(s) \longrightarrow 4Zn^{2+}(aq) + 8e^-$$
$$2NO_3^-(aq) + 8e^- + 10H^+ \longrightarrow N_2O(g) + 5H_2O$$

$$\overline{4Zn(s) + 2NO_3^-(aq) + 10H^+ \longrightarrow 4Zn^{2+}(aq) + N_2O(g) + 5H_2O}$$

(d) $P(s) + NO_3^-(aq) \longrightarrow H_2PO_4^-(aq) + NO(g)$
We have

$$\underset{Oxidation}{\text{Oxidation}} \qquad \overset{0}{P(s)} \longrightarrow \overset{+5}{H_2PO_4^-(aq)}$$

$$\underset{Reduction}{\text{Reduction}} \qquad \overset{+5}{NO_3^-(aq)} \longrightarrow \overset{+2}{NO(g)}$$

Adding electrons we have

$$\underset{Oxidation}{\text{Oxidation}} \qquad \overset{0}{P(s)} \longrightarrow \overset{+5}{H_2PO_4^-}(aq) + 5e^-$$

$$\underset{Reduction}{\text{Reduction}} \qquad \overset{+5}{NO_3^-}(aq) + 3e^- \longrightarrow \overset{+2}{NO(g)}$$

Now balance charges by adding hydrogen ions and balance oxygen atoms by adding H_2O.

$$P(s) + 4H_2O \longrightarrow H_2PO_4^-(aq) + 6H^+ + 5e^-$$
$$NO_3^-(aq) + 4H^+ + 3e^- \longrightarrow NO(g) + 2H_2O$$

Eliminate the electrons by multiplying the first equation by three and the second equation by five, adding and also eliminating redundancies in H^+ and H_2O.

$$3P(s) + 12H_2O \longrightarrow 3H_2PO_4^-(aq) + 18H^+ + 15e^-$$
$$5NO_3^-(aq) + 20H^+ + 15e^- \longrightarrow 5NO(g) + 10H_2O$$

$$\overline{3P(s) + 5NO_3^-(aq) + 2H^+ + 2H_2O \longrightarrow 3H_2PO_4^-(aq) + 5NO(g)}$$

(e) $NO_3^-(aq) + I_2(s) \longrightarrow IO_3^-(aq) + NO_2(g)$
We have

$$\underset{Oxidation}{\text{Oxidation}} \qquad \overset{0}{I_2(g)} \longrightarrow \overset{+5}{2IO_3^-(aq)}$$

Note: Atoms other than hydrogen and oxygen are balanced at this stage. Since 2 I atoms are involved, the total change is 10e.

$$\underline{\text{Reduction}} \qquad \overset{+5}{NO_3^-}(aq) \longrightarrow \overset{+4}{NO_2}(g)$$
Adding electrons we have

$$\underline{\text{Oxidation}} \qquad \overset{0}{I_2}(s) \longrightarrow 2\overset{+5}{IO_3^-}(aq) + 10e^-$$

$$\underline{\text{Reduction}} \qquad \overset{+5}{NO_3^-}(aq) + e^- \longrightarrow \overset{+4}{NO_2}(g)$$

Now balance charges by adding hydrogen ions and balance oxygen atoms by adding H_2O

$$I_2(s) + 6H_2O \longrightarrow 2IO_3^-(aq) + 10e^- + 12H^+$$
$$NO_3^-(aq) + e^- + 2H^+ \longrightarrow NO_2(g) + H_2O$$

Eliminate the electrons by multiplying the second equation by two, adding and also eliminating redundancies in H^+ and H_2O.

$$I_2(s) + 6H_2O \longrightarrow 2IO_3^-(aq) + 10e^- + 12H^+$$
$$10NO_3^-(aq) + 10e^- + 20H^+ \longrightarrow 10NO_2(g) + 10H_2O$$

$$\overline{10NO_3^-(aq) + I_2(s) + 8H^+ \longrightarrow 2IO_3^-(aq) + 10NO_2(g) + 4H_2O}$$

18. (a) $MnO_4^-(aq) + I^-(aq) \longrightarrow MnO_2(s) + IO^-(aq)$
We have

$$\underline{\text{Oxidation}} \qquad \overset{-1}{I^-}(aq) \longrightarrow \overset{+1}{IO^-}(aq)$$

$$\underline{\text{Reduction}} \qquad \overset{+7}{MnO_4^-}(aq) \longrightarrow \overset{+4}{MnO_2}(s)$$
Adding electrons we have

$$\underline{\text{Oxidation}} \qquad \overset{-1}{I^-}(aq) \longrightarrow \overset{+1}{IO^-}(aq) + 2e^-$$

$$\underline{\text{Reduction}} \qquad \overset{+7}{MnO_4^-}(aq) + 3e^- \longrightarrow \overset{+4}{MnO_2}(s)$$

Now balance charges by adding hydroxide ions and balance oxygen and hydrogen atoms by adding H_2O.

$$I^-(aq) + 2OH^- \longrightarrow IO^-(aq) + 2e^- + H_2O$$
$$MnO_4^-(aq) + 3e^- + 2H_2O \longrightarrow MnO_2(s) + 4OH^-$$

Eliminate the electrons by multiplying the first reaction by three and the second equation by two, adding and also eliminating redundancies in OH^- and H_2O

$$3I^-(aq) + 6OH^- \longrightarrow 3IO^-(aq) + 6e^- + 3H_2O$$
$$2MnO_4^-(aq) + 6e^- + 4H_2O \longrightarrow 2MnO_2(s) + 8OH^-$$

$$\overline{2MnO_4^-(aq) + 3I^-(aq) + H_2O \longrightarrow 2MnO_2(s) + 3IO^-(aq) + 2OH^-}$$

(b) $Br_2(aq) \longrightarrow Br^-(aq) + BrO_3^-(aq)$
We have

$$\underline{\text{Oxidation}} \qquad \overset{0}{Br_2}(aq) \longrightarrow 2\overset{+5}{BrO_3^-}(aq)$$

$$\overset{0}{Br_2}(aq) \longrightarrow \overset{-1}{2Br^-}(aq)$$

Reduction

Note: Atoms other than hydrogen and oxygen are balanced at this stage.

Adding electrons we have

Oxidation
$$\overset{0}{Br_2}(aq) \longrightarrow \overset{+5}{2BrO_3^-}(aq) + 10e^-$$

Reduction
$$\overset{0}{Br_2}(aq) + 2e^- \longrightarrow \overset{-1}{2Br^-}(aq)$$

Now balance charges by adding hydroxide ions and balance oxygen and hydrogen atoms by adding H_2O.

$$Br_2(aq) + 12OH^- \longrightarrow 2BrO_3^-(aq) + 10e^- + 6H_2O$$
$$Br_2(aq) + 2e^- \longrightarrow 2Br^-(aq)$$

Eliminate electrons by multiplying the second equation by five and adding

$$Br_2(aq) + 12OH^- \longrightarrow 2BrO_3^-(aq) + 10e^- + 6H_2O$$
$$5Br_2(aq) + 10e^- \longrightarrow 10Br^-(aq)$$
_____
$$6Br_2(aq) + 12OH^- \longrightarrow 2BrO_3^-(aq) + 10Br^-(aq) + 6H_2O$$
or $\quad 3Br_2(aq) + 6OH^- \longrightarrow BrO_3^-(aq) + 5Br^-(aq) + 3H_2O$

(c) $\quad I^-(aq) + ClO^-(aq) \longrightarrow IO_3^-(aq) + Cl^-(aq)$

We have

Oxidation
$$\overset{-1}{I^-}(aq) \longrightarrow \overset{+5}{IO_3^-}(aq)$$

Reduction
$$\overset{+1}{ClO^-}(aq) \longrightarrow \overset{-1}{Cl^-}(aq)$$

Adding electrons we have

Oxidation
$$\overset{-1}{I^-}(aq) \longrightarrow \overset{+5}{IO_3^-}(aq) + 6e^-$$

Reduction
$$\overset{+1}{ClO^-}(aq) + 2e^- \longrightarrow \overset{-1}{Cl^-}(aq)$$

Now balance charges by adding hydroxide ions and balance oxygen and hydrogen by adding H_2O

$$I^-(aq) + 6OH^- \longrightarrow IO_3^-(aq) + 3H_2O + 6e^-$$
$$ClO^-(aq) + 2e^- + H_2O \longrightarrow Cl^-(aq) + 2OH^-$$

Eliminate the electrons by multiplying the second equation by 3, adding and also eliminating redundancies in OH^- and H_2O.

$$I^-(aq) + 6OH^- \longrightarrow IO_3^-(aq) + 3H_2O + 6e^-$$
$$3ClO^-(aq) + 6e^- + 3H_2O \longrightarrow 3Cl^-(aq) + 6OH^-$$
_____
$$I^-(aq) + 3ClO^-(aq) \longrightarrow IO_3^-(aq) + 3Cl^-(aq)$$

(d) $\quad SO_3^{2-}(aq) + MnO_4^-(aq) \longrightarrow SO_4^{2-}(aq) + MnO_2(s)$

We have

Oxidation
$$\overset{+4}{SO_3^{2-}}(aq) \longrightarrow \overset{+6}{SO_4^{2-}}(aq)$$

Reduction
$$\overset{+7}{MnO_4^-}(aq) \longrightarrow \overset{+4}{MnO_2}(s)$$

145

See part (i) for balancing this half-reaction.
Adding electrons we have

$$\underline{\text{Oxidation}} \qquad \overset{+4}{SO_3^{2-}}(aq) \longrightarrow \overset{+6}{SO_4^{2-}}(aq) + 2e^-$$

Now balance charges by adding hydroxide ions and balance oxygen and hydrogen by adding H_2O

$$SO_3^{2-}(aq) + 2OH^- \longrightarrow SO_4^{2-}(aq) + 2e^- + H_2O$$
$$MnO_4^-(aq) + 3e^- + 2H_2O \longrightarrow MnO_2(s) + 4OH^-$$

Eliminate the electrons by multiplying the first equation by three and the second equation by two, adding and also eliminating redundancies in OH^- and H_2O

$$3SO_3^{2-}(aq) + 6OH^- \longrightarrow 3SO_4^{2-}(aq) + 6e^- + 3H_2O$$
$$2MnO_4^-(aq) + 6e^- + 4H_2O \longrightarrow 2MnO_2(s) + 8OH^-$$

$$3SO_3^{2-}(aq) + 2MnO_4^-(aq) + H_2O \longrightarrow 3SO_4^{2-}(aq) + 2MnO_2(s) + 2OH^-$$

19. The oxidation numbers are obtained using the proceeding outlined in previous chapters. In all cases but H_2O_2 here, the O is 2- and H is +1 and Cl is -1, which determines the oxidation numbers for the other atoms:

$$\overset{+3\ -2\ +1-2}{Al_2O_3 \cdot xH_2O} \qquad , \qquad \overset{+3-1}{AlCl_4^-}, \quad \overset{+4-2}{SiO_2}$$

$$\overset{+4-2}{SiO_3^{2-}} \qquad , \qquad \overset{+2\ -2+1}{Pb(OH)_4^{2-}}, \quad \overset{+4-1}{PbCl_4}$$

$$\overset{+3\ -2}{Fe_2O_3} \qquad \overset{+2\ -3+1}{Cu(NH_3)_4^{2+}}, \text{ since in } NH_3 \text{ since H is +1, N is -3;}$$
thus Cu is 2+.

20.

Acid	Anhydride
H_2SO_4	SO_3
HNO_3	N_2O_5
H_2CO_3	CO_2
$HClO_4$	Cl_2O_7

21.

Basic	$K_2O + H_2O \longrightarrow$	$2KOH$
Basic	$SrO + H_2O \longrightarrow$	$Sr(OH)_2$
Acidic	$SO_2 + H_2O \longrightarrow$	H_2SO_3
Acidic	$SO_3 + H_2O \longrightarrow$	H_2SO_4
Acidic	$CO_2 + H_2O \longrightarrow$	H_2CO_3
Acidic	$P_4O_6 + 6H_2O \longrightarrow$	$4H_3PO_3$
Acidic	$Cl_2O_7 + H_2O \longrightarrow$	$2HClO_4$

22. Al_2O_3 is more basic than SiO_2, and SO_2 is more acidic than SiO_2, since oxide acidity increases from left to right across the periodic table.

23. a) $Li_2O + SiO_2 \longrightarrow Li_2SiO_3$ since O^{2-} reacts with
$$SiO_2 \longrightarrow SiO_3^{2-}$$

b) $Na_2O + N_2O_5 \longrightarrow 2NaNO_3$

c) $6CaO + P_4O_{10} \longrightarrow 2Ca_3(PO_4)_2$

24. a) $AlCl_3 + 3NaOH \longrightarrow Al(OH)_3(s) + 3NaCl(aq)$
      white precipitate appears; it dissolves in excess NaOH.

     b) $CuSO_4 + 2NaOH \longrightarrow Cu(OH)_2(s) + Na_2SO_4(aq)$
      Pale blue precipitate forms.

     c) $FeSO_4 + 2NaOH \longrightarrow Fe(OH)_2(s) + Na_2SO_4(aq)$
      Dirty white precipitate forms; it rapidly turns brown.

     d) $Pb(NO_3)_2 + 2NaOH \longrightarrow Pb(OH)_2(s) + 2NaNO_3(aq)$
      White precipitate forms; it dissolves in excess NaOH.

25. The Lewis structures are

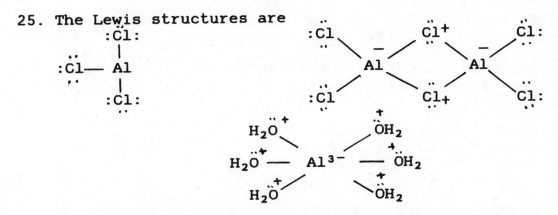

26. a) $2Al(OH)_3 \xrightarrow{\text{heat}} Al_2O_3 + 3H_2O$

     b) $2Fe(OH)_3 \xrightarrow{\text{heat}} Fe_2O_3 + 3H_2O$

     c) $Cu(OH)_2 \xrightarrow{\text{heat}} CuO + H_2O$

27. **$CuSO_4$** solution reacts with a base to form Cu(II) hydroxide
$$Cu^{2+} + 2OH^- \longrightarrow Cu(OH)_2$$
The blue gelatinous precipitate of $Cu(OH)_2$ dissolves in aqueous ammonia to give a deep blue solution of the ion $[Cu(NH_3)_4]^{2+}$.

$Al_2(SO_4)_3$ No reaction with HCl(aq). Reaction with a base produces a white gelatinous precipitate of aluminum hydroxide, $Al(OH)_3$,
$$Al_2(SO_4)_3 + 6NaOH \longrightarrow 2Al(OH)_3 + 3Na_2SO_4$$
In excess solution of base the precipitate of aluminum hydroxide dissolves to form the aluminate ion
$$Al(OH)_3(s) + OH^- \longrightarrow Al(OH_4)^-$$

$Pb(NO_3)_2$ reacts with HCl in solution to produce a white precipitate of sparingly soluble lead chloride, $PbCl_2$. Lead iodide, PbI_2 is also sparingly soluble and may be precipitated as a yellow solid when Pb(II) salts react with a soluble iodide in solution.

FeSO₄ Iron(II) sulphate reacts with hydroxide ion in solution to form a white precipitate of iron(II) hydroxide $Fe(OH)_2$ which rapidly becomes discoloured due to its oxidation to iron(III) hydroxide, $Fe(OH)_3$, a brown gelatinous precipitate.

28. a) $2Al + 2NaOH + 6H_2O \longrightarrow 2NaAl(OH)_4 + 3H_2$

    b) $Al_2O_3 + 3C + 3Cl_2 \longrightarrow 2AlCl_3 + 3CO$

    c) $2(NH_4)Al(SO_4)_2 \cdot 12H_2O \longrightarrow 2NH_3 + 4H_2SO_4 + Al_2O_3 + 21H_2O$

29. The normal salts of iron and copper that may be produced from HNO_3, H_2SO_4 and H_3PO_4 are

    HNO₃: $Cu(NO_3)_2$ Copper(II) Nitrate
                 $Fe(NO_3)_2$ Iron(II) Nitrate
                 $Fe(NO_3)_3$ Iron(III) Nitrate

    H₂SO₄: Cu_2SO_4 Copper(I) Sulfate
                 $CuSO_4$ Copper(II) Sulfate
                 $FeSO_4$ Iron(II) Sulfate
                 $Fe_2(SO_4)_3$ Iron(III) Sulfate

    H₃PO₄: Cu_3PO_4 Copper(I) Phosphate
                 $Cu_3(PO_4)_2$ Copper(II) Phosphate
                 $Fe_3(PO_4)_2$ Iron(II) Phosphate
                 $FePO_4$ Iron(III) Phosphate

30.

	Substance	Formula	Systematic Name
a)	Limestone	$CaCO_3$	Calcium carbonate
b)	Alumina	Al_2O_3	Aluminum oxide
c)	Magnetite	Fe_3O_4 (or) $Fe(II)Fe(III)_2O_4$	Iron(II)Iron(III) mixed oxide
d)	Pyrite	FeS_2	Iron(II) disulfide
e)	Coke	C	Carbon
f)	Red lead	Pb_3O_4 (or) $Pb(II)_2Pb(IV)O_4$	Lead(II)lead(IV) mixed oxide
g)	Rust	$Fe_2O_3 \cdot H_2O$	Hydrated iron(III) oxide

31. In the modern blast furnace process to manufacture steel, a mixture of iron ore, coke and limestone is added at the top of the furnace while preheated air, or oxygen, is blown in at the bottom. The iron ore is reduced, by carbon monoxide formed by the incomplete combustion of the coke, according to the overall process

$$Fe_2O_3 + 3CO \longrightarrow 2Fe + 3CO_2$$

The purpose of the limestone, $CaCO_3$, is to form calcium oxide, CaO, which combines with silica impurities to form slag, $CaSiO_3$. The molten slag forms on top of the molten

148

iron protecting it from re-oxidation.
The molten iron tapped off from the blast furnace is called
pig iron and contains impurities, notably carbon, silicon and
sulfur. Purification of the molten iron is, therefore,
carried out and this is accomplished by a process called the
basic oxygen process.
The basic oxygen process consists of blowing oxygen through
the molten pig iron, converting the impurities to their
oxides, and leaving behind the final product steel.

32. Iron corrodes readily in moist air. The reactions which
     occur are
$$2Fe(s) + 4H^+(aq) + O_2(g) \longrightarrow 2Fe^{2+}(aq) + 2H_2O$$
     This inital stage, which produces Fe^{2+} ions, is followed by
     the oxidation of the iron from the +2 to the +3 oxidation
     state by oxygen
$$4Fe^{2+}(aq) + O_2(g) + 4H_2O \longrightarrow 2Fe_2O_3(s) + 8H^+(aq)$$
     to form insoluble iron(III) oxide. The overall process,
     obtained by summing these two reactions, is
$$4Fe(s) + 3O_2(g) \longrightarrow 2Fe_2O_3(s)$$

33. Slag consists of fused impurities from ore extraction
     processes. In the blast furnace process to produce iron, the
     slag is chiefly calcium silicate, $CaSiO_3$, formed by the
     reaction of calcium oxide, CaO, with the silica impurities in
     the iron ore. It serves a useful purpose by forming a
     protective layer on top of the molten iron, preventing
     reoxidation of the iron.

34. $H_2Al_2(SiO_4)_2 \cdot H_2O$ has a molar mass of
     $2\times1.01+2\times26.98+2(28.09+4\times16.00)+2\times1.01+16.00$ g mol^{-1}
     = 258.18 g mol^{-1}
     This mass of the clay contains $2\times26.98 = 53.96$ g Al.
     Therefore %Al by mass $= \dfrac{53.96}{258.18} \times 100 = 20.90\%$.

35. From the information given, 0.250 g of aluminum combined with
     $1.236 - 0.250 = 0.986$ g of chlorine. We can calculate the
     mole ratio of aluminum to chlorine as follows:

	Al		Cl
Mass ratio	0.250 g	:	0.986 g
Mole ratio	$\dfrac{0.250 \text{ g}}{26.98 \text{ g mol}^{-1}}$	:	$\dfrac{0.986 \text{ g}}{35.45 \text{ g mol}^{-1}}$
=	9.27×10^{-3} mol	:	2.78×10^{-2} mol
=	$\dfrac{9.27\times10^{-3}}{9.27\times10^{-3}}$	:	$\dfrac{2.78\times10^{-2}}{9.27\times10^{-3}}$
=	1.00	:	3.00

The empirical formula is, therefore, $AlCl_3$.
Empirical formula mass = 133.33 g mol^{-1}. The number of
moles of aluminum chloride contained in 1.236 g of the
substance may be obtained by substituting the given data in
the ideal gas equation in the form

$$n = \frac{PV}{RT} = \frac{\frac{720}{760} \times \frac{210}{1000}}{0.0821 \times 523}$$

(Note conversions to atmospheres, litres and kelvins.)

$$n = 4.63 \times 10^{-3} \text{ mol.}$$

The molar mass of the substance will, therefore, be

$$\frac{1.236 \text{ g}}{4.63 \times 10^{-3} \text{ mol}} = 267 \text{ g mol}^{-1}$$

This is just twice the empirical formula mass, and therefore yields a molecular formula of $(AlCl_3)_2$.

36. We can calculate the mass of tin in the alloy from the mass of the hydrated oxide $SnO_2 \cdot 2H_2O$ which has a molar mass of $118.69 + 2 \times 16.00 + 2(2 \times 1.01 + 16.00) = 186.73$ g mol^{-1}. The calculation is

$$0.778 \text{ g } SnO_2 \cdot 2H_2O \times \frac{1 \text{ mol } SnO_2 \cdot 2H_2O}{186.73 \text{ g } SnO_2 \cdot 2H_2O} \times \frac{1 \text{ mol } Sn}{1 \text{ mol } SnO_2 \cdot 2H_2O}$$

$$\times \frac{118.69 \text{ g } Sn}{1 \text{ mol } Sn} = 0.495 \text{ g } Sn$$

The mass percentage of lead in the solder sample will, therefore, be given by

$$\frac{1.00 - 0.495}{1.00} \times 100\% = 50.5\%$$

37. The reactions involved are

a) $3Pb + 2O_2 \longrightarrow Pb_3O_4$

        Red lead - a mixed oxide of Pb(II) and Pb(IV)
        The two oxides react differently:

b) $Pb_3O_4 + 4HNO_3 \longrightarrow 2Pb(NO_3)_2 + PbO_2 + 2H_2O$

        Lead(II) nitrate   Lead(IV) oxide
        (soluble)   (insoluble brown compound)

In effect, only the lead(II) reacts with nitric acid; the PbO_2 is unaffected.

c) $Pb(NO_3)_2 + 2KI \longrightarrow PbI_2 + 2KNO_3$

        Lead(II) iodide   Potassium nitrate
        (yellow insoluble compound)   (soluble)

From the balanced equations we may deduce that
1. From equations (a) and (b) 3 moles of lead will produce a maximum of one mole of PbO_2.
2. From equations (a), (b), and (c), 3 moles of lead will produce a maximum of two moles of PbI_2.

The maximum mass of PbO_2 formed will be given by

$$2.00 \text{g Pb} \times \frac{1 \text{ mol Pb}}{207.19 \text{ g Pb}} \times \frac{1 \text{ mol } PbO_2}{3 \text{ mol Pb}} \times \frac{239.19 \text{ g } PbO_2}{1 \text{ mol } PbO_2} = 0.770 \text{ g.}$$

The maximum mass of PbI_2 formed will be given by

$$2.00 \text{ g Pb} \times \frac{1 \text{ mol Pb}}{207.19 \text{ g Pb}} \times \frac{2 \text{ mol PbI}_2}{3 \text{ mol Pb}} \times \frac{460.99 \text{ g PbI}_2}{1 \text{ mol PbI}_2} = 2.97 \text{ g.}$$

38. The reactions are

a) $2Fe + 3Cl_2 \longrightarrow 2FeCl_3$
   Iron(III) chloride
   (red-black solid)

b) $FeCl_3 + 3NaOH \longrightarrow Fe(OH)_3 + 3NaCl$
   Iron(III) hydroxide Sodium chloride
   (gelatinous brown precipitate)

c) $2Fe(OH)_3 \xrightarrow{\text{heat}} Fe_2O_3 + H_2O$

   Iron(III) oxide
   (red brown powder)

From the balanced equations (a), (b) and (c) it may be deduced that two moles of iron will produce a maximum of one mole of Fe_2O_3. The maximum mass of Fe_2O_3, the red-brown powder, which may be prepared from 1.50 g of iron will, therefore, be given by

$$1.50 \text{ g Fe} \times \frac{1 \text{ mol Fe}}{55.85 \text{ g Fe}} \times \frac{1 \text{ mol Fe}_2O_3}{2 \text{ mol Fe}} \times \frac{159.70 \text{ g Fe}_2O_3}{1 \text{ mol Fe}_2O_3}$$

$$= 2.14 \text{ g Fe}_2O_3.$$

CHAPTER 10

1. Each carbon in diamond forms covalent single bonds to four
    neighboring carbons. The geometry about each carbon is
    exactly tetrahedral. A giant 3-D structure of carbon atoms
    is thereby produced.

2. Graphite consists of planar sheets of carbon atoms, with
    only relatively weak intermolecular forces joining one sheet
    to another at relatively long separation. Each carbon is
    surrounded in a trigonal planar geometry by three other
    carbon atoms; it forms a double covalent bond with one of
    these atoms and a single covalent bond with each of the
    other two.

3. Since graphite contains multiple bonds on each atom, a form
    of metallic bonding occurs; thus graphite will conduct
    electricity along a sheet. In addition, since the sheets
    are only weakly joined to each other, they slide easily over
    each other and make graphite a good lubricant. In contrast,
    diamond neither conducts electricity nor is a lubricant
    since all the atoms are held together by strong bonds in a
    3-D arrangement. Thus diamond is a very hard, high-melting
    substance.

4. C, NaCl, MgO, SiO_2 and Al all are network solids since they
    do not contain individual molecules, and the structure
    extends indefinitely. S_8, CO_2, and P_4O_6 are molecular
    solids (at sufficiently low temperatures; of course CO_2 is
    at gas at normal temperatures).

5. In order that a molecular solid melt, it is necessary only
    to break the weak intermolecular forces between the
    molecules. Thus they melt at a much lower temperature than
    do network solids, for which (strong) covalent (or ionic)
    bonds between atoms must be broken before the atoms are
    sufficiently mobile to slide by each other.

6. a) Weak intermolecular (London) forces.

    b) Covalent single bonds.

    c) Ionic bonds between Mg^{2+} and O^{2-}.

    d) Polar covalent single bonds.

7. Polymeric SO_3 consists of long chains of alternating S and O atoms joined by single bonds, with each S also forming double bonds to two other sulfur atoms (see text for diagram). Since the molecules are long and thin, and since different strands will be attracted to each other by dipole-dipole interactions which will be optimum when the strands are parallel or wind around each other, the crystals are needlelike. Plastic sulfur consists of long chains of sulfur atoms which are weakly attracted to each other by London forces. They become tangled with each other, thus forming a soft, rubbery solid.

8. Amorphous solids are those which contain a random, disordered arrangement of atoms rather than the regular, periodic arrangement which is characteristic of crystalline solids. An example is glass. Amorphous solids do not have a sharp melting point because heating only increases the motion of the atoms; in contrast for a crystalline solid the regular arrangement is largely destroyed at the melting point, whereas the arrangement already is relatively random in an amorphous solid.

9. a) Silica, SiO_2, contains Si-O single bonds in a three-dimensional network solid. In contrast, carbon dioxide consists of discrete O=C=O molecules which even in the solid are only weakly attracted to each other. Thus SiO_2 is a high-melting solid, whereas CO_2 is a gas.

    b) Oxygen consists of O_2 molecules, and since they attract each other weakly, the element is a gas. Sulfur consists of S_8 rings with each S joined to two others by single bonds. Since eight, rather than two, atoms are involved, the London forces are greater and sulfur is a solid.

10. A 2-D network solid is one in which the network extends indefinitely only in two dimensions. Examples include graphite, black phosphorus, and magnesium chloride.

11. A space lattice is a regular, repeating arrangement of points in space.

12. A unit cell is a set of points (four for a 2-D lattice, eight for a 3-D) joined together, and which shows the full symmetry of the lattice. By moving it repeatedly by distances equal to the cell edge, the complete lattice is generated.

13. See Figure 10.16b of the text for the diagrams requested here. The primitive cubic unit cell contains eight points, one at each corner. The body-centered cube is identical, except for the addition of one point in the center of the cube. The face-centered cubic has six points more than the primitive, one in the center of each of the six faces.

153

14. a) Since each of the eight points are shared with seven other cubes as well, each contributes 1/8 to the cell. Thus lattice points = 8 x 1/8 = 1.

    b) Same a (a), plus one unshared point in the center for a total of 2.

    c) Same as (a), plus six points on the faces, each of which is shared between two cubes:
       1 + 6 x (1/2) = 4 lattice points total.

15. The three common structures of metals are the body-centered cubic, the face-centered cube and hexagonal. In each case the motif is a single atom at a lattice point. The complete structures usually are described as monatomic body-centered cubic, cubic close-packed, and hexagonal close-packed respectively.

16. Copper is face-centered cubic (cubic close-packed), sodium is body-centered cubic; in both cases there is an atom at each lattice point. Diamond is based upon the face-centered cubic unit cell, but with four additional carbon atoms located one-fourth of the way along each of the body diagonals.

17. KCl and BaO have the sodium chloride structure - i.e. are based upon a face-centered cubic lattice, with the anions half-way along each cell edge. CuCl has the sphalerite (ZnS) structure, which is also based upon the face-centered cubic lattice but with anions at the lattice points and cations one-quarter the distance along each body diagonal.

18. The structures differ in that the sequence of layers types is ABCABCABC--- in cubic close-packing, whereas it is ABABABAB-- in hexagonal close-packing.

19. The solution is shown as Figure 10.20 of the textbook.

20. This problem is very similar to Example 10.3 of the text; see it for details.
    Volume of unit cell = $(4.05 \times 10^{-8} \text{ cm})^3 = 6.64 \times 10^{-23} \text{ cm}^3$.
    Mass of unit cell = Vd = $6.64 \times 10^{-23} \text{ cm}^3 \times 2.70 \text{ g cm}^{-3}$
        = 1.79×10^{-22} g.
    The mass per atom of aluminum is $26.98/6.022 \times 10^{23}$
        = 4.480×10^{-23} g.
    Since the ratio of unit cell mass to atomic mass is $1.79 \times 10^{-22}/4.480 \times 10^{-23} = 4.00$, thus there are four atoms per unit cell, and it must therefore be a face-centered cubic lattice.

21. The volume of the unit cell is $(392 \text{ pm})^3$, i.e.
    $(392 \times 10^{-10} \text{ cm})^3$, since 1 pm = 10^{-12} m = 10^{-10} cm.

volume per atom is 1.50×10^{-23} cm^3, i.e. there are 6.64×10^{22} atoms per cm^3. Since the density is 21.5 g cm^{-3}, we conclude that

6.64 x 10^{22} atoms have a mass of 21.5 g

and thus 1 mole of platinum has a mass of

$$\frac{21.5 \text{ g}}{6.64 \times 10^{22} \text{ atoms}} \times \frac{6.022 \times 10^{23} \text{ atoms}}{1 \text{ mole}} = 195 \text{ g/mole.}$$

Thus the atomic mass of platinum is 195.

22. According to Example 10.1 in the text, the length of a face diagonal b is $\sqrt{2}a$, where a is the unit cell edge. Thus the face diagonal is $\sqrt{2} \times 405$ pm = 573 pm. In the structure, the face diagonal equals four times the radius, which therefore is 143 pm.

23. a) To deduce the dimensions of the unit cell, we first deduce its volume. Now we know that four formula units of CuCl occupy one unit cell (since it has the ZnS structure); let us therefore establish the volume associated with four formula units.

3.41 g CuCl x $\dfrac{1 \text{ mole CuCl}}{98.99 \text{ g CuCl}}$ x $\dfrac{6.022 \times 10^{23} \text{ formula units CuCl}}{1 \text{ mole CuCl}}$

= 2.07×10^{22} formula units CuCl in 1 cm^3.

Thus 1 formula unit occupies 4.83×10^{-23} cm^3, and 4 formula units occupy 1.93×10^{-22} cm^3. The length of the edge of the unit cell is the cube root of the value, i.e. 5.78×10^{-8} cm, or 578 pm, since there are 4 units in each unit cell.

b) To deduce the Cu$^+$ to Cl$^-$ distance, we first recall that if the Cu are at the lattice points, the Cl$^-$ ions are one-quarter along the body diagonals. Thus we calculate the length of a body diagonal: see text Example 10.1.
    Body diagonal = $\sqrt{3}$ x unit cell edge length
                  = $\sqrt{3}$ x 578 pm
                  = 1000 pm.
One-quarter this value is 250 pm, and is the shortest Cu-Cl length.

c) Since the Cl$^-$ radius is 180 pm and the sum of those for Cu$^+$ and Cl$^-$ must be 250 pm, that for Cu$^+$ must be 70 pm.

24. The value of the unit cell is $(450 \times 10^{-10}$ cm$)^3$; i.e. 9.11×10^{-23} cm^3. From the density of 1.45 g cm^{-3}, we can deduce the atoms per cm^3:

$$\frac{1.45 \text{ g Ne}}{1 \text{ cm}^3} \times \frac{1 \text{ mole Ne}}{20.18 \text{ g Ne}} \times \frac{6.022 \times 10^{23} \text{ atoms Ne}}{1 \text{ mole Ne}}$$

$$= 4.33 \times 10^{22} \text{ atoms/cm}^3.$$

Thus in one unit cell there are

$$\frac{4.33 \times 10^{22} \text{ atoms}}{1 \text{ cm}^3} \times \frac{9.11 \times 10^{-23} \text{ cm}^3}{1 \text{ unit cell}} = 3.95 \text{ atoms/cell}.$$

We conclude there are four atoms per unit cell, so neon has a face-centered cubic lattice. As in Q. 22, from the edge length of 450 pm, we deduce that the face diagonal has length $2 \times 450 = 636$ pm, and thus the atomic radius is $636/4 = 159$ pm.

25. a) See text Figure 10.20 for diagram of the unit cell.

   b) For cubic close-packed structures, there are four atoms per cell.

   c) Since the cell edge is 559 pm, the cell volume is $(559 \times 10^{-10} \text{ cm})^3 = 1.75 \times 10^{-22} \text{ cm}^3$. Thus the volume per atom is $4.37 \times 10^{-23} \text{ cm}^3$ (since there are four atoms per cell). Now the mass of one atom is determined as follows:

$$\frac{83.80 \text{ g Kr}}{1 \text{ mole Kr}} \times \frac{1 \text{ mole Kr}}{6.022 \times 10^{23} \text{ atoms}} = 1.39 \times 10^{-22} \text{ g/atom}.$$

   Since density = mass/volume, thus using the mass and volume values appropriate to one atom:

$$d = \frac{m}{V} = \frac{1.39 \times 10^{-22} \text{ g}}{4.37 \times 10^{-23} \text{ cm}^3} = 3.18 \text{ g/cm}^3.$$

   d) Since the edge is 559 pm, the face diagonal is $\sqrt{2} \times 559 = 791$ pm, and the radius therefore is $791/4 = 198$ pm (see Q. 22).

   e) The radii differ since 791 pm (part (d)) refers to the volume occupied by a neutral Kr atom when it is not bonded to its neighbors but just weakly attracted to them by London forces. The value in Figure 4.8 refers to the size of a Kr atom when it is bonded, i.e. to a highly electronegative atom.

26. From the edge length, the volume is $(407 \times 10^{-10} \text{ cm})^3 = 6.74 \times 10^{-23} \text{ cm}^3$, i.e. $1.69 \times 10^{-23} \text{ cm}^3$ per atom since there are four atoms per cell. The number of atoms per 1 cm^3 is therefore $1/(1.69 \times 10^{-23} \text{ cm}^3) = 5.92 \times 10^{22}$. Now in this 1 cm^3 there is 19.329 g of gold, which is

$$19.329 \text{ g} \quad \text{x} \quad \frac{1 \text{ mole}}{196.97 \text{ g}} \quad = \quad 0.098132 \text{ mole}.$$

Since 0.098132 mole therefore contains 5.92×10^{22} atoms, 1 mole contains 6.033×10^{23} atoms. Thus our estimate of the Avogadro constant is 6.033×10^{23} atoms/mole.

27. Since NaCl has the face-centered lattice, there are four NaCl units per cell. From Figure 10.24, we see that the length of an edge is twice the NaCl distance, i.e. 2 x 281 = 562 pm, and thus the unit cell volume is $(562 \times 10^{-10}$ cm$)^3$, or 4.44×10^{-23} per NaCl pair. Thus the pairs per cm^3 is 2.25×10^{22}. The moles of NaCl in 1 cm^3 is

$$2.165 \text{ g NaCl} \times \frac{1 \text{ mole NaCl}}{58.44 \text{ g NaCl}} = 0.03705 \text{ moles}.$$

Thus the Avogadro constant is $\dfrac{2.25 \times 10^{22} \text{ NaCl pairs}}{0.03705 \text{ moles NaCl pairs}}$

$= 6.07 \times 10^{23}$ pairs/mole.

28. The methodology is identical to that for Q. 26, since Cu also has cubic close-packed structure. We obtain 6.03×10^{23} atoms per mole as the estimate of the Avogadro constant.

29. From the density, in 1 cm^3 there is

$$3.180 \text{ g CaF}_2 \times \frac{1 \text{ mole CaF}_2}{78.08 \text{ g CaF}_2} \times \frac{6.022 \times 10^{23} \text{ units CaF}_2}{1 \text{ mole CaF}_2}$$
$= 2.453 \times 10^{22}$ units of CaF$_2$.

Thus the volume per unit is $1/(2.453 \times 10^{22}) = 4.077 \times 10^{-23}$ cm^3. The volume of the unit cell is $(546.3 \times 10^{-10}$ cm$)^3 = 1.630 \times 10^{-22}$ cm^3. Thus the number of units per unit cell is 1.630×10^{-22} cm^3/4.077×10^{-21} cm^3 unit^{-1} = 4.00 units. Thus there are four units per unit cell.

30. For 1 cm^3, since the mass of KF is 2.481 g, and its molar mass is 58.10 g, the number of moles it contains is 2.481/58.10 = 0.04270 moles, i.e. 2.572×10^{22} formula units. Thus the volume occupied by 1 formula unit is 3.889×10^{-23} cm^3; that for four formula units, the number in one unit cell, is 1.556×10^{-22} cm^3. The edge length in the unit cell is the cube root of the volume, i.e. 5.38×10^{-8} cm. Since the K to F distance is over half this length, we obtain 2.69×10^{-8} cm, i.e. 269 pm, as the answer.

31. Face-centered cubic, Si atoms are at the lattice points, and an O atom exists between each of the closest pair of Si atoms.

CHAPTER 11   ANSWERS

1. a) $CO + H_2 \longrightarrow CH_2O$ (methanal) $\xrightarrow{H_2}$ CH_3OH(methanol)

    b) $2CO + O_2 \longrightarrow 2CO_2$

    c) $CO + Cl_2 \longrightarrow COCl_2$ (carbonyl chloride)

    d) $CO + H_2O \rightleftarrows CO_2 + H_2$

    e) $3CO + Fe_2O_3 \longrightarrow 2Fe + 3CO_2$

2. a) i. $C + H_2O \longrightarrow CO + H_2$
        ii. $CH_4 + 2H_2O \longrightarrow CO + 3H_2$
        or iii. $2C + O_2 \longrightarrow 2CO$

    b) i. $C + O_2 \longrightarrow CO_2$
        ii. $CaCO_3 \longrightarrow CaO + CO_2$

    c) $C + 2S \longrightarrow CS_2$

3. The required Lewis Structures are as follows; see Chapters 6
    and 8 if you encounter difficulties in deducing them:

    a) $\ddot{O} = C = \ddot{O}$

    b) $^{-}:C \equiv O:^{+}$

    c) $^{-}:C \equiv N:$

    d) $^{-}:C \equiv C:^{-}$

    e) $H - C \equiv N:$

    f) $O = C \diagdown \begin{matrix} \ddot{C}l: \\ \ddot{C}l: \end{matrix}$

4. The two Lewis structures which may be written for the
    thiocyanate ion SCN^{-} are

    i) $\ddot{S} = C = \ddot{\ddot{N}}$

    ii) $:\ddot{S} - C \equiv N:$

Structure ii is the preferred structure and agrees with the
bond length data. Of the main group elements carbon, oxygen
and nitrogen most readily form multiple bonds while nitrogen
readily forms triple bonds, as for example in the
particularly stable N_2 molecule. However, sulfur and other
atoms of its period do not readily form double bonds. Thus
ii is more important than is i.

158

5. The two Lewis structures for CS_2 are

    i) $:\ddot{S} = C = \ddot{S}:$

           2−   2+

    ii) $:\ddot{C} = S = \ddot{S}:$

Structure ii) requires the presence of formal charges whereas structure i) does not.

It is a general rule that the Lewis structure of a molecule which has the smallest number of formal charges has a lower energy and, therefore, is more stable than those with a larger number of formal charges. Clearly structure i) above is the preferred Lewis structure.

6. We may determine the empirical and molecular formulas from the given data for the compound formed by the dehydration of malonic acid as follows:

	C	O
% composition by mass	53.0	47.0
mole ratios	$\dfrac{53.0}{12.01}$	$\dfrac{47.0}{16.00}$
	= 4.41	= 2.94
Atomic ratios	= $\dfrac{4.41}{2.94}$	$\dfrac{2.94}{2.94}$
	= 1.50	1.00
Ratio of integers	= 3	2

The empirical formula is, therefore, C_3O_2. The number of moles contained in 0.200 g of the compound is calculated by means of the ideal gas equation in the form

$$n = \frac{PV}{RT}$$

Substituting $n = \dfrac{\frac{740}{760} \times \frac{74.3}{1000}}{0.0821 \times 300} = 2.94 \times 10^{-3}$ mol.

Therefore molar mass $= \dfrac{0.200 \text{ g}}{2.94 \times 10^{-3} \text{ mol}} = 68.1$ g mol^{-1}

The empirical formula mass of $C_3O_2 = 68.0$ g mol^{-1} and so, in this case, empirical formula mass and true formula mass are identical. The substance is C_3O_2 – <u>carbon suboxide</u>. The equation for its formation from malonic acid is

$$CH_2(COOH)_2 \xrightarrow[\text{Dehydration}]{P_4O_{10}} C_3O_2 + 2H_2O$$

A possible Lewis structure for C_3O_2 is

$$\ddot{O} = C = C = C = \ddot{O}$$

This molecule would be linear with no formal charges. Since
the vector sum of the - C = O dipoles will be zero, the
molecule as a whole will be non-polar, i.e. would have no
dipole moment.

7. First deduce the empirical formula and then by determining
   the molar mass of the compound from the data given, deduce
   the molecular formula.

	C	Br	O
% composition by mass	6.4	85.0	8.6
Mole Ratios	$\dfrac{6.4}{12.01}$	$\dfrac{85.0}{79.91}$	$\dfrac{8.6}{16.00}$
	= 0.533	1.064	0.538
Atomic ratios	$\dfrac{0.533}{0.533}$	$\dfrac{1.064}{0.533}$	$\dfrac{0.538}{0.533}$
Integer ratio	= 1	2	1

The empirical formula is, therefore, $COBr_2$.
The number of moles of the compound contained in 0.94 g may
be calculated by applying the ideal gas equation in the form

$$n = \frac{PV}{RT}$$

Substituting $\quad n = \dfrac{1.00 \times 0.122}{0.0821 \times 298} = 4.99 \times 10^{-3}$ mol.

Therefore molar mass $= \dfrac{0.94 \text{ g}}{4.99 \times 10^{-3} \text{ mol}} = 188$ g mol^{-1}

The empirical formula mass of $COBr_2$ is 188 g mol^{-1}. The
molecular formula is, therefore, $COBr_2$. A Lewis structure
for this compound is

$$\ddot{:}\text{O} = \text{C} \begin{array}{c} \ddot{\text{Br}}\text{:} \\ \ddot{\text{Br}}\text{:} \end{array}$$

There are no formal charges and the molecular type is AX_3 —
a planar triangular molecule.

8. If we assume that all the carbon in the aluminum carbide has
   been converted to methane we can calculate the mass of carbon
   in 0.50 g of the carbide by applying the ideal gas equation
   to calculate the number of moles of carbon and then its
   mass in the methane sample.

$$n = \frac{PV}{RT}$$

Substituting $\quad n = \dfrac{1.02 \times 0.250}{0.0821 \times 298} = 1.04 \times 10^{-2}$ mol.

Therefore mass of carbon, since 1 mol methane contains 1 mol carbon, will be 1.04×10^{-2} mol C $\times \dfrac{12.01 \text{ g C}}{1 \text{ mol C}} = 0.125$ g C.

Therefore, the mass of aluminum in the sample will be $0.50 - 0.125 = 0.375$ g Al.

We may now deduce the empirical formula.

	Al	C
Composition by mass	0.375 g	0.125 g
Mole ratios	$\dfrac{0.375}{26.98}$	$\dfrac{0.125}{12.01}$
	$= 1.39 \times 10^{-2}$	1.04×10^{-2}
Atom ratios	$= \dfrac{1.39 \times 10^{-2}}{1.04 \times 10^{-2}}$	$\dfrac{1.04 \times 10^{-2}}{1.04 \times 10^{-2}}$
Ratio	1.34	1.00
Ratio of integers	4	3

The empirical formula for the aluminum carbide is, therefore, Al_4C_3.

The amount of CH_4 to be produced is 0.818 mol (from PV=nRT);

$$0.818 \text{ mol } CH_4 \times \frac{1 \text{ mol } Al_4C_3}{3 \text{ mol } CH_4} \times \frac{143.95 \text{ g } Al_4C_3}{1 \text{ mol } Al_4C_3} = 39.2 \text{ g } Al_4C_3$$

9. The reaction of the weak acid HCN with water may be depicted as:

$$\underset{\text{acid}_1}{HCN} + \underset{\text{base}_2}{H_2O} \rightleftharpoons \underset{\substack{\text{conjugate}\\\text{acid}_2}}{H_3O^+} + \underset{\substack{\text{conjugate}\\\text{base}_1}}{CN^-}$$

Sodium cyanide, NaCN, would be expected to form a basic solution in water due to the reaction with water of the CN^- ion which acts as a base.

$$\underset{\text{base}}{CN^-} + \underset{\text{acid}}{H_2O} \rightleftharpoons \underset{\substack{\text{conjugate}\\\text{acid}}}{HCN} + \underset{\substack{\text{conjugate}\\\text{base}}}{OH^-}$$

10. The balanced reaction equations are
    a) $NaCN + H_2SO_4 \longrightarrow NaHSO_4 + HCN$

    b) $2NaCN + 2H_2O + \underset{\text{(conc.)}}{2H_2SO_4} \longrightarrow (NH_4)_2SO_4 + Na_2SO_4 + 2CO$

    c) $4HCN + 5O_2 \longrightarrow 2N_2 + 4CO_2 + 2H_2O$

    d) $3CS_2 + 6NaOH \longrightarrow 2Na_2CS_3 + Na_2CO_3 + 3H_2O$

Note that reaction (b) also involves water molecules.
Reaction (c) is an oxidation-reduction; nitrogen is being

oxidized while oxygen is being reduced. In all other cases, no changes occur to the oxidation states.

11. a) The empirical and molecular formulas of compound X may be obtained from the data given by first calculating the empirical formula.

	C	N
% composition = mass in 100 g sample	46.2	53.8

Mole ratios	$\dfrac{46.2}{12.01}$	$\dfrac{53.8}{14.01}$
=	3.85	3.84
or	1	1

The empirical formula is, therefore, CN.
The molar mass of X is calculated by applying the ideal gas equation in the form

$$n = \frac{PV}{RT}$$

Substituting, $n = \dfrac{0.95 \times 0.1263}{0.0821 \times 373} = 3.92 \times 10^{-3}$ mol.

The mass of the sample of X was 0.208 g and so the molar

mass of X is $\dfrac{0.208 \text{ g}}{3.92 \times 10^{-3} \text{ mol}} = 53.1$ g mol^{-1}.

The empirical formula mass of CN $= 26.0$ g mol^{-1} which is approximately one half of the molar mass. The molecular formula must be $(CN)_2$, the formula for the gas cyanogen.

b) The reduction product
$$H_2N - CH_2 - CH_2 - NH_2 \qquad \text{ethylenediamine}$$
gives us the clue that the structure is NCCN, cyanogen.

c) The Lewis structure is

$$:N \equiv C - C \equiv N:$$

This is a linear molecule, since it is type AX_2 and therefore linear about each carbon atom.

d) There will be no dipole moment since the vector sum of the two $- C \equiv N$ dipoles is zero in this linear molecule.

12. The evidence all points towards the gas being COS, carbon oxysulphide. Thus when burned in oxygen
$$2COS + 3O_2 \longrightarrow 2CO_2 + 2SO_2$$
the sole products are CO_2 and SO_2. The molar mass may be deduced by applying the ideal gas equation in the form
$$M = \frac{mRT}{PV} \qquad \text{where n the number of moles of}$$

162

$$gas = \frac{m}{M}$$

m = mass of gas, M = molar mass of gas

Substituting $M = \dfrac{0.246 \times 0.0821 \times 298}{1.00 \times 0.100} = 60.2$ g mol^{-1}

which agrees with the molar mass of COS. Remembering that, at constant temperature and pressure, V α n, we can write the equation for the combustion of COS according to the given data as

	COS	+	3/2 O$_2$	$\longrightarrow$	CO$_2$	+	SO$_2$
Before reaction	100 mL		200 mL		0		0

	COS	+	3/2 O$_2$	$\longrightarrow$	CO$_2$	+	SO$_2$
After reaction	0		(200-3/2x100)mL = 50 mL.		100 mL		100 mL

Both CO$_2$ and SO$_2$ are soluble in water and will dissolve, leaving only the 50 mL of oxygen undissolved which agrees with observation. A heated platinum wire decomposes the gas in a manner consistent with the equation

$$COS(g) \xrightarrow{\text{Heated Pt wire}} CO(g) + S(s)$$

No volume change is expected at constant temperature and pressure conditions since sulphur is present as a solid. The reaction

COS + 4KOH $\longrightarrow$ 4K$^+$(aq) + CO$_3{}^{2-}$(aq) + S^{2-}(aq) + 2H$_2$O

requires a 4:1 mol ratio of KOH to COS to bring about complete reaction. This is in agreement with the given data since

50.00mL 0.2M KOH contains 0.0500Lx0.2 mol L^{-1} = 1.00x10^{-2} mol KOH
25.00mL 0.1M COS contains 0.02500Lx0.2 mol L^{-1}= 2.50x10^{-3} mol COS

Therefore $\dfrac{\text{moles KOH}}{\text{moles COS}} = \dfrac{1.00 \times 10^{-2}}{2.50 \times 10^{-3}} = 4.$

The Lewis structure for COS is analogous to that for CO$_2$

O = C = S

The molecule is linear but is in this case polar: the vector sum of the - C = O and - C = S dipoles is not zero since they are non-identical. The COS molecule, therefore, has a dipole moment.

13. When the alkanes are heated to a sufficiently high temperature by themselves, they decompose to give a mixture of products including smaller alkanes, other hydrocarbons containing unsaturated linkages, and hydrogen. For example when propane, C$_3$H$_8$, is heated a mixture of products is obtained as follows

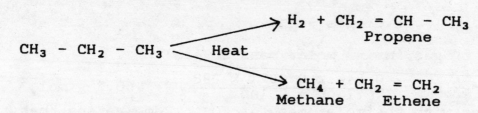

$$CH_3 - CH_2 - CH_3 \begin{array}{c} \longrightarrow H_2 + CH_2 = CH - CH_3 \\ \quad\quad\quad\quad\quad\text{Propene} \\ \text{Heat} \\ \longrightarrow CH_4 + CH_2 = CH_2 \\ \quad\quad\text{Methane}\quad\quad\text{Ethene} \end{array}$$

14. First, reaction of calcium oxide with carbon yields calcium carbide, CaC_2

$$CaO + 3C \longrightarrow CaC_2 + CO$$

In turn, calcium reacts with water to form ethyne:

$$CaC_2 + 2H_2O \longrightarrow Ca(OH)_2 + C_2H_2$$

The first of these two reactions is normally carried out in the electric furnace.

15. An addition reaction is a reaction in which two molecules combine to give a third molecule. Two examples of addition reactions involving hydrocarbons are

1. $CH_2 = CH - CH_3 + Cl_2 \longrightarrow CH_2Cl - CHCl - CH_3$
    Propene   1,2-Dichloropropane

2. $CH_2 = CH_2 + H_2 \xrightarrow[\text{catalyst}]{\text{High Temp}} CH_3 - CH_3$
    Ethene   Ethane

An elimination reaction involves the decomposition of a molecule into two molecules, one of which, normally the smaller of the two, is said to be eliminated. An elimination reaction is the opposite of an addition reaction.
Two examples are

1. the elimination of hydrogen in the cracking of ethane

    $$CH_3 - CH_3 \longrightarrow H_2 + CH_2 = CH_2$$
    Ethane   Ethene

2. the dehydration of ethanol by concentrated sulphuric acid

    $$CH_3CH_2OH \xrightarrow{H_2SO_4} CH_2 = CH_2 + H_2O$$
    Ethanol   Ethene

16. For all examples, compare the atoms bonded to each carbon with those on ethyne itself, i.e. $HC\equiv CH$, to see what needs to be added.

a) Ethyne will add two molecules of chlorine across the triple bond to produce a molecule which has two Cl's on each carbon:

$$CH \equiv CH + 2Cl_2 \longrightarrow CHCl_2 - CHCl_2$$

b) Since we want two Cl atoms added to one carbon but only one to the other, this two stage reaction involves first, addition of a molecule of chlorine followed by addition of a molecule of HCl (or vice-versa):

$$CH \equiv CH + Cl_2 \longrightarrow CHCl = CHCl$$
$$CHCl = CHCl + HCl \longrightarrow CH_2Cl - CHCl_2$$

164

c) This process requires addition of one Br and one Cl to each carbon, and can be accomplished by a two stage reaction which employs successively a molecule of chlorine and a molecule of bromine.

$$CH \equiv CH + Cl_2 \longrightarrow CHCl = CHCl$$
$$CHCl = CHCl + Br_2 \longrightarrow CHBrCl - CHBrCl$$

(or first the Br_2 and then the Cl_2)

d) First a molecule of chlorine is added across the triple bond, followed by the addition of a molecule of HBr (or vice-versa). In this manner, one carbon adds an H and a Cl at the other a Br and a Cl.

$$CH \equiv CH + Cl_2 \longrightarrow CHCl = CHCl$$
$$CHCl = CHCl + HBr \longrightarrow CH_2Cl - CHBrCl$$

17. The ring bonds in cyclopropane are strained. Reaction with chlorine, for example, causes bond scission followed by addition, the characteristic reaction of an alkene.

$$\begin{array}{c} \diagup CH_2 \diagdown \\ CH_2 \!-\!\!-\!\!-\! CH_2 \end{array} + Cl_2 \longrightarrow CH_2Cl-CH_2-CH_2Cl$$

cyclopropane   1,3-dichloropropane

On the other hand alkanes react with halogens to give substitution products.

$$CH_3 - CH_2 - CH_3 + Cl_2 \longrightarrow CH_3 - CH_2 - CH_2Cl + HCl$$

18. Examples of the required reactions are

a) $CH_3 - CH_2 - CH_3 + 5O_2 \longrightarrow 3CO_2 + 4H_2O$
    propane

b) $CH_3 - CH_2 - CH_3 \xrightarrow{\text{heat}} CH_4 + CH_2 = CH_2$
    Propane   Methane   Ethene

c) An alcohol is a compound which contains an OH group bonded to carbon.

$$CH_3 - CH_2OH \xrightarrow{\text{conc. } H_2SO_4} CH_2 = CH_2 + H_2O$$
Ethanol   Ethene

d) $CH_2 = CH - CH_3 + Cl_2 \longrightarrow CH_2Cl - CHCl - CH_3$
    Propene   1,2-dichloropropane

19. The required reactions are

a) $CH_3 - CH_2 - CH_3 + 5O_2 \longrightarrow 3CO_2 + 4H_2O$

b) $CH_2 = CH_2 + Cl_2 \longrightarrow CH_2Cl - CH_2Cl$

c) $CH_3 - CH_3 + Cl_2 \longrightarrow CH_3 - CH_2Cl + HCl$

d) $CaC_2 + 2H_2O \longrightarrow CH \equiv CH + Ca(OH)_2$

e) $n(CH_2 = CH_2) \xrightarrow{\text{catalyst}} (-CH_2 - CH_2-)_n$

f) $CH_3 - CH_3 \xrightarrow{\text{heat}} CH_2 = CH_2 + H_2$

20. a) Cyclobutane is more reactive than butane because of the strained ring system in the former. Breaking a bond in the ring followed by addition is a common reaction of the strained ring cycloalkanes, i.e. cyclopropane and cyclobutane.

   b) Cyclohexene and cyclohexane both contain rings of carbon-carbon bonds relatively free of strain. However cyclohexene is the more reactive of the two by virtue of its double bond which readily enter into addition reactions while cyclohexane is unreactive like other alkanes.

   c) Cyclohexene is more reactive than benzene because it readily undergoes addition reactions by virtue of its double bond. On the other hand, benzene will only undergo addition reactions under extreme conditions, preferring to undergo substitution reactions instead.

21. a) <u>Cracking</u> is the process whereby alkanes, when heated to a sufficiently high temperature, decompose to form a mixture of molecules including smaller alkanes, unsaturated hydrocarbons and hydrogen. For example

   $$CH_3 - CH_3 \xrightarrow{\text{Heat}} H_2 + CH_2 = CH_2$$
   $\qquad$ Ethane $\qquad\qquad\qquad\qquad$ Ethene

   b) <u>Polymerization</u> - a polymerization reaction is one in which a large number of small molecules (monomers) combine to form a very large molecule (polymer). For example

   $$n(CH_2 = CH_2) \xrightarrow{\text{Catalyst}} (-CH_2 - CH_2-)_n$$
   $\qquad$ Ethene $\qquad\qquad\qquad\qquad$ Polyethylene

   c) <u>Addition Reaction</u> - a reaction in which two molecules combine to give a third molecule. In organic chemistry they are normally reactions of the double or triple bond. For example

   $$H_2C = CH_2 + H_2 \longrightarrow H_3C—CH_3$$

   <u>Hydrogenation</u> - a particular type of addition reaction in which one of the two combining molecules is hydrogen, H_2. For example

   $$C_6H_{10} + H_2 \xrightarrow{\text{Catalyst}} C_6H_{12}$$
   $\quad$ Cyclohexene $\qquad\qquad\qquad\qquad$ Cyclohexane

   d) <u>Cyclic Hydrocarbon</u> - a hydrocarbon containing a closed chain or ring of carbon atoms. For example cyclobutane.

e) <u>Alkyl Group</u> - a substituent group formed from an alkane by the removal of one hydrogen atom and replacing the -ane ending by -yl. For example,

$$CH_3 - CH_3 \qquad\qquad CH_3 - CH_2 -$$
$$\text{ethane} \qquad\qquad\qquad \text{ethyl group}$$

f) <u>Aromatic Hydrocarbon</u> - The name given to members of the arene series of hydrocarbons - hydrocarbons containing the benzene ring or fuzed benzene ring systems. The name originally described the pleasant odors associated with many of these compounds. An example is benzene.

g) <u>Conformation</u> - Conformations are the different arrangements of the atoms and groups that are possible as a result of rotations about single bonds. An example is the eclipsed conformation of ethane.

22. Cyclopropane undergoes ring scission and subsequent addition of hydrogen due to the high strain energy of the carbon-carbon bonds in the ring. On the other hand the carbon-carbon bonds in cyclopentane are relatively unstrained and the addition of hydrogen does not occur. The reaction of cyclopropane may be shown as:

The product is propane.

23.

The Lewis diagram of C_2F_4 illustrates that the geometry about each carbon atom is AX_3 - triangular planar. Thus both carbon atoms and the fluorine atoms attached to them must be coplanar since no rotation is possible about the double bond.

24. We would expect the F - C - F bond angle in tetrafluoroethene to be less than the H - C - H bond angle in ethene because fluorine is more electronegative than hydrogen. This decreases the space occupied by the bonding electron pair in the C - F bond due to the greater force of attraction exerted by the more electronegative atom. This permits the electron pairs in the carbon-carbon double bond even greater space, thus reducing the F - C - F bond angle.
It is generally observed that bond angles decrease as the electronegativity of the ligands increases.

25. The four isomeric forms of C_4H_6 referred to in the question may be depicted as follows:

A)

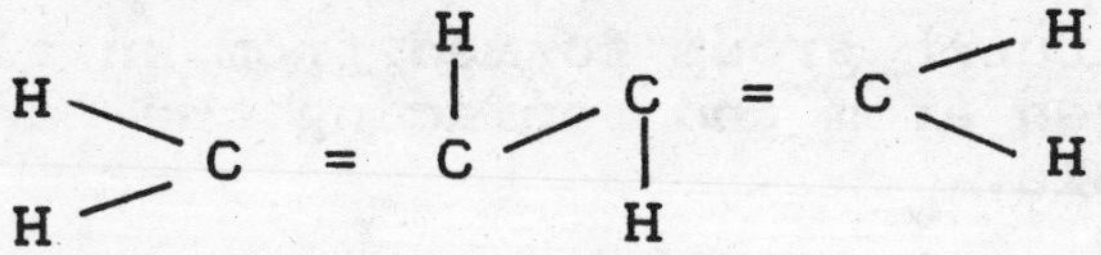

$$H \underset{H}{\overset{H}{>}} C = C \overset{H}{\underset{H}{<}} C \overset{H}{\underset{H}{>}} C = C \overset{H}{\underset{H}{<}}$$ 1,3-butadiene

B) $CH_3 - C \equiv C - CH_3$ 2-butyne

C) 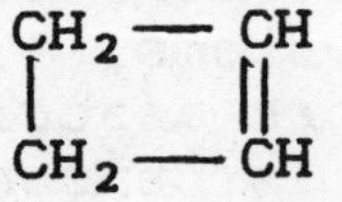
$$\begin{array}{c} CH_2 - CH \\ | \quad\quad \| \\ CH_2 - CH \end{array}$$ cyclobutene

D) $CH \equiv C - CH_2 - CH_3$ 1-butyne

Alternatives to (C) are 3-methylcyclopropene and bicyclobutane.

26. The Kekule structure contains three double bonds and would be expected to undergo addition reactions. However, benzene undergoes substitution reactions with halogens, rather than the expected addition. Spectroscopic studies have demonstrated that all the C-C bonds in the ring are identical, with bond lengths of 140 pm. We now consider benzene to be a resonance hybrid of the two Kekule structures, with a bond order obtained by taking the sum of the bond order for any bond in the two structures (1+2=3) and dividing by the number of structures (2), giving an average bond order of 1.5. The observed bond length of 140 pm is consistent with this bond order.

27. Conformations are different arrangements of atoms that can be converted into one another by rotation about single bonds. Thus two conformations of ethane, C_2H_6, are the eclipsed and staggered conformations

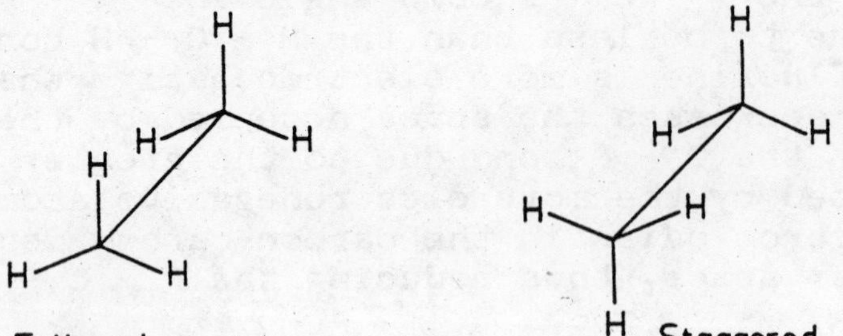

Eclipsed   Staggered

For cyclohexane, C_6H_{12}, two conformations are the boat and chair forms.

168

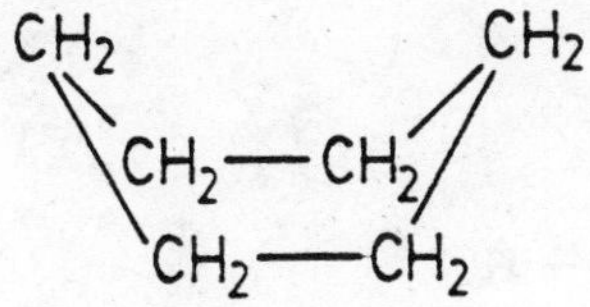

```
   CH₂            CH₂              CH₂
    \            /                 \    CH₂ — CH₂
    CH₂ — CH₂                      CH₂ — CH₂
                                           \
    CH₂ — CH₂                              CH₂
       Boat Form                        Chair Form
```

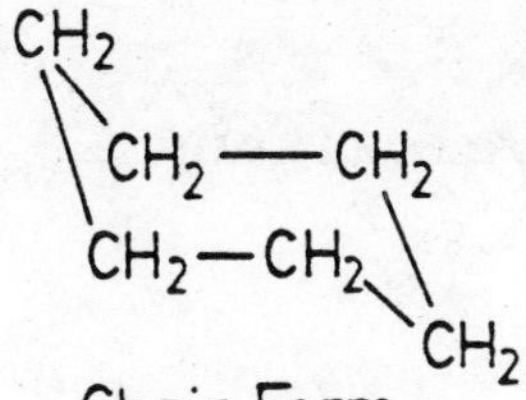

28. An alkene contains one or more double bonds between carbon atoms. An alkane contains only single covalent bonds.

29. A saturated hydrocarbon contains only single covalent bonds. An unsaturated hydrocarbon contains double and/or triple bonds.

30.

a) methane, alkane

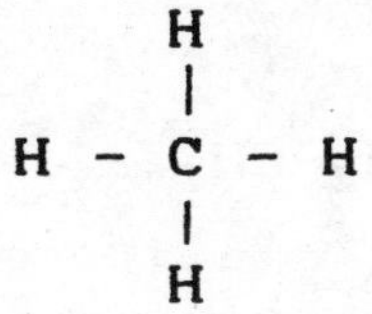

```
        H
        |
    H - C - H
        |
        H
```

b) ethylene, alkene

```
    H           H
     \         /
      C  =  C
     /         \
    H           H
```

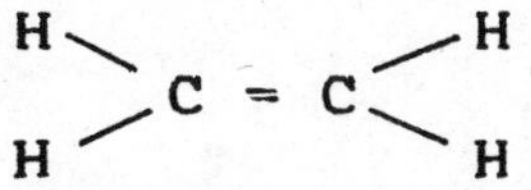

c) methylacetylene, alkyne

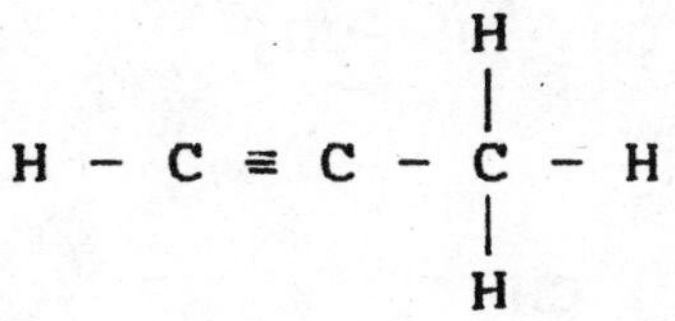

```
                    H
                    |
    H - C ≡ C - C - H
                    |
                    H
```

d) cyclobutane, cycloalkane

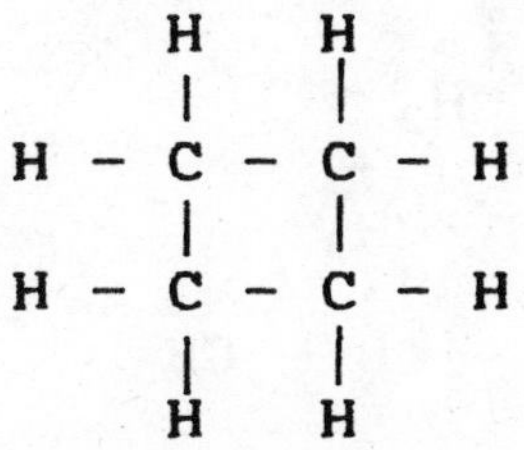

```
        H   H
        |   |
    H - C - C - H
        |   |
    H - C - C - H
        |   |
        H   H
```

169

e) cyclopropene, cycloalkene

$$\begin{array}{c} H \\ | \\ C \\ \diagup\!\!\!\diagdown \\ H-C\!=\!C-H \\ | \\ H \end{array}$$

31. The strategy here is to draw as many unique isomers as possible that have a continuous chain of seven C atoms; then try six C, then five C, etc. Thus, the nine isomers of heptane are

   i) $CH_3-CH_2-CH_2-CH_2-CH_2-CH_2-CH_3$:   heptane or n-heptane

  ii) $CH_3-CH-CH_2-CH_2-CH_2-CH_3$:   2-methylhexane
            $|$
          CH_3

 iii) $CH_3-CH_2-CH-CH_2-CH_2-CH_3$:   3-methylhexane
                $|$
             CH_3

  iv) $CH_3-CH-CH-CH_2-CH_3$:   2,3-dimethylpentane
          $|$ $|$
        $CH_3 CH_3$

   v) $CH_3-CH-CH_2-CH-CH_3$:   2,4-dimethylpentane
            $|$ $|$
         CH_3 CH_3

  vi) CH_3
               $|$
       $CH_3-C-CH_2-CH_2-CH_3$:   2,2-dimethylpentane
               $|$
              CH_3

 vii) CH_3
                  $|$
       $CH_3-CH_2-C-CH_2-CH_3$:   3,3-dimethylpentane
                  $|$
                 CH_3

viii) CH_3 CH_3
              $|$ $|$
       $CH_3 - C - CH - CH_3$:   2,2,3-trimethylbutane
              $|$
           CH_3

  ix) $CH_3-CH_2-CH-CH_2-CH_3$:   3-ethylpentane
                $|$
             CH_2
             $|$
            CH_3

32. a) Alkanes have the general formula C_nH_{2n+2} and so the alkane with 22 carbon atoms will have the molecular formula $C_{22}H_{46}$.
b) Alkenes with one double bond have the general formula C_nH_{2n} (shared with the cycloalkanes) and so the alkene having 19 carbon atoms and one double bond will have the molecular formula $C_{19}H_{38}$.
c) Alkynes with one triple bond have the general formula C_nH_{2n-2} and so the alkyne having 12 carbon atoms will have the molecular formula $C_{12}H_{22}$.
d) The cycloalkane with 10 carbon atoms will have the molecular formula $C_{10}H_{20}$. See (b) above.

33.

2-butene

$$\begin{array}{c} H \\ \\ CH_3 \end{array}\!\!\!>\!\!C = C\!\!<\!\!\!\begin{array}{c} H \\ \\ CH_3 \end{array}$$, the cis-form of which

is shown, may have a geometrical isomer, the trans form, by interchanging hydrogen and the methyl group at one carbon atom, since no free rotation is possible about the the double bond:

$$\begin{array}{c} CH_3 \\ \\ H \end{array}\!\!\!>\!\!C = C\!\!<\!\!\!\begin{array}{c} H \\ \\ CH_3 \end{array}$$ trans-2-butene

On the other hand 2-butyne,

$$CH_3 - C \equiv C - CH_3$$

can have no geometric isomers. The molecule is linear and only one group is attached to each carbon atom making up the triple bond; thus no different spatial arrangements of groups or atoms are possible as with 2-butene.

34. The IUPAC names are
a) 2-methylpropane since the longest continuous chain has 3 carbons

b) 4-(2-propyl)octane since the longest continuous chain has 8 carbons, and a 2-propyl group is attached to carbon 4.
c) propene

d) 2-methyl-2-butene

e) 2-hexene

f) 1,1,2,3-tetramethylcyclobutane

g) 1,4-hexadiene

35.
a)
$$\begin{array}{ccccccc} & & CH_3 & & & CH_3 & \\ & & | & & & | & \\ CH_3 & - & C & - & CH_2 & - & CH & - & CH_3 \\ & & | & & & & \\ & & CH_3 & & & & \end{array}$$

b)
$$\begin{array}{cc} CH & = & CH \\ | & & | \\ CH & = & CH \end{array}$$

c) 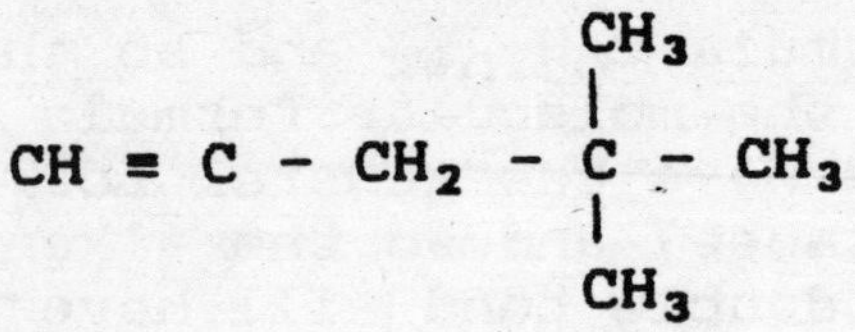 $CH \equiv C - CH_2 - \overset{\displaystyle CH_3}{\underset{\displaystyle CH_3}{\overset{|}{\underset{|}{C}}}} - CH_3$

d)

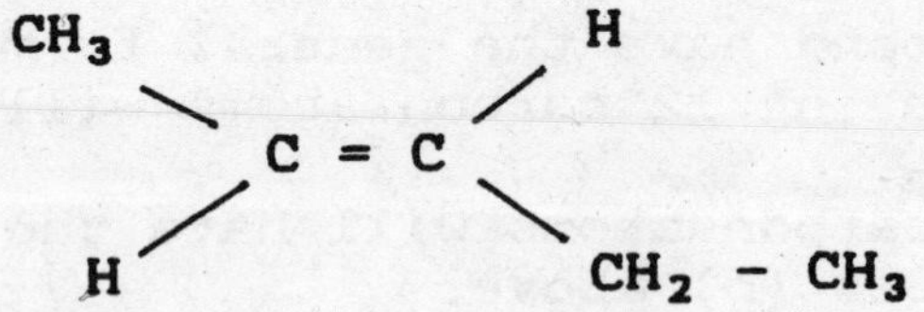

e) $CH_2 = CH - CH = CH_2$

f)

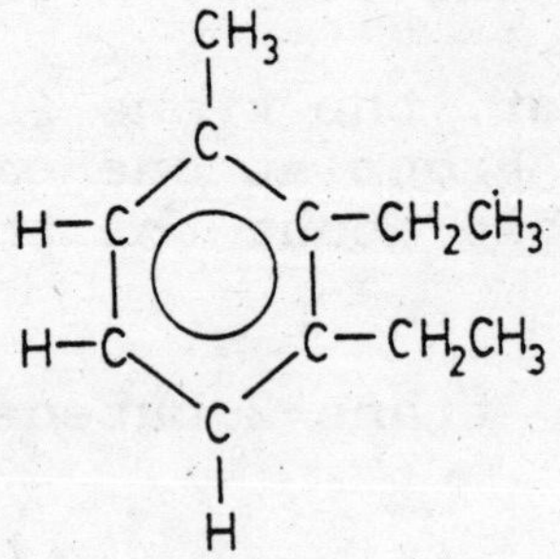

g)

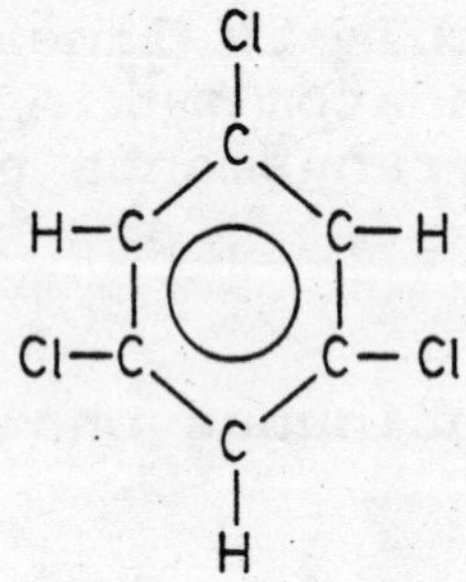

36. Again the strategy is to start with the longest possible
    chain, and place the C=C at all unique positions within it,
    then consider successively shorter chains. Finally consider
    the largest rings, then the next largest, etc.

    a) $CH_2 = CH - CH_2 - CH_2 - CH_3$: 1-pentene

    b) $CH_3 - CH = CH - CH_2 - CH_3$: 2-pentene

    c) 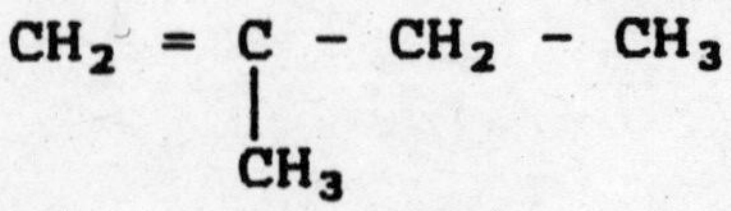 $CH_2 = \overset{\displaystyle }{\underset{\displaystyle CH_3}{\overset{}{\underset{|}{C}}}} - CH_2 - CH_3$: 2-methyl-1-butene

    d) 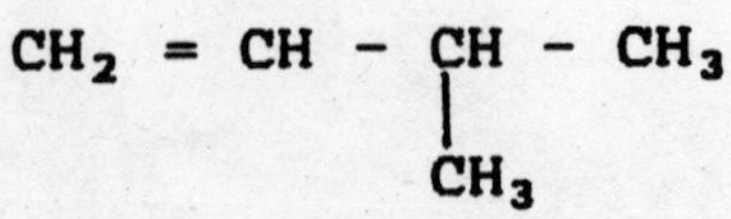 $CH_2 = CH - \overset{\displaystyle }{\underset{\displaystyle CH_3}{\overset{}{\underset{|}{CH}}}} - CH_3$: 3-methyl-1-butene

172

e) 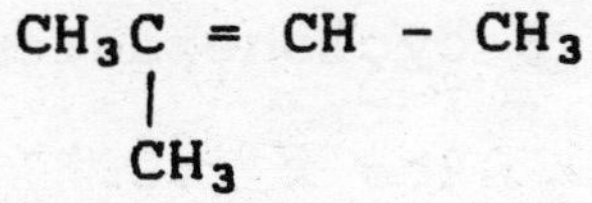 $CH_3C = CH - CH_3$
    |
    CH_3

: 2-methyl-2-butene

f)

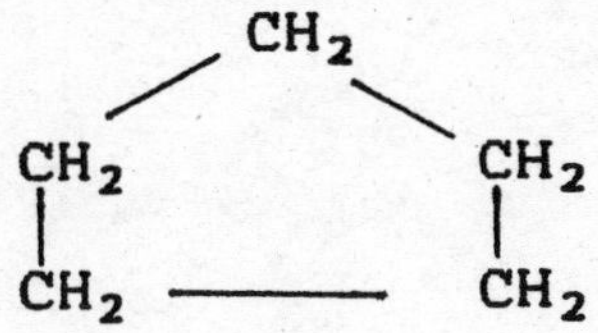

$$
\begin{array}{c}
CH_2 \\
CH_2 \qquad\quad CH_2 \\
CH_2 \text{———} CH_2
\end{array}
$$

: cyclopentane

g) 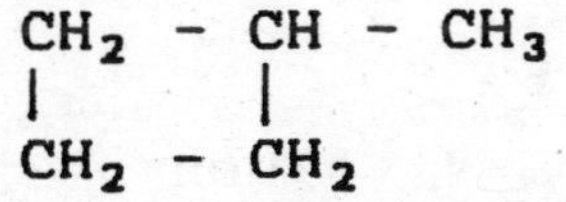 $CH_2 - CH - CH_3$
    | |
    $CH_2 - CH_2$

: 1-methylcyclobutane

h)

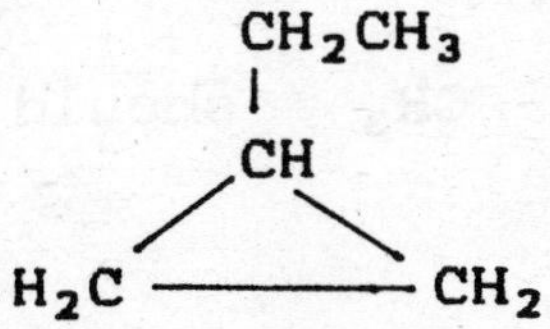

CH_2CH_3
    |
    CH
H_2C ——— CH_2

: 1-ethylcyclopropane

i)

CH_3
    |
    CH
H_2C ——— CH —CH_3

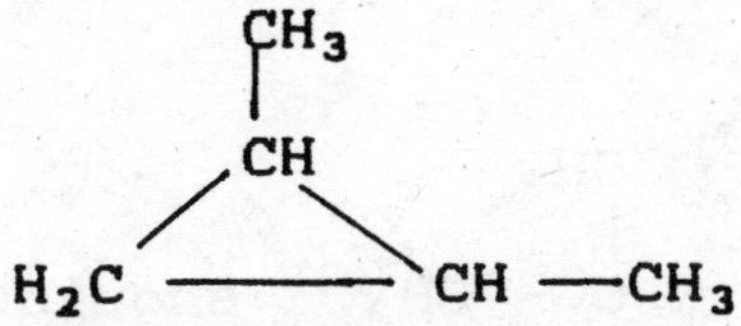

: 1,2-dimethylcyclopropane

j)

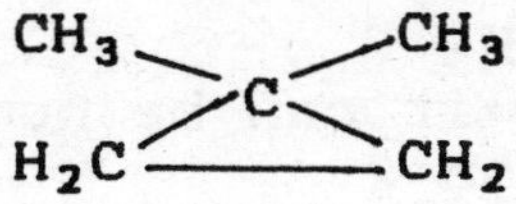

CH_3 CH_3
      \ /
       C
H_2C ——— CH_2

: 1,1-dimethylcyclopropane

37. a) $CCl_2 = CH_2$

: 1,1-dichloroethene

b)

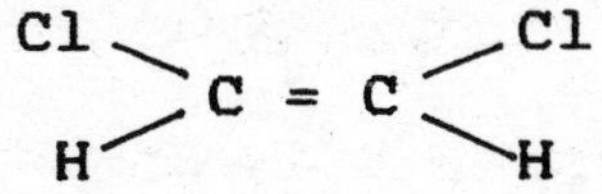

Cl Cl
  \   /
   C = C
  /   \
H H

: cis-1,2-dichloroethene

c)

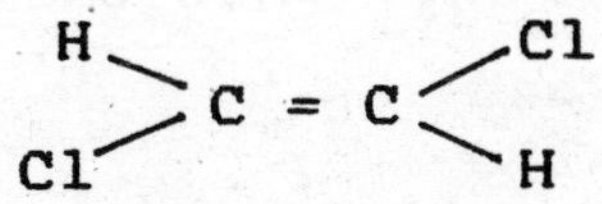

H Cl
  \   /
   C = C
  /   \
Cl H

: trans-1,2-dichloroethene

38. a)

$$
\begin{array}{c}
H \\
| \\
C \\
H-C \qquad\qquad C-H \\
H-C \text{====} C-H \\
| \qquad\qquad | \\
H \qquad\qquad H
\end{array}
$$

: 1,3-cyclopentadiene

173

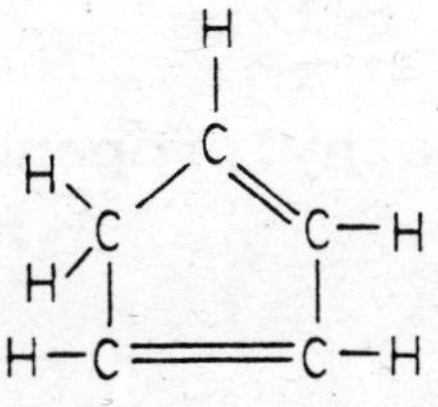

b)

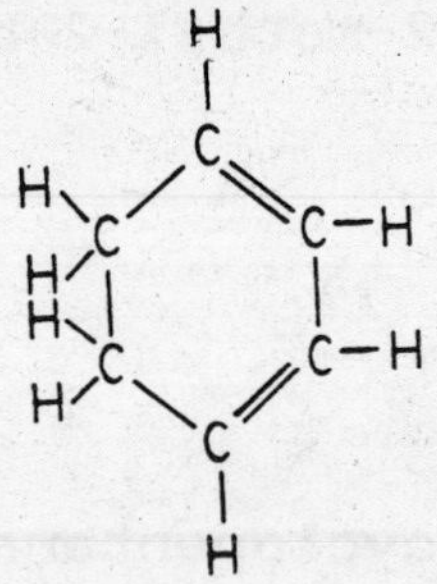

1,3-cyclohexadiene

c) 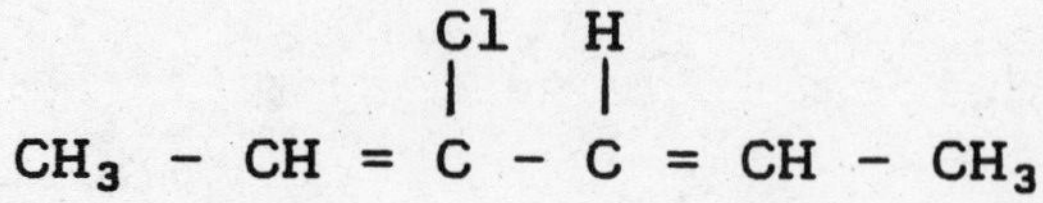
$$CH_3 - CH = \overset{\overset{\displaystyle Cl}{|}}{C} - \overset{\overset{\displaystyle H}{|}}{C} = CH - CH_3 \qquad \text{3-chloro-2,4-hexadiene}$$

39. a) 2-ethylbutane $\quad CH_3 - \overset{\underset{\displaystyle CH_2 - CH_3}{|}}{CH} - CH_2 - CH_3 \quad$ should have

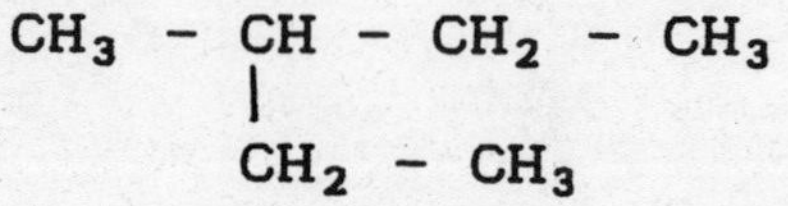

the name 3-methylpentane, since the longest chain has five carbons.

b) 3,3-dimethylbutane $\quad CH_3 - CH_2 - \overset{\overset{\displaystyle CH_3}{|}}{\underset{\underset{\displaystyle CH_3}{|}}{C}} - CH_3 \quad$ should have

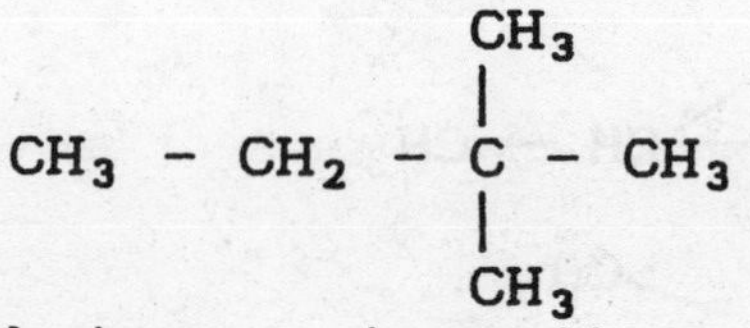

the name 2,2-dimethylbutane, since it can be numbered so that the methyl groups are on carbon 2.

c) 1-ethylpropane $\quad CH_2 - CH_2 - CH_3 \quad$ should have the name
   pentane $\qquad \overset{\underset{\displaystyle CH_2 - CH_3}{|}}{}$

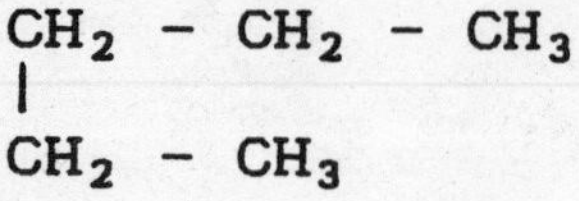

d) 2,2-dimethylpropane $\quad CH_3 - \overset{\overset{\displaystyle CH_3}{|}}{\underset{\underset{\displaystyle CH_3}{|}}{C}} - CH_3 \quad$ has the correct
   IUPAC name.

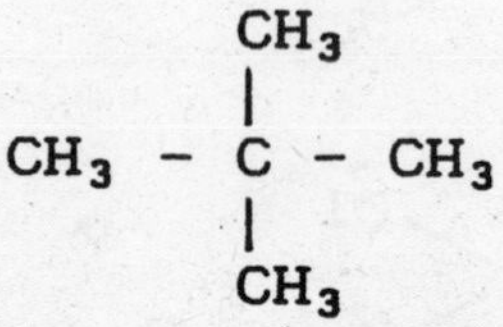

40. The following are the isomeric structures of C_4H_8.
    a) $CH_2 = CH - CH_2 - CH_3$ $\qquad\qquad\qquad$ 1-butene

    b) 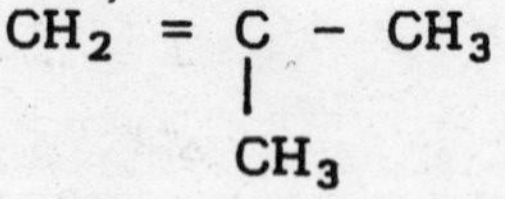 $CH_2 = \overset{\underset{\displaystyle CH_3}{|}}{C} - CH_3$ $\qquad\qquad\qquad$ methylpropene

    c) 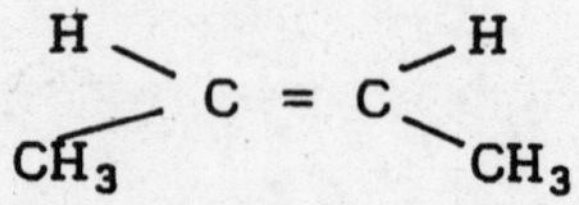 $\qquad\qquad$ cis-2-butene

    d) 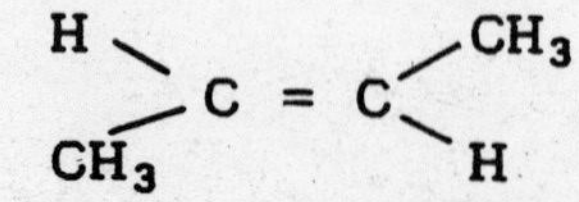 $\qquad\qquad$ trans-2-butene

174

e)
$$
\begin{array}{c}
CH_2 - CH_2 \\
|\qquad\quad| \\
CH_2 - CH_2
\end{array}
$$
cyclobutane

f)
$$
\begin{array}{c}
CH_3 \\
| \\
CH \\
CH_2 \!-\!\!-\!\!-\! CH_2
\end{array}
$$
methylcyclopropane

41. The two circles in the structural formula for naphthalene each represent six electrons. However, two of these electrons are common to both rings of carbon atoms. The total number of electrons delocalized over both rings in naphthalene, therefore, is ten.

42. a) $CH_3 - CH_2 - CH_2 - CH_3$ and $CH_3 - CH = CH - CH_3$ are NOT isomers because they have different molecular formulas.

b) $CH_3(CH_2)_5CH(CH_3)_2$ and $CH_3(CH_2)_4CH(CH_3)CH_2CH_3$ share the same molecular formula but have different structures and are, therefore, isomers.

c)
$$
\begin{array}{c}
H \qquad\qquad Br \\
\diagdown\; C = C \;\diagup \\
\diagup \qquad\qquad \diagdown \\
H \qquad\qquad H
\end{array}
\quad\text{and}\quad
\begin{array}{c}
H \qquad\qquad H \\
\diagdown\; C = C \;\diagup \\
\diagup \qquad\qquad \diagdown \\
Br \qquad\qquad H
\end{array}
\quad\text{are not}
$$
isomers although they have the same molecular formula. Their structures are identical, as can be seen by rotating one by 180° about the center of the C=C bond.

d) These two structures are equivalent, since one can be rotated into the other. Thus they are not isomers.

e) The two structures represent different molecules with the same molecular formula, and they are therefore isomers. Notice that the first isomer has no carbons between the two that bear Cl's, whereas the second has one intervening carbon atom.

43. a) $CO + Cl_2 \longrightarrow COCl_2$ addition reaction, and also an oxidation-reduction since the oxidation state of Cl and of C change.

b) $CH_4 + 2H_2O \longrightarrow CO + H_2$ oxidation-reduction

c) $CO + H_2 \longrightarrow H_2CO$ addition reaction, and also an oxidation-reduction

d) $CS_2 + 3Cl_2 \longrightarrow CCl_4 + S_2Cl_2$ oxidation-reduction

e) $CaC_2 + 2H_2O \longrightarrow Ca(OH)_2 + C_2H_2$ acid-base, since H^+ is transferred from H_2O to C_2^{2-}.

175

f) $C_2H_6 \longrightarrow C_2H_4 + H_2$ elimination, and
                                                       ox-red

44. a) C_6H_{10} $+$ Br_2 $\longrightarrow$ $C_6H_{10}Br_2$
      cyclohexene   1,2-dibromocyclohexane

    b) $C_3H_8 + 5O_2 \longrightarrow 3CO_2 + 4H_2O$

    c) $C_2H_5OH + H_2SO_4 \xrightarrow[\text{conc } H_2SO_4]{\text{Heat}} C_2H_4 + H_3O^+HSO_4^-$

       or $C_2H_5OH \xrightarrow[\text{Heat}]{} CH_2 = CH_2 + H_2O$

    d) $CH_4 + NH_3 \xrightarrow[\text{catalyst}]{\text{Heat}} HCN + 3H_2$

45. a) Natural gas is a mixture of gaseous hydrocarbons, mainly methane, which occur in the earth's crust.

    b) Petroleum or crude oil is a liquid mixture of hydrocarbons which occur in the earth's crust.

    c) Coal tar is a liquid distillate formed when coal is heated in the absence of air. It is a valuable source of organic chemicals.

    d) Synthesis gas is a mixture of carbon monoxide and hydrogen formed by the action of steam on methane in the presence of a catalyst.
        $CH_4 + H_2O \longrightarrow CO + 3H_2$
                     synthesis gas
Synthesis gas is a valuable industrial fuel as well as being a source of hydrogen.

46. The strategy here is to mentally compare the reactions of the two compounds in question, and find one type which allows you to easily distinguish between the two.
    a) C_2H_6 or $CH_3 - CH_3$, ethane is a saturated hydrocarbon while C_2H_2 or $CH \equiv CH$, ethyne is unsaturated. Ethyne will decolorize aqueous bromine when bubbled through it Ethane will not.

    b) Bubbling each gas through lime water – $Ca(OH)_2$ solution – will give a precipitate in the case of CO_2 but not in the case of C_3H_8 – propane. The relevant reaction is
       $CO_2 + Ca(OH)_2 \longrightarrow CaCO_3 + H_2O$
                            (insoluble)

The milkiness of the solution is due to the precipitation of calcium carbonate, $CaCO_3$.

c) Both CO and CH_4 burn in air. However, a cold watchglass brought to the mouth of the tube containing the methane will show the condensation of water upon its surface. CO does not produce water on combustion.

$$2CO + O_2 \longrightarrow 2CO_2$$
$$CH_4 + 2O_2 \longrightarrow CO_2 + 2H_2O$$

d) The bromine water test may be applied here also. When shaken with bromine water in a test-tube, ethene will decolourize the solution due to the presence of the double bond. Saturated propane would have no effect on bromine water.

Molecular Formulas

47. The percentage composition of the hydrocarbon can be used first to deduce the empirical formula:

	C	H
By %	82.6%	17.4%
By mass, in 100 g	82.6 g	17.4 g
Mole ratio	$\dfrac{82.6}{12.01}$	$\dfrac{17.4}{1.01}$
= atomic ratio		
=	6.88	17.2
=	1.00	2.50 or 2:5

The empirical formula is, therefore, C_2H_5 with an empirical formula mass = $2 \times 12.01 + 5 \times 1.01$
= 29.07

The molar mass is obtained by application of the ideal gas equation

$$PV = nRT$$

or $\quad PV = \dfrac{m}{M} RT \quad$ where M = molar mass of the gas

m = mass of gas in grams

or $\quad M = \dfrac{mRT}{PV}$

Substituting the given values

$$M = \dfrac{0.47 \times 0.0821 \times 298}{\dfrac{750}{760} \times 0.199}$$

= 58.6 g mol^{-1} or a molecular mass of 58.6 u.

This value is approximately twice the empirical formula weight and so the molecular formula will be $(C_2H_5)_2$ or C_4H_{10}, i.e. Butane.

Without further information it would not be possible to write down a unique structural formula for the compound since butane can exist in two isomeric forms:

$CH_3 - CH_2 - CH_2 - CH_3$ and $CH_3 - CH - CH_3$
$\quad$ n-butane $\qquad\qquad\qquad\qquad\qquad |$
$\qquad\qquad\qquad\qquad\qquad\qquad\qquad CH_3$
$\qquad\qquad\qquad\qquad\qquad$ 2-methylpropane

48. The percentage composition of the hydrocarbon can be used to

determine the empirical formula, as follows:

	C	H
By %	85.6%	14.4%
By mass in 100 g	85.6 g	14.4 g
Mole ratio	$\dfrac{85.6}{12.01}$	$\dfrac{14.4}{1.01}$
= atomic ratio		
=	7.13	14.3
=	1.00	2.01

The empirical formula is, therefore, CH_2 with an empirical formula mass = 12.01 + 2 x 1.01
= 14.03

The flask was sealed after equilibrium had been reached at one atmosphere pressure and so the increase in mass of the flask would give the mass of gas present in the flask at equilibrium. We now apply the ideal gas law in the form derived in the answer to question 47, in order to deduce the molecular mass:

$$M = \frac{mRT}{PV}$$ where

m = 0.687 g
R = 0.0821 ℓ atm mol^{-1} K^{-1}
T = 373 K (273 + 100)
P = 1 atmosphere
V = 0.250 ℓ

and so $$M = \frac{0.687 \times 0.0821 \times 373}{1 \times 0.250}$$
= 84.2 g mol^{-1} or a molecular mass of 84.2 u.
This molecular mass is almost exactly six times the empirical mass and so the molecular formula will be $(CH_2)_6$ or C_6H_{12}. Although it is not possible to assign a unique structural formula to this molecule since it could be one of the isomeric family of hexenes, or cyclohexane.

49. We first obtain the empirical formula for the hydrocarbon

	C	H
% composition	85.71	14.29
Mole Ratios =	$\dfrac{85.71}{12.01}$	$\dfrac{14.29}{1.01}$
=	7.14	14.1
=	1.00	1.97
Ratio of lowest integers =	1	2

The empirical formula is, therefore, CH_2.
The molar mass may be calculated directly from the ideal gas law in the form

$$M = \frac{mRT}{PV}$$ where m = Mass of gas in g.
M = molar mass

Substituting, $$M = \frac{0.200 \times 0.0821 \times 300}{0.921 \times 0.0953} = 56.1 \text{ g mol}^{-1}$$

The empirical formula mass is 14.02 g mol^{-1}, and thus the ratio of molecular to empirical mass is 4 to 1.
Therefore the molecular formula must be $(CH_2)_4$ or C_4H_8. See the answer to Q. 40 for all possible structures.

CHAPTER 12

1. The strategy here is to search for a chemical in the overall equation which appears only once in the set of reactions for which $\Delta H°$ values are given. In this case, both $CuCl_2$ and $CuCl$ (but not Cu) fill the bill. If we choose $CuCl_2$, we see that in order to have it on the left side of the equation, we must reverse the first reaction; hence the $\Delta H°$ changes sign:

$$CuCl_2 \longrightarrow Cu + Cl_2 \qquad\qquad \Delta H° = +206 \text{ kJ}$$

To eliminate Cl_2 (which we want to do since it does not appear in the overall equation), we must add in the second equation; i.e. to the above reaction we add

$$2Cu + Cl_2 \longrightarrow 2CuCl \qquad\qquad \Delta H° = -36 \text{ kJ}$$

and thus obtain

$$CuCl_2 + 2Cu + Cl_2 \longrightarrow Cu + Cl_2 + 2CuCl$$
$$\Delta H° = +206-36 = +170 \text{ kJ}$$

After cancelling terms common to both sides, we see that the equation is identical to the overall reaction given in the text:

$$CuCl_2 + Cu \longrightarrow 2CuCl \qquad\qquad \Delta H° = +170 \text{ kJ}$$

2. As in Q. 1, we pick a chemical (here F_2, O_2, HF or H_2O) that appears only once in the given reactions. Choosing F_2, we see that the first equation needs to be doubled since the overall reaction has $2F_2$:

$$2H_2 + 2F_2 \longrightarrow 4HF \qquad\qquad \Delta H° = -542\times2 = -1084 \text{ kJ}$$

No H_2 appears in the overall equation; we can eliminate it by adding to the above equation the reverse of the second thermochemical equation listed: i.e. we add the above to

$$2H_2O \longrightarrow 2H_2 + O_2 \qquad\qquad \Delta H° = +572 \text{ kJ}$$

and obtain, after cancellation of $2H_2$,

$$2F_2 + 2H_2O \longrightarrow 4HF + O_2 \qquad\qquad \Delta H° = -1084+572$$
$$= -512 \text{ kJ}$$

Since the above equation is the overall reaction, the answer is $\Delta H° = -512$ kJ.

3. The methodology is the same as for Q. 1 and Q. 2. We multiply the first equation by 2, and then add the reverse of the second to eliminate C(graphite) and obtain the desired equation:

$$2C(graphite) + 2O_2 \longrightarrow 2CO_2 \qquad\qquad \Delta H° = -787.0 \text{ kJ}$$
$$2CO \longrightarrow 2C(graphite) + O_2 \qquad\qquad \Delta H° = +110.5 \text{ kJ}$$

Thus for

$$2CO + 2O_2 \longrightarrow 2CO_2 \qquad\qquad \Delta H° = -676.5 \text{ kJ}$$

4. The methodology is the same as for Q. 1 and 2. We choose first to obtain either FeO or Fe as it appears in the overall equation. To have one mole of FeO on the left, we need to

179

reverse the first equation and divide it by 3.

$FeO + 1/3\ CO_2 \longrightarrow 1/3\ Fe_3O_4 + 1/3\ CO$ $\quad \Delta H° = -38/3 = -12.7$ kJ

To have one mole of Fe on the right, we divide the third thermochemical equation by two, i.e.

$1/2\ Fe_2O_3 + 3/2\ CO \longrightarrow Fe + 3/2\ CO_2$ $\quad \Delta H = -28/2 = -14.0$ kJ

and add the above two equations, to obtain

$FeO + 1/2\ Fe_2O_3 + 7/6\ CO \longrightarrow 1/3\ Fe_3O_4 + Fe + 7/6\ CO_2$
$$\Delta H = -12.7 - 14.0$$
$$= -26.7 \text{ kJ}$$

(Common terms in CO and CO_2 have been combined.) To eliminate Fe_2O_3 and Fe_3O_4, we first multiply the second thermochemical equation by one-sixth to obtain $1/3\ Fe_3O_4$ and $1/2\ Fe_2O_3$, i.e.

$1/3\ Fe_3O_4 + 1/6\ CO_2 \longrightarrow 1/2\ Fe_2O_3 + 1/6\ CO$
$$\Delta H = +59/6 = +9.8 \text{ kJ}$$

and combine it with the preceding equation, to obtain

$FeO + CO \longrightarrow Fe + CO_2$ $\quad \Delta H = -26.7 + 9.8 = -16.9$ kJ

5. The methodology is the same as for Q. 1-4. To obtain $3NO_2$ as reactant, we reverse the first thermochemical equation and multiply it by 3/2:

$3NO_2 \longrightarrow 3NO + 3/2\ O_2$ $\qquad \Delta H° = +173 \times 3/2$
$$= +259.5 \text{ kJ}$$

To obtain $2HNO_3$ as product, we multiply the second thermochemical equation by one-half

$N_2 + 5/2\ O_2 + H_2O \longrightarrow 2HNO_3$ $\qquad \Delta H° = -255/2 = -127.5$ kJ

and add it to the above equation to obtain

$3NO_2 + N_2 + 5/2\ O_2 + H_2O \longrightarrow 3NO + 3/2\ O_2 + 2HNO_3$
$$\Delta H° = 259.5 - 127.5 = +132.0 \text{ kJ}$$

After cancellation of common O_2, this equation is

$3NO_2 + N_2 + O_2 + H_2O \longrightarrow 3NO + 2HNO_3$
$$\Delta H° = +132.0 \text{ kJ}$$

To eliminate N_2 and O_2 and some of the NO, we take the reverse of the third thermochemical equation, i.e.

$2NO \longrightarrow N_2 + O_2$ $\qquad \Delta H° = -181$ kJ

and add it to the previous equation, to obtain the overall equation given in the problem:

$3NO_2 + H_2O \longrightarrow NO + 2HNO_3$ $\qquad \Delta H° = +132.0 - 181 = -49$ kJ

6. Since the standard $\Delta H°$ values are available for the two compounds involved (see also Table 12.1) we can deduce $\Delta H°$ from the relationship

$\Delta H° = \text{Sum } \Delta H_f°(\text{Products}) - \text{Sum } \Delta H_f°(\text{Reactants})$

The balanced reaction is

$2C_6H_{12}(g) \longrightarrow 3C_4H_8(g)$

and thus

$\Delta H° = 3\Delta H_f°(C_4H_8, g) - 2\Delta H_f°(C_6H_{12}, g)$
$$= 3 \times 28.4 - 2 \times (-123.3)$$
$$= 331.8 \text{ kJ}$$

7. The $\Delta H_f°$ values for all chemicals in the reaction are either given in the problem or in Table 12.1; thus we deduce $\Delta H°$ as in Q. 6; here

$$\Delta H^\circ = \Delta H_f^\circ(C_6H_{12}O_6,g) + 6\Delta H_f^\circ(O_2,g) - 6\Delta H_f^\circ(CO_2,g)$$
$$- 6\Delta H_f^\circ(H_2O,\ell)$$
$$= -1273 + 6 \times 0 - 6 \times (-393.5) - 6 \times (-285.8)$$
$$= +2803 \text{ kJ mol}^{-1}$$

Since the molar mass of glucose, $C_6H_{12}O_6$, is 180.18 g,

$$\Delta H^\circ = \frac{2803 \text{ kJ}}{1 \text{ mole glucose}} \times \frac{1 \text{ mole glucose}}{180.18 \text{ g glucose}}$$
$$= 15.56 \text{ kJ/g glucose}$$

8. The reaction is
$$SO_3(g) + H_2O(g) \longrightarrow H_2SO_4(\ell)$$
As in Q. 6, and using data from Table 12.1 in the text,
$$\Delta H^\circ = \Delta H_f^\circ(H_2SO_4,\ell) - \Delta H_f^\circ(SO_3,g) - \Delta H_f^\circ(H_2O,g)$$
$$= -814.0 - (-395.7) - (-241.8)$$
$$= -176.5 \text{ kJ}$$

9. From the general equation for ΔH° (see Q. 6), we obtain for this reaction
$$\Delta H^\circ = \Delta H_f^\circ(C_2H_6,g) - \Delta H_f^\circ(C_2H_2,g) - 2\Delta H_f^\circ(H_2,g)$$
Thus
$$\Delta H_f^\circ(C_2H_2,g) = -\Delta H^\circ + \Delta H_f^\circ(C_2H_6,g) - 2\Delta H_f^\circ(H_2,g)$$
$$= +312 - 84.7 - 2 \times 0$$
$$= +227 \text{ kJ}$$

10. By definition, ΔH_f°(element)=0 when the element is in its standard state; usually this is the most stable form at 25°C and 1 atmosphere pressure. Since the most stable state for Br_2 is liquid and for I_2 is solid, the ΔH_f° values for $Br_2(g)$ and $I_2(g)$ are not zero. By contrast, the stable forms for F_2 and Cl_2 are gases, and their ΔH_f° values are zero.

11. To obtain the enthalpy of formation, we require ΔH° for the reaction
$$Mg(s) + O_2(g) + H_2(g) \longrightarrow Mg(OH)_2(s)$$
since $Mg(s)$, $O_2(g)$ and $H_2(g)$ are the stablest forms for these elements. We can follow the methodology of Q. 1-5 to obtain this value. To obtain $Mg(s)$, we divide the first equation by 2:
$$Mg + 1/2 \, O_2 \longrightarrow MgO \qquad \Delta H^\circ = -601.8 \text{ kJ}$$
To obtain $Mg(OH)_2$, we add the second thermochemical equation to this one, and then have (after cancellation of MgO)
$$Mg + 1/2 \, O_2 + H_2O \longrightarrow Mg(OH)_2 \qquad \Delta H^\circ = -601.8-36.7$$
$$= -638.5 \text{ kJ}$$
To eliminate H_2O, we take the reverse of one-half the third thermochemical equation, i.e.
$$H_2 + 1/2 \, O_2 \longrightarrow H_2O \qquad \Delta H = -572.4/2=-286.2 \text{ kJ}$$
Now add this equation to the one above it, to obtain the first overall equation given in this solution (after H_2O is cancelled from both sides):
$$Mg + O_2 + H_2 \longrightarrow Mg(OH)_2 \qquad \Delta H = -638.5-286.2$$
$$= -924.7 \text{ kJ}$$

12. The balanced reaction here is
$$C_4H_{10}(\ell) + 13/2\ O_2(g) \longrightarrow 4CO_2(g) + 5H_2O(g)$$
(Combustion, unless otherwise indicated, always involves $O_2(g)$). On a molar basis,
$$\begin{aligned}
\Delta H^\circ &= 4\Delta H_f^\circ(CO_2,g) + 5\Delta H_f^\circ(H_2O,g) - \Delta H_f^\circ(C_4H_{20},\ell) \\
&\qquad - 13/2\ \Delta H_f^\circ(O_2,g) \\
&= 4 \times (-393.5) + 5 \times (-241.8) - (-127) - 13/2 \times 0 \\
&= -2656\ kJ
\end{aligned}$$
We convert to 1 gram butane using unit factors:

$$\frac{-2656\ kJ}{1\ mole\ C_4H_{10}} \times \frac{1\ mole\ C_4H_{10}}{58.14\ g\ C_4H_{10}} = -45.68\ kJ/g\ C_4H_{10}$$

13. The balanced reactions, for one mole of oxide each, are
$$\begin{aligned}
NO + 1/2\ O_2 &\longrightarrow NO_2 \\
SO_2 + 1/2\ O_2 &\longrightarrow SO_3 \\
O_2 + 1/2\ O_2 &\longrightarrow O_3
\end{aligned}$$
Since $\Delta H_f^\circ(g) = 0$ for O_2, in each case
$$\Delta H^\circ = \Delta H_f^\circ \text{ (oxide on right side)} - \Delta H_f^\circ \text{ (oxide on left side)}$$
Using the ΔH_f° values in Table 12.1 of the text, we obtain
$$\begin{aligned}
\Delta H^\circ &= -57.1\ kJ \text{ for } NO \to NO_2 \\
&= -98.9\ kJ \text{ for } SO_2 \to SO_3 \\
&= +142.7\ kJ \text{ for } O_2 \to O_3
\end{aligned}$$
The latter value is per mole of O_3 formed; it would be 95.1 per mole of O_2 consumed.

14. Combustion is reaction with $O_2(g)$; thus the reaction is
$$C_3H_8(g) + 5O_2(g) \longrightarrow 3CO_2(g) + 4H_2O(g)$$
We are told that the heat, q, released when one gram of C_3H_8 burns is 46.3 kJ; since $\Delta H^\circ = -q$ and since the molar mass of C_3H_8 is 44.11 g, we obtain
$$\begin{aligned}
\Delta H^\circ &= \frac{-46.3\ kJ}{1\ g\ C_3H_8} \times \frac{44.11\ g\ C_3H_8}{1\ mole\ C_3H_8} \\
&= -2042\ kJ\ mol^{-1}
\end{aligned}$$
For the overall reaction, we can write
$$\Delta H^\circ = 3\Delta H_f^\circ(CO_2,g) + 4\Delta H_f^\circ(H_2O,g) - \Delta H_f^\circ(C_3H_8,g) - 5\Delta H_f^\circ(O_2,g)$$
Since the ΔH_f° values are available in Table 12.1 for CO_2, H_2O, and O_2, we can solve for $\Delta H_f^\circ(C_3H_8,g)$:
$$\Delta H_f^\circ(C_3H_8,g) = 3\Delta H_f^\circ(CO_2,g) + 4\Delta H_f^\circ(H_2O,g) - \Delta H^\circ$$
since $\Delta H_f^\circ(O_2,g) = 0$. Substituting values, we obtain
$$\begin{aligned}
\Delta H_f^\circ(C_3H_8,g) &= 3 \times (-393.5) + 4 \times (-241.8) - (-2042) \\
&= -106\ kJ\ mol^{-1}
\end{aligned}$$

15. The methodology is similar to Q. 1-5. To obtain 2 moles of H_2 as reactant, double the fourth thermochemical equation:
$$2H_2(g) + O_2(g) \longrightarrow 2H_2O(\ell) \qquad \Delta H^\circ = 2 \times (-285.8)$$
$$= -571.6\ kJ$$
To obtain 1 mole CO as reactant, reverse the second thermochemical equation
$$CO(g) \longrightarrow C(graphite) + 1/2\ O_2(g) \qquad \Delta H^\circ = +110.5\ kJ$$
To obtain CH_3OH as product, reverse the first equation:
$$CO_2(g) + 2H_2O(\ell) \longrightarrow CH_3OH(\ell) + 3/2\ O_2(g) \qquad \Delta H^\circ = +726.6$$

Adding these three equations gives
$$2H_2(g) + O_2(g) + CO(g) + CO_2(g) + 2H_2O(\ell)$$
$$\longrightarrow\ 2H_2O(\ell) + C(graphite) + 1/2\ O_2(g) + CH_3OH(\ell) + 3/2\ O_2(g)$$
which, after cancelling common terms, gives
$$2H_2(g) + CO(g) + CO_2(g) \longrightarrow C(graphite) + CH_3OH(\ell) + O_2(g)$$
$$\Delta H° = +265.5\ kJ$$
To eliminate C(graphite), $O_2(g)$ and $CO_2(g)$ we take the third thermochemical equation, i.e.
$$C(graphite) + O_2(g) \longrightarrow CO_2(g) \qquad \Delta H° = -393.5\ kJ$$
and add it to our above equation, to obtain
$$2H_2(g) + CO(g) \longrightarrow CH_3OH(\ell) \qquad \Delta H° = +265.5 - 393.5$$
$$= -128.0\ kJ$$

16. First write the combustion reactions to see the reactions for which $\Delta H°$ values are given!

$C(graphite) + O_2(g) \longrightarrow CO_2(g)$		$\Delta H° = -393.5\ kJ$
$H_2(g) + 1/2\ O_2(g) \longrightarrow H_2O(\ell)$		$\Delta H° = -285.8\ kJ$
$C_2H_6(g) + 7/2\ O_2(g) \longrightarrow 2CO_2(g) + 3H_2O(\ell)$		$\Delta H° = -1559.8\ kJ$
$C_3H_8(g) + O_2(g) \longrightarrow 3CO_2(g) + 4H_2O(\ell)$		$\Delta H° = -2219.9\ kJ$

The enthalpy of formation for C_2H_6 is, by definition, the $\Delta H°$ of
$$2C(graphite) + 3H_2(g) \longrightarrow C_2H_6(g)$$
By using the usual methodology with Hess's Law, this reaction is found to be twice the first thermochemical equation, plus three times the second reaction, plus the reverse of the third equation. Thus
$$\Delta H° = 2 \times (-393.5) + 3 \times (-285.8) - (-1559.8) = -84.6\ kJ$$
Similarly, the $\Delta H_f°$ for C_3H_8 is the $\Delta H°$ of
$$3C(graphite) + 4H_2(g) \longrightarrow C_3H_8(g)$$
This reaction can be obtained by multiplying the first thermochemical equation by 3, adding it to four times the second, and finally adding the reverse of the fourth reaction. Thus
$$\Delta H° = 3 \times (-393.5) + 4 \times (-285.8) - (-2219.9)$$
$$= -103.8\ kJ$$
The ΔH_f and ΔH combustion values for butane can be calculated by assuming that the increments between C_4H_{10} and C_3H_8 in each instance is equal to the increment from C_3H_8 to C_2H_6. (This is approximately correct since bond energies in alkanes are almost constant.) Thus we obtain
$$\Delta H_f°(butane) \approx -123\ kJ$$
$$\Delta H_c°(butane) \approx -2219.9 + (-2219.9 + 1559.8)$$
$$= -2880\ kJ$$

17. The heat evolved per mole is obtained by dividing the heat by the mass, and multiplying by the molar mass; e.g.
$$q = \frac{71\ kJ}{3.2\ g\ CH_3OH} \times \frac{32.04\ g\ CH_3OH}{1\ mole\ CH_3OH} = 710\ kJ\ mol^{-1}$$

Since $\Delta H° = -q$, the $\Delta H°(combustion) = -q(per\ mole)$. The results are listed below. The values increase with increasing chain length, as there is more and more carbon to oxidize as the chain lengthens.

Alcohol	m	q	q per mole	ΔH per mole
CH_3OH	3.20	71	710	−710
C_2H_5OH	9.20	268	1342	−1342
C_3H_7OH	7.50	251	2011	−2011
$1-C_4H_9OH$	7.40	263	2635	−2635
$2-C_4H_9OH$	8.20	288	2604	−2604

(Given the significant figures in m and q, the q and ΔH per mole probably should be reported to only three significant figures.)

18. The balanced equation for the combustion is
$$C_2H_5OH + 3O_2(g) \longrightarrow 2CO_2(g) + 3H_2O(\ell)$$
(Liquid water is assumed to be the product.) In algebraic terms,
$$\Delta H° = 2\Delta H_f°(CO_2,g) + 3\Delta H_f°(H_2O,\ell) - \Delta H_f°(C_2H_5OH) - 3\Delta H_f°(O_2,g)$$
Rearrangement leads to isolation of the unknown in terms of terms whose values are known (see Table 12.1):
$$\Delta H_f°(C_2H_5OH) = 2\Delta H_f°(CO_2,g) + 3\Delta H_f°(H_2O,\ell) - 3\Delta H_f°(O_2,g) - \Delta H°$$
$$= 2 \times (-393.5) + 3 \times (-285.8) - 3 \times 0 - (-1370)$$
$$= -274 \text{ kJ mol}^{-1}$$

19. Methodology similar to Q. 18. The balanced equation is
$$C_3H_8 + 5O_2(g) \longrightarrow 3CO_2(g) + 4H_2O(\ell)$$
$$\Delta H° = 3\Delta H_f°(CO_2,g) + 4\Delta H_f°(H_2O,g) - \Delta H_f°(C_3H_8) - 5\Delta H_f°(O_2,g)$$
so
$$\Delta H_f°(C_3H_8) = 3\Delta H_f°(CO_2,g) + 4\Delta H_f°(H_2O,g) - 5\Delta H_f°(O_2,g) - \Delta H°$$
$$= 3 \times (-393.5) + 4 \times (-241.8) - 5 \times 0 - (-2044)$$
$$= -104 \text{ kJ mol}^{-1}$$

20. By definition, the dissociation energy in O_2 is the $\Delta H°$ for
$$O_2(g) \longrightarrow 2O(g)$$
Now for this reaction,
$$\Delta H° = 2\Delta H_f°(O,g) - \Delta H_f°(O_2,g)$$
$$= 2 \times 249 - 0$$
$$= 498 \text{ kJ}$$
Similarly, for nitrogen the dissociation energy is $\Delta H°$ for
$$N_2(g) \longrightarrow 2N(g)$$
$$\Delta H° = 2\Delta H_f°(N,g) - \Delta H_f°(N_2,g)$$
$$= 2 \times 473 - 0$$
$$= 946 \text{ kJ}$$
The double bond value times 3/2 gives 747 kJ, so the triple bond is stronger than this.

21. The molecule C_2H_6 contains six C–H bonds and one C–C bond; thus its total bonding energy is estimated to be
$$TBE = 6E(C–H) + E(C–C)$$
$$= 6 \times 413 + 348$$
$$= 2826 \text{ kJ}$$
This TBE is, by definition, the estimated $\Delta H°$ for the process
$$C_2H_6(g) \longrightarrow 2C(g) + 6H(g)$$
We can work $\Delta H_f°$ for C_2H_6 into our calculations by expressing the $\Delta H°$ for this process in terms of $\Delta H_f°$'s:
$$\Delta H° = 2\Delta H_f°(C,g) + 6\Delta H_f°(H,g) - \Delta H_f°(C_2H_6,g)$$
Solving for our unknown, we obtain:

$$\Delta H_f°(C_2H_6,g) = 2\Delta H_f°(C,g) + 6\Delta H_f°(H,g) - \Delta H°$$

We use values from Table 12.1 for $\Delta H_f°$(atoms), and our bond energy estimate for $\Delta H°$:

$$\Delta H_f°(C_2H_6,g) = 2 \times 716.7 + 6 \times 218.0 - 2826$$
$$= -85 \text{ kJ mol}^{-1}$$

22. The total bonding energy in PCl_3 is the $\Delta H°$ of the reaction

$$PCl_3(g) \longrightarrow P(g) + 3Cl(g)$$

$$\Delta H° = \Delta H_f°(P,g) + 3\Delta H_f°(Cl,g) - \Delta H_f°(PCl_3,g)$$
$$= 316.2 + 3 \times 121.7 - (-287.0)$$
$$= 968.3 \text{ kJ}$$

This value can be identified with $3E(P-Cl)$, since PCl_3 contains three P-Cl bonds; thus

$$E(P-Cl) = 968.3/3 = 322.8 \text{ kJ mol}^{-1}$$

The energy associated with the two additional bonds in PCl_5 is $\Delta H°$ for the reaction

$$PCl_5(g) \longrightarrow PCl_3(g) + 2Cl(g)$$

$$\Delta H° = \Delta H_f°(PCl_3,g) + 2\Delta H_f°(Cl,g) - \Delta H_f°(PCl_5,g)$$
$$= -287.0 + 2 \times 121.7 - (-374.7)$$
$$= 331.1 \text{ kJ}$$

Thus the fourth and fifth bonds have an average energy of $331.1/2 = 165.6$ kJ.

23. We can deduce $2E(O-H)$ as the $\Delta H°$ for the reaction

$$H_2O(g) \longrightarrow 2H(g) + O(g)$$

$$\Delta H° = 2\Delta H_f°(H,g) + \Delta H_f°(O,g) - \Delta H_f°(H_2O,g)$$
$$= 2 \times 218.0 + 249.1 - (-241.8)$$
$$= 926.9$$

Thus $E(O-H) = 463.4$ kJ.

From the Lewis structure H-O-O-H for H_2O_2, we conclude that its total bonding energy is equivalent to $2E(O-H) + E(O-O)$; we can deduce this value as the $\Delta H°$ for

$$H_2O_2(g) \longrightarrow 2H(g) + 2O(g)$$

i.e. $\Delta H° = 2\Delta H_f°(H,g) + 2\Delta H_f°(O,g) - \Delta H_f°(H_2O_2,g)$
$$= 2 \times 218.0 + 2 \times 249.1 - (-136.4)$$
$$= 1070.6 \text{ kJ}$$

Subtracting $2E(O-H)$ from this total yields

$$E(O-O) = 143.7 \text{ kJ mol}^{-1}$$

From Q. 20, we have $E(O=O) = 498$ kJ. Thus the O-O bond strength of 143.7 is much less than half the O=O value.

24. For CO, the bond strength is the $\Delta H°$ for

$$CO(g) \longrightarrow C(g) + O(g)$$

From the $\Delta H_f°$ values, we obtain $\Delta H° = 1076.3$ kJ here. For CO_2, the strength of the pair of CO interactions is the $\Delta H°$ for

$$CO_2(g) \longrightarrow C(g) + 2O(g)$$

From the $\Delta H_f°$ values, we obtain $\Delta H° = 1608.4$ kJ, so each CO interaction here is 804.2 kJ in strength. Thus the average C=O bond energy in CO_2 is less than the CO bond in CO, which is not unexpected given that the later is a triple bond $^-C\equiv O^+$ in one of its most important Lewis structures.

25. Since H_2CO contains 2 C-H and one C=O bonds, the $\Delta H°$ for its atomization reaction
$$H_2CO(g) \longrightarrow 2H(g) + C(g) + O(g)$$
of 1517.7 kJ (obtained from the $\Delta H_f°$ values given) can be expressed as
$$2E(C-H) + E(C=O) = 1517.7$$
Using $E(C-H) = 413$ kJ from Table 12.2, we obtain
$$E(C=O) = 692 \text{ kJ}$$
Since the average C=O value in CO_2 is 804.2 kJ (see Q. 24 solution), we conclude that the CO_2 value is greater.

26. The $\Delta H°$ values for gas-phase reactions can be estimated from the bond energies of the constituent molecules using the equation
$$\Delta H° = \text{Sum(BE's for Reactants)} - \text{Sum(BE's for Products)}$$
a) The reactants contain two S-H bonds and one Cl-Cl bond, and the products possess two S-Cl and one H-H bonds; thus
$$\begin{aligned}\Delta H° &= 2E(S-H) + E(Cl-Cl) - 2E(S-Cl) - E(H-H) \\ &= 2 \times 364 + 239 - 2 \times 276 - 436 \\ &= -21 \text{ kJ}\end{aligned}$$
where we obtain bond energy values from Table 12.2 of the text.

b) Similarly,
$$\begin{aligned}\Delta H° &= 4E(C-H) + 2E(F-F) - 2E(C-H) - 2E(C-F) - 2E(H-F) \\ &= -964 \text{ kJ}\end{aligned}$$

c) Similarly,
$$\begin{aligned}\Delta H° &= 2E(C-H) + 2E(C-Cl) + 4E(C-H) - 6E(C-H) - 2E(C-Cl) \\ &= 0 \quad \text{(since the number of bonds of each type is the} \\ &\qquad\qquad \text{same in reactants and products)}\end{aligned}$$

27. The methodology is the same as for Q. 26.
a) $\begin{aligned}\Delta H° &= E(C\equiv C) + 2E(C-H) + E(C-C) + 6E(C-H) - 2E(C=C) - 8E(C-H) \\ &= E(C\equiv C) + E(C-C) - 2E(C=C) \\ &= -78 \text{ kJ}\end{aligned}$

b) $\begin{aligned}\Delta H° &= 4E(O-H) + 2E(O-O) - 4E(O-H) - E(O=O) \\ &= 2E(O-O) - E(O=O) \\ &= -218 \text{ kJ}\end{aligned}$

c) $\begin{aligned}\Delta H° &= E(C\equiv O) + E(H-H) - 2E(C-H) - E(C=O) \\ &= -27 \text{ kJ}\end{aligned}$

28. The Kekule structure for naphthalene contains 8 C-H, 5 C=C and 6 C-C bonds (see text Chapter 11); thus its expected total bonding energy is
$$8E(C-H) + 5E(C=C) + 6E(C-C)$$
From the bond energies in Table 12.2, we calculate this value to be 8487 kJ. This is the expected value for the reaction
$$C_{10}H_8(g) \longrightarrow 10C(g) + 8H(g)$$
for which we can also write the expression
$$\Delta H° = 10\Delta H_f°(C,g) + 8\Delta H_f°(H,g) - \Delta H_f°(C_{10}H_8,g)$$

Rearranging to isolate $\Delta H_f°$ for naphthalene, we obtain
$$\Delta H_f°(C_{10}H_8, g) = 10\Delta H_f°(C, g) + 8\Delta H_f°(H, g) - \Delta H°$$
Substituting $\Delta H_f°$ values from Table 12.1 and our estimate of $\Delta H°$ leads to an estimated $\Delta H_f°$ value for $C_{10}H_8$ of 424 kJ. Since the experimental $\Delta H_f°$ is +151 kJ, we conclude that naphthalene is more stable by 273 kJ than expected from bond energies; i.e. its resonance energy is 273 kJ. This value is slightly less than twice the 146 kJ value for benzene, (see text), perhaps only because the bond energies vary slightly between compounds even when no resonance is involved.

29. The methodology is similar to that of Q. 28 in terms of the strategy to estimate the $\Delta H_f°$ values. From their structures (se Chapter 11 of the text)
Total Expected Bonding Energy of Cyclobutane
$= 4E(C-C) + 8E(C-H) = 4696$ kJ
Total Expected Bonding Energy of Cyclohexane
$= 6E(C-C) + 12E(C-H) = 7044$ kJ
We equate each to the corresponding $\Delta H°$ expression of the reactions
$$C_4H_8(g) \longrightarrow 4C(g) + 8H(g)$$
$$\text{and} \quad C_6H_{12}(g) \longrightarrow 6C(g) + 12H(g)$$
e.g. $4696 = 4 \times 716.7 + 8 \times 218.0 - \Delta H_f°(C_4H_8, g)$
and thus $\Delta H_f°(C_4H_8, g) = -85$ kJ is expected.
Similarly $\Delta H_f°(C_6H_{12}, g) = -128$ kJ is expected.
The value for C_6H_{12} is within 5 kJ of the experimental value (of -123.3; see Table 12.1) but that for C_4H_8 is 113 kJ more negative than the experimental value. The discrepancy for cyclobutane arises because it is strained.

30. The $\Delta H°$ value can be calculated from $\Delta H_f°$ values listed in Table 12.1; the difference between $\Delta E°$ and $\Delta H°$ can be evaluated as $P\Delta V$.
First we write the balanced equation for the reaction:
$$C_2H_6(g) + 7/2\ O_2(g) \longrightarrow 2CO_2(g) + 3H_2O(\ell)$$
Thus
$\Delta H° = 2\Delta H_f°(CO_2, g) + 3\Delta H_f°(H_2O, \ell) - \Delta H_f°(C_2H_6, g) - 3.5\Delta H_f°(O_2, g)$
$= 2 \times (-393.5) + 3 \times (-285.8) - (-84.7) - 3.5 \times 0$
$= -1559.7$ kJ
If gaseous H_2O is formed, then by a similar calculation we find $\Delta H° = -1427.7$ kJ.
For any reaction, we can evaluate $P\Delta V$ using the equation
$$P\Delta V = \Delta nRT = RT\Delta n$$
where Δn is the moles of gaseous products minus moles of gaseous reactants. When liquid water is formed, then from the balanced equation above
$$\Delta n = 2 - 1 - 3.5 = -2.5$$
Thus $RT\Delta n = 8.314$ J K^{-1} mole^{-1} $\times$ 298 K $\times$ $(-2.5$ mole$)$
$= -6.2$ kJ
$= P\Delta V$
Now $\Delta E° = \Delta H° - P\Delta V$
thus $\Delta E° = -1559.7 - (-6.2)$
$= -1553.5$ kJ

When $H_2O(g)$ is formed, then
$$\Delta n = 2 + 3 - 1 - 3.5 = +0.5$$
$$\text{and } RT\Delta n = 8.314 \times 298 \times (+0.5)$$
$$= +1.2 \text{ kJ}$$
$$= P\Delta V$$
For this case
$$\Delta E° = \Delta H° - P\Delta V = -1427.7 - 1.2 = -1428.9 \text{ kJ}$$

31. Since the reaction occurs in a bomb calorimeter, the volume is constant and
$$q = -\Delta E$$
We can evaluate ΔE from ΔH and $P\Delta V$ for the reaction, where ΔH is obtained from $\Delta H_f°$ values:
$$n\text{-}C_4H_{10}(g) + 13/2 \ O_2(g) \longrightarrow 4CO_2(g) + 5H_2O(\ell)$$

$$\Delta H° = 4\Delta H_f°(CO_2,g) + 5\Delta H_f°(H_2O,\ell) - \Delta H_f°(n\text{-}C_4H_{10},g) - 13/2\Delta H_f°(O_2,g)$$
$$= 4 \times (-393.5) + 5 \times (-285.8) - (-126.1) - 13/2 \times 0$$
$$= -2876.9 \text{ kJ}$$
From the chemical equation, $\Delta n = 4 - 1 - 13/2 = -3.5$
Since $P\Delta V = \Delta nRT = RT\Delta n$
then $P\Delta V = 8.314 \text{ J K}^{-1} \text{ mole}^{-1} \times 298 \text{ K} \times (-3.5 \text{ mole})$
$$= -8.7 \text{ kJ}$$

Now $\Delta E° = \Delta H° - P\Delta V$
$$= -2876.9 - (-8.7)$$
$$= -2868.2 \text{ kJ}$$
This value applies to one mole of $n\text{-}C_4H_{10}$; since only 2.42 g were reacted, ΔE will be
$$2.42 \text{ g } C_4H_{10} \times \frac{1 \text{ mole } C_4H_{10}}{58.14 \text{ g } C_4H_{10}} \times \frac{-2868.2 \text{ kJ}}{1 \text{ mole } C_4H_{10}} = -119 \text{ kJ}$$
Thus the heat q released is 119 kJ.

32. The 1303 value refers to a constant volume process; thus
$$\Delta E° = -1303 \text{ kJ}$$
Since $\Delta H° = \Delta E° + P\Delta V$
we can obtain $\Delta H°$ from $\Delta E°$ by evaluating $P\Delta V$. For this purpose we need the balanced equation:
$$C_2H_2(g) + 5/2 \ O_2(g) \longrightarrow 2CO_2(g) + H_2O(\ell)$$
Here $\Delta n = 2 - 1 - 5/2 = -1.5$
Now $P\Delta V = RT\Delta n$
$$= 8.314 \text{ J K}^{-1} \text{ mole}^{-1} \times 298 \text{ K} \times (-1.5 \text{ mole})$$
$$= -3.7 \text{ kJ}$$
Thus $\Delta H° = -1303 + (-3.7)$
$$= -1307 \text{ kJ}$$

33. All the heat of reaction is used here to warm the 1500 g of water. Thus the heat q is
q = Specific heat capacity of H_2OxMass H_2Oxtemperature increase
$$= 4.184 \text{ J g}^{-1} \text{ K}^{-1} \times 1500 \text{ g} \times (26.386 - 25.246) \text{ K}$$
$$= 7155 \text{ J}$$
Since $\Delta H_3 = -q$, and since the molar mass of C_8H_{18} is 114.26, we obtain

$$\frac{-7155 \text{ J}}{0.150 \text{ g C}_8\text{H}_{18}} \times \frac{114.26 \text{ g C}_8\text{H}_{18}}{1 \text{ mole C}_8\text{H}_{18}} = -5,450,000 \text{ J/mole}$$

Thus the enthalpy of combustion is -5450 kJ mole^{-1}

34. The amount of NaOH available is
$$\frac{50.0 \text{ mL}}{1000 \text{ mL L}^{-1}} \times \frac{0.400 \text{ moles NaOH}}{1 \text{ L}} = 0.0200 \text{ moles NaOH}$$

and of H_2SO_4 is

$$\frac{20.00 \text{ mL}}{1000 \text{ mL L}^{-1}} \times \frac{0.500 \text{ moles H}_2\text{SO}_4}{1 \text{ L}} = 0.0100 \text{ moles H}_2\text{SO}_4$$

The reaction is $2\text{NaOH} + \text{H}_2\text{SO}_4 \longrightarrow \text{Na}_2\text{SO}_4 + 2\text{H}_2\text{O}$
Thus we have the correct ratio of moles of the two reactants.
The total amount of heat evolved during the reaction is the
sum of that received by the calorimeter and the solution; we
take the specific heat capacity of the latter to be 4.184 J
g^{-1} K^{-1} and the mass of the 70 mL equal to 70 g, since it is
a dilute aqueous solution.
q = Heat received by calorimeter + Heat received by solution
  = 39.0 J K^{-1} x 3.60 K + 4.184 J g^{-1} K^{-1} x 70 g x 3.60 K
  = 1195 J
Thus ΔH = $-1/95$ J per 0.0100 mole H_2SO_4, and therefore
    ΔH = -119.5 kJ per mole H_2SO_4.

35. The methodology is the same as for Q. 34.
q = 350 J K^{-1} x 2.60 K + 4.184 J g^{-1} K^{-1} x 505.4 g x 2.60 K
  = 6408 J
$$\Delta H = -\frac{6408 \text{ J}}{5.40 \text{ g CaO}} \times \frac{56.08 \text{ g CaO}}{1 \text{ mole CaO}} = -66.5 \text{ kJ/mole}$$

36. The energy of combustion of hexane is obtained as the $\Delta H°$ of
the reaction
  $\text{C}_6\text{H}_{14}(\ell) + 19/2 \text{ O}_2(g) \longrightarrow 6\text{CO}_2(g) + 7\text{H}_2\text{O}(\ell)$
$\Delta H°$ = $6\Delta H_f°(\text{CO}_2,g) + 7\Delta H_f°(\text{H}_2\text{O},\ell) - \Delta H_f°(\text{C}_6\text{H}_{14},\ell) -$
    $19/2 \ \Delta H_f°(\text{O}_2,g)$
  = 6 x (-393.5) + 7 x (-285.8) - (-199) - 19/2 x 0
  = -4162.6 kJ
Thus 4162.6 kJ of heat energy are obtained from the
combustion of 1 mole of C_6H_{14}. To deduce the cost per joule,
we transform this value into heat per litre of gasoline:
$$\frac{4162.6 \text{ kJ}}{1 \text{ mole C}_6\text{H}_{14}} \times \frac{1 \text{ mole C}_6\text{H}_{14}}{86.20 \text{ g C}_6\text{H}_{14}} \times \frac{1.38 \text{ g C}_6\text{H}_{14}}{1 \text{ mL C}_6\text{H}_{14}} \times \frac{1000 \text{ mL}}{1 \text{ L}}$$
  = 66,600 kJ L^{-1}
If you know the local gasoline cost in dollars per liter,
you can deduce number of kilojoules of energy that can be
bought per dollar in your area by using gasoline. (If
gasoline is sold by the gallon in your area, use conversion
factors in Chapter 1.) In Canada in 1985, the cost was about
\$0.50 per litre; thus one could obtain 66,600 kJ per \$0.50,

i.e. about 133,000 kJ per dollar.

For electricity, one kilowatt-hour corresponds to

$$1000 \text{ watts} \times 1 \text{ hour}$$
$$= 1000 \text{ J s}^{-1} \times 3600 \text{ s}$$
$$= 3600 \text{ kJ}$$

Dividing this number by the dollar cost of a kilowatt-hour yields the number of kilojoules of electrical energy you can obtain per dollar. If this amount is higher than the amount of heat from gasoline per dollar, then electricity is the "best buy". (In most areas, gasoline will be the best buy.)

37. Although each carbon participates in one C=C and two C-C bonds, one can associate only one half the energies of such bond with a particular carbon. Thus the energy per carbon required is

$$\frac{E(C=C) + 2E(C-C)}{2}$$

$$= (619 + 2 \times 348)/2$$

$$= 657.5 \text{ kJ}$$

38. a) The standard enthalpy of formation is the ΔH° for the reaction in which 1 mole of a compound is formed from its elements, each of which is in its most stable state; the elements and compound are all in standard states. The ΔH_f° for $MgCO_3(s)$ is the ΔH° for

$$Mg(s) + C(s) + 3/2\ O_2(g) \longrightarrow MgCO_3(s)$$

b) The heat capacity of the calorimeter and contents can be obtained from the results of the second experiment:

$$\frac{506 \text{ J}}{1.02 \text{ K}} = 496 \text{ J K}^{-1}$$

Thus the heat q released in the first experiment is

$$q = 496 \text{ J K}^{-1} \times 8.61 \text{ K} = 4270 \text{ J} = -\Delta H$$

This value now can be converted to a molar basis:

$$\frac{-4270 \text{ J}}{0.203 \text{ g Mg}} \times \frac{24.31 \text{ g Mg}}{1 \text{ mole Mg}} = -5.11 \times 10^5 \text{ J/mole}$$

$$= -511 \text{ kJ/mole}$$

c) From (b), we have

$$Mg(s) + 2HCl(aq) \longrightarrow MgCl_2(aq) + H_2(g)$$
$$\Delta H^\circ = -511 \text{ kJ}$$

From the information listed,

$$MgCO_3(s) + 2HCl(aq) \longrightarrow MgCl_2(aq) + H_2O(\ell) + CO_2(g)$$
$$\Delta H^\circ = -90.4 \text{ kJ}$$

We require $\Delta H_f^\circ(MgCO_3)$, i.e. the ΔH° for the reaction given in part (a). If we reverse the second of the two equations above and add the two, we obtain an equation related to the formation reaction for $MgCO_3$:

$$Mg(s) + CO_2(g) + H_2O(\ell) \longrightarrow MgCO_3(s) + H_2(g)$$
$$\Delta H^\circ = -511+90.4$$
$$= -421 \text{ kJ}$$

For this reaction,
$$\Delta H^\circ = \Delta H_f^\circ(MgCO_3,s) + \Delta H_f^\circ(H_2,g) - \Delta H_f^\circ(Mg,s)$$
$$- \Delta H_f^\circ(CO_2,g) - \Delta H_f^\circ(H_2O,\ell)$$
Since $\Delta H_f^\circ(H_2,g) = \Delta H_f^\circ(Mg,s) = 0$, then by rearrangement,
$$\Delta H_f^\circ(MgCO_3,s) = \Delta H + \Delta H_f^\circ(CO_2,g) + \Delta H_f^\circ(H_2O,\ell)$$
$$= -421 + (-393.5) + (-285.8)$$
$$= -1100 \text{ kJ mole}^{-1}$$

1. In sublimation, the material passes from the solid state directly to the gas, but this process is equivalent to passing from solid to liquid and then liquid to gas. Since each of these two processes requires energy, the enthalpy of sublimation must be larger than either one of the above, e.g. the enthalpy for vaporization (liquid to gas).

2. a) As the temperature rises, the average kinetic energy of the molecules of the liquid increases, and a greater proportion of them have sufficient energy to escape the surface and become gaseous. Thus the vapor pressure increases with increasing temperature.

   b) A liquid boils when its vapor pressure equals that of the atmosphere. Since that of toluene is greater than that of benzene at 20°C, then if we assume that this superiority is maintained as the temperature is increased, toluene's vapor pressure will equal 760 mm Hg at a lower temperature than will that for benzene. Thus benzene should have a higher boiling point. (This is contrary to fact, so the data quoted must be in error.)

3. The porous clay pot soaks up the water which evaporates on a warm day. Since the molar enthalpy of vaporization of water is large, the contents of the pot are kept cool since heat is abstracted from them for use in evaporation.

4. Assuming liquid H_2O is formed in the process, the reaction is
$$CH_4(g) + 2O_2(g) \rightarrow CO_2(g) + 2H_2O(\ell).$$
So
$$\Delta H° = \Delta H_f°(CO_2,g) + 2\Delta H_f°(H_2O,\ell) - \Delta H_f°(CH_4,g) - 2\Delta H_f°(O_2,g)$$
$$= -393.5 + 2\times(-285.8) - (-74.5) - 2 \times 0$$
$$= -890.6 \text{ kJ mol}^{-1}$$
where the data have been taken from Table 12.1.
Now the amount of heat energy required to vaporize 1000 kg of water is

$$1,000,000 \text{ g } H_2O \times \frac{1 \text{ mole } H_2O}{18.02 \text{ g } H_2O} \times \frac{40.7 \text{ kJ}}{1 \text{ mole } H_2O}$$

$$= 2.26 \times 10^6 \text{ kJ}.$$

Thus the number of moles of CH_4 required is

$$\frac{2.26 \times 10^6 \text{ kJ}}{890.6 \text{ kJ mole}^{-1}} = 2.54 \times 10^3 \text{ mole}.$$

Converting to mass, we find that the amount of CH_4 required is 4.07×10^4 g, i.e. 40.7 kg.

5.   a)   Since the sample was collected over water,
$$P_{total} = P_{O_2} + P_{H_2O}$$
and $P_{total} = P_{atmosphere}$ since the water levels were adjusted to be equal. At 21°C, by linear extrapolation of the values in Table 13.4, P_{H_2O} = 18.8 mm Hg = 18.8 torr.

Thus
$$P_{O_2} = P_{total} - P_{H_2O} = 745 - 18.8 = 726 \text{ torr.}$$

b)   From the data, V = 365 mL when P_{O_2} = 726 torr and T = 294 K. For P_{O_2} = 760 torr (since "dry" O_2 is specified, none of the 760 torr is due to H_2O) and T = 273, since the sample has the same amount of O_2 then
$$P_2V_2/T_2 = P_1V_1/T_1$$
i.e. $V_2 = P_1V_1T_2/P_2T_1$
 = 726 torr x 365 mL x 273 K/(760 torr x 294 K)
 = 324 mL.

6.   The mass of H_2O is 0.115 g, i.e. 0.00638 moles. The Ideal Gas Law applies to the H_2O component of the original sample:
$$P_{H_2O}V = n_{H_2O}RT$$
$$P_{H_2O} = n_{H_2O}RT/V$$
$\phantom{P_{H_2O}}$ = 0.00638 x 0.0821 x 298/5.00
$\phantom{P_{H_2O}}$ = 0.0312 atm, i.e. 23.7 torr.

7.   The reaction is LiH + H_2O → LiOH + H_2(g).   Thus

$$0.54 \text{ g LiH} \times \frac{1 \text{ mole LiH}}{7.95 \text{ g LiH}} \times \frac{1 \text{ mole } H_2}{1 \text{ mole LiH}} = 0.068 \text{ mole } H_2.$$

Now the total pressure of 754 torr equals that of H_2 plus that of 23.8 torr from the water vapor; thus
$$P_{H_2}V = n_{H_2}RT$$
$$V = n_{H_2}RT/P_{H_2}$$
 = 0.068 x 0.0821 x 298/(730/760)
 = 1.7 L.
As in Q.5, one can convert readily to STP for dry H_2:
$V_2 = P_1V_1T_1/P_2T_1$
 = 730 x 1.7 L x 273/(760 x 298)
 = 1.5 L.
The molarity of LiOH can be obtained from the moles of LiOH

produced, which is the same as the moles of H_2:

   $[LiOH]$ = 0.068 moles/0.0505 L = 1.3 M.

8. Given the hardness and very high melting point, boron is unlikely to be a molecular solid. Its lack of conductivity does not rule out the possibility that it is an ionic solid since even solid NaCl does not conduct, but since it contains only one element it presumably is not ionic. All the information is however consistent with a covalent network solid. It is unlikely to be soluble in water, since all the 3-D networks of bonds would have to be broken to achieve this, and since boron atoms are not likely to be strongly bound to H_2O.

9. Presumably $SnCl_4$ is a molecular substance, since it is a gas at a relatively low temperature and this is possible only for small molecules held together by weak intermolecular forces. In contrast, $SnCl_2$ could be an ionic solid or a network solid since its melting point is quite high.

10. a) Since N≡N bonds are strong, and N-N relatively weak, N_2 will exist as a molecular solid of weakly attracted N_2 molecules rather than as a 2-D or 3-D network of N atoms singly bonded to each other.

    b) There is no conceivable covalent bond network H_2S can form. Further, sulfur and hydrogen do not differ sufficiently in electronegativity such that an ionic solid could form. Thus H_2S will form a molecular solid.

    c) Since Cr is a metal, we expect it to form a network solid held together by metallic bonding.

    d) CaO contains a metal and a non-metal, and thus the bonding is ionic. We expect it to form a network solid since ionic substances always find it energetically profitable to do so.

    e) Molecular solid, for the same reason as (b).

    f) Network solid, since Si-O single bonds are preferred to Si=O and the only way in which sufficient Si-O bonds can form to fulfill the valencies is by formation of a network.

    g) Since KOH is K^+OH^-, it will form a network solid of ionic bonds.

    h) Molecular solid, for the same reason as (b).

11. a) BrF since its bonds are more ionic (the electronegativity difference between Br and F is greater than between Cl and F) and also because Br has more

electrons; thus both dipole-dipole and London forces greater in BrF than in ClF.

b) BrCl for the same reasons as in (a); note that only London forces occur in Cl_2.

c) KBr since it is ionic (since K is a metal) whereas BrCl is polar covalent since both atoms are non-metals.

d) K because it is a network solid (although held together only by metallic bonding) whereas Br_2 is a molecular solid with molecules attracted only by van der Waals forces.

12. Since Cl has more electrons than does H, it is more polarizable. Thus the intermolecular attractions increase if it is substituted by Cl, and thus the boiling points of C_6H_5Cl is greater than those for C_6H_6 and that for C_6Cl_6 is much greater.

13. a) London forces (since molecules are covalent).

b) Ionic since CaO consists of Ca^{2+} and O^{2-} ions.

c) London forces

d) Dipole-dipole forces (since CN bonds are polar).

e) Hydrogen bonds (i.e. a special type of dipole-dipole force).

14. LiF and BeF_2 are ionic solids and thus each atom is an ion which is held to the 3-D array of other ions by strong electrostatic forces. In BF_3 through OF_2 the forces of attraction are all dipole-dipole and London; those in F_2 are London forces.

15. The water molecules are attracted to each other by hydrogen bonds and therefore are not easily vaporized, whereas the hydrocarbon molecules in gasoline are attracted to each other by the much weaker London type of force and thus are more readily vaporized.

16. a) H_2O since hydrogen bonding will provide substantial intermolecular attraction; no hydrogen bonding is possible in Cl_2O.

b) CBr_4 since it contains more electrons and thus the London forces will be stronger.

c) Toluene, for the same reason as in (b).

d) Methanol, for the same reason as in (a).
e) Acetic acid, for the same reason as in (a).

17. Of the list, molecular mass, covalent radius, electronegativity and covalent bond strength would <u>not</u> be expected to depend upon intermolecular forces since they are properties of individual molecules or atoms. The other entries – boiling point, density, solubility, and viscosity – are properties of the entire sample rather than of isolated molecules and thus will depend on intermolecular forces.

18. a) HCl is soluble in H_2O (since HCl is polar and can form ions) but insoluble in pentane (since it is nonpolar).

    b) H_2O is soluble in HF (since they can form hydrogen bonding with each other) but insoluble in gasoline (since no hydrogen bonds between H_2O and gasoline are possible), and the bond types differ (see answer to Q. 15).

    c) $CHCl_3$ is insoluble in water (since no hydrogen bonds can be formed by $CHCl_3$) but soluble in CCl_4 since the bond types are similar.

    d) Naphthalene is insoluble in water since it cannot form hydrogen bonds, but soluble in benzene since the bond types are identical.

    e) N_2 is insoluble in water since it can form neither ions nor hydrogen bonds and contains ony a nonpolar bond; HCN is soluble since it contains a polar bond and can donate a proton to H_2O to form ions.

    f) Benzene is insoluble in water (since it cannot form hydrogen bonds and its bonds are quite nonpolar) but soluble in toluene since the bond types are identical.

19. a) Ar: Induced dipole-induced dipole (London).

    b) Cl_2: Induced dipole-induced dipole (London).

    c) LiF: Electrostatic attraction of Li^+ for F^- ions.

    d) $AlCl_3 \cdot 6H_2O$: This system is really $Al(H_2O)_6^{3+}$ and Cl^- ions which are held together by electrostatic attraction; within the cation the H_2O molecules are covalently bonded to the Al^{3+} ion.

    e) CH_3OH: The most important will be hydrogen bonds between the H(-O) atom of one molecule and the oxygen of another.

    f) H_2SO_4: Dipole-dipole attractions of S-O bonds and also hydrogen bonds (between H of one molecule and O of an adjacent one).

g) HCl: Dipole-dipole attractions.

h) C_2F_6: London forces.

20. The trend is to lower boiling pont with a lesser number of O-H groups, as they are replaced by F atoms; thus the intermolecular attraction falls as OH is replaced by F. Although both S-O and S-F bonds are polar, only OH groups can engage in hydrogen bonds between molecules; this decrease in ability to engage in hydrogen bonding causes the boiling point trend.

21. a) Ice is less dense than is water at 0°-4°C; thus any solid water is found at the top and floats on the more dense liquid layer.

b) n-Octane molecules are long and thin, and therefore can approach each other more closely and consequently experience greater London forces of attraction than can the more spherical, branched octane molecules.

c) NH_3 molecules attract each other via hydrogen bonding, whereas H_2 molecules are attracted only by much weaker London forces; thus NH_3 should show a greater deviation from ideal gas behavior than H_2, with respect both to deviations caused by intermolecular attraction, and also to size since NH_3 is larger than H_2.

22. a)
    CO_2: London forces.
    H_2O: Hydrogen bonding.
    HF: Hydrogen bonding.
    I_2: London forces (induced dipole-induced dipole).
    ICl: Dipole-dipole or London forces.
    He: London forces.

b)
    C_6H_6: London forces
    C_2H_5OH: Hydrogen bonding between different molecules
    C_2H_6: London forces
    CaO: Ionic attraction between oppositely-charged ions, Ca^{2+} and O^{2-}.
    Cl_2: London forces.
    HCl: Dipole-dipole attractions, and London forces.

23. a) Ca since more electrons are involved in the metallic bonding, and each is attracted to 2^+ cores, thus giving stronger metallic bonding.

b) SiH_4 since it has more electrons, and therefore is more polarizable, than CH_4.

c) C_4H_{10} since it has more electrons than C_3H_8.

199

d) NH_3 since strong hydrogen bonds exist between the molecules, and this overrides the London force trend which favors the species with the greater number of electrons.

e) Cl_2 since it has more electrons than F_2.

f) SiO_2 since it is a network solid (i.e. one giant molecule) whereas SO_2 consists of molecules weakly attracted to each other (by London and dipole-dipole forces).

24. a) Of the six substances listed, only CO, H_2S and CH_2Cl_2 possess non-zero dipole moments (since the bond dipoles cancel in CCl_4 and CH_4); thus only for these three molecules will there be dipole-dipole interactions.

b) To display hydrogen bonding, a molecule must contain a hydrogen atom bonded to an electronegative atom, and there must be a lone pair available as well. Thus of the list of eight molecules, only CH_3OH, NH_3, H_2N-NH_2, and CH_3COOH have hydrogen-bonding.

25. a) H_2O_2 since it can form hydrogen bonds, whereas benzene cannot. Any hydrocarbon solvent would be better for benzene.

b) Ethanediol for the same reason as (a); any hydrocarbon.

c) Sugar for the same reason as (a); any hydrocarbon.

d) Magnesium chloride since it consists of ions which can be solvated whereas $CHCl_3$ cannot form hydrogen bonds or ions; a chloro-substituted hydrocarbon would be better.

e) HI since it forms H_3O^+ and I^-; any nonpolar liquid solvent such as CCl_4 would be better for I_2.

f) LiCl since it consists of ions; any hydrocarbon or halocarbon liquid would be better for CCl_4.

g) CH_3OH as in (c); any hydrocarbon for ethane.

26. Unless indicated otherwise, all reactions proceed at 25°C.

a) $CaC_2 + 2H_2O \longrightarrow Ca(OH)_2 + C_2H_2$.
Acid-base since H^+ is transferred from H_2O to C_2^{2-} ion.

b) $SO_2 + H_2O \longrightarrow$ "H_2SO_3" ($+ H_2O \rightleftharpoons H_3O^+ + HSO_3^-$).

The first reaction is a Lewis acid-base reaction, and the second is a Bronsted-Lowry acid-base reaction since H^+ is transferred

198

c) $SO_3 + H_2O \longrightarrow H_2SO_4 + H_2O \longrightarrow H_3O^+ + HSO_4^-$.
The first reaction is a Lewis acid-base process;
the second is a Bronsted-Lowry acid-base process
since H^+ is transferred.

d) $Mg_3N_2 + 6H_2O \longrightarrow 3Mg(OH)_2 + 2NH_3$.
Acid-base since H^+ is transferred from H_2O to N^{3-}.

e) At high temperatures only, CO reacts with water in the
form of steam:
   $CO + H_2O \longrightarrow CO_2 + H_2$.
This is an oxidation-reduction reaction.

f) $NaNH_2 + H_2O \longrightarrow NaOH + NH_3$.
Acid-base since H^+ is transferred from H_2O to NH_2^-.

g) $P_4 + H_2O \longrightarrow$ N.R.

h) $PCl_3 + 3H_2O \longrightarrow H_3PO_3 + 3HCl$.
Lewis acid base, since H_2O adds to PCl_3 first, then HCl
splits off.

i) $PCl_5 + 5H_2O \longrightarrow H_3PO_4 + 5HCl$.
Lewis acid-base, as for (h).

j) $COCl_2 + H_2O \longrightarrow 2HCl + CO_2$.
Lewis acid-base, as for (h).

k) $Ca + 2H_2O \longrightarrow Ca(OH)_2 + H_2$.
Oxidation-reduction, since Ca is oxidized (to Ca^{2+}),
and since hydrogen is produced by reduction of water.

l) $Na_2O + H_2O \longrightarrow 2NaOH$.
Acid-base since H^+ is transferred from H_2O to O^{2-}.

m) $2F_2 + 2H_2O \longrightarrow 4HF + O_2$.
Oxidation-reduction, since F is reduced and H_2O is
oxidized to O_2.

n) $Br_2 + H_2O \rightleftharpoons HBr + HOBr$
Oxidation-reduction, as in part (m).

27. If H_2O is to behave as a Lewis base, it must donate an
electron pair to another molecule and thereby form a bond
with it; in general

$$H_2\overset{..}{O}: + X \longrightarrow \underset{H}{\overset{H}{\diagdown}}\overset{+}{\underset{..}{O}}\!\!-\!\!\overset{-}{X}$$

Examples in the text include $X=SO_3$, CO_2, and P_4O_{10}:
   $H_2O + SO_3 \longrightarrow H_2SO_4$
   $H_2O + CO_2 \rightleftharpoons H_2CO_3$

199

$$6H_2O + P_4O_{10} \longrightarrow 4H_3PO_4$$

28. If H_2O is to behave as a Bronsted-Lowry acid, it must donate H^+ to another species X, thus forming XH^+ and OH^-. Examples include molecules X which are weak bases, e.g. $X=NH_3$ or H_2O:

$$H_2O + NH_3 \rightleftharpoons OH^- + NH_4^+$$
$$H_2O + H_2O \rightleftharpoons OH^- + H_3O^+$$

29. When H_2O behaves as an oxidizing agent, it accepts electrons from another molecule or ion; in the process H_2 is released since the oxidation number of H changes from +1 to 0 (oxygen cannot be further reduced since it already is in the -2 state). Thus the unbalanced reaction is
$$H_2O \longrightarrow H_2.$$
After balancing, this reaction is (in alkaline solution)
$$2e^- + 2H_2O \longrightarrow 2OH^- + H_2.$$
   When H_2O behaves as a reducing agent, it supplies electrons to another molecule or ion; in the process O_2 is released since O changes in oxidation number from -1 to 0. The unbalanced reaction is
$$H_2O \longrightarrow O_2$$
which upon balancing for acid solution is
$$2H_2O \longrightarrow 4H^+ + O_2 + 4e^-.$$

30. A Bronsted-Lowry base accepts H^+; thus H_2O becomes H_3O^+ when it acts as a base. Examples are
$$H_2O + HCl \longrightarrow H_3O^+ + Cl^-$$
$$H_2O + HNO_3 \longrightarrow H_3O^+ + NO_3^-.$$

31. Water is described as amphoteric because it can behave as an acid or as a base depending upon whether a base or an acid is dissolved in it.

32. Since pure water at 1.00 atm boils at 100.0°C, the elevation ΔT in the boiling point is $\Delta T = 101.0° - 100.0° = 1.0°C$. The molality of the solution is then obtained from
$$\Delta T = K_b m$$
$$m = \Delta T/K_b = 1.0°C/0.52°C \text{ kg mol}^{-1}$$
$$= 1.92 \text{ mol/kg}.$$
The actual mass of solution is 250 g (assuming the density of water to be exactly 1 g/mL); thus the amount of sugar is
$$\frac{1.92 \text{ mol sugar}}{1 \text{ kg water}} \times 0.250 \text{ kg water} \times \frac{342.34 \text{ g sugar}}{1 \text{ mole sugar}} = 164 \text{ g sugar}$$

33. $\Delta T_b = 78.89 - 78.41 = 0.48$
$$\Delta T_b = K_b m$$
so $m = \Delta T_b/K_b = 0.48/1.19 = 0.40$ molal.
In 100.0 g of ethanol there would therefore be 0.040 moles of solute, and thus its molar mass $= 5.00$ g/0.040 moles $= 125$ g/mole. From the formula, the molar mass of camphor is 152.26 and that of naphthalene is 128.18, so the mothballs were naphthalene.

200

34. In all cases, one can compute the lowering of the freezing point, relative to that of 0°C for pure water, by the equation

$$\Delta T = K_f m$$

where from Table 13.10, $K_f = 1.86°C$ kg mol^{-1}.

a) Here the solute, sugar, is not ionic, so m = 0.10 and
$$\Delta T = 1.86 \times 0.10 = 0.19°C$$
Thus the freezing point is - 0.19°C.

b) Since 1 mole of NaCl gives 2 moles of ions, i = 2.
Thus the freezing point is - 0.37°C, not - 0.19°C, since
$$\Delta T = iK_f m = 2 \times 1.86 \times 0.1.$$

c) Similar to (b); since $CaCl_2 \longrightarrow Ca^{2+} + 2Cl^-$, here i = 3 so the freezing point is -0.56°C.

35. From the information given one can deduce the molality of the solution since from Table 13.10, $K_f = 5.10°C$ kg mol^{-1} for this substance:
$$m = \Delta T/K_f = 0.099°C/5.10°C \text{ kg mol}^{-1}$$
$$= 0.019 \text{ mol kg}^{-1}.$$

Now from the actual mass of solvent, we deduce moles of solute:

$$\frac{0.019 \text{ mol solute}}{1 \text{ kg solvent}} \times 0.100 \text{ kg solvent} = 0.0019 \text{ mol solute.}$$

Since the mass of this amount of solute is 1.00 g, thus its
molar mass = 1.00 g/0.0019 mol
= 530 g mol^{-1}.

Now the empirical formula mass for $AlBr_3$ is 266.68 g mol^{-1}, the molar mass is 530/266.68 = 2.0 times the empirical; thus the molecular formula is Al_2Br_6. The Lewis formula involves two bridging Br atoms:

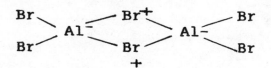

36. If the molality of NaCl is 5.8, then i = 2 since NaCl $\longrightarrow$ $Na^+ + Cl^-$.
Thus $\Delta T = iK_f m$
$$= 2 \times 1.86 \times 5.8 = 21.6.$$
Thus NaCl could lower the freezing point of water to -21.6°C.

37. Osmotic pressure Π is 7.2 mm Hg, i.e. $7.2/760 = 9.5 \times 10^{-3}$ atm. If we consider a sample of volume V = 1.000 L, hence of mass = 1000 g, then the moles of solute can be computed from

$$\Pi V = nRT$$

$$n = \Pi V/RT = 9.5 \times 10^{-3} \text{ atm} \times 1.000 \text{ L}/0.0821 \text{ L atm K}^{-1}$$
$$\text{mol}^{-1} \times 298 \text{ K}$$

$$= 3.9 \times 10^{-4} \text{ mol.}$$

The mass of solute is 1% of 1000 g, i.e. 10 g, and thus the molar mass is

$$\frac{10 \text{ g}}{3.9 \times 10^{-4} \text{ mol}} = 26,000 \text{ g mol}^{-1}.$$

Now the empirical formula mass is 342.34, and thus the ratio of molar mass to empirical formula mass is 26,000/342.34 = 76. Thus there are about 76 monomer units in each polymer molecule.

38. Methodology is similar to Q. 37.

$$n = \Pi V/RT = 0.427 \text{ atm} \times 0.050 \text{ L}/0.0821 \text{ L atm mol}^{-1} \text{ K}^{-1} \times$$
$$298 \text{ K}$$

$$= 8.7 \times 10^{-4} \text{ mol.}$$

Molar mass = 5.00 g/8.7 $\times 10^{-4}$ mol = 5700 g mol^{-1}.

CHAPTER 14

1. In each case, K is equal to the concentration (or pressure) of the products, each raised to its coefficient in the equation as given, divided by those for the reactants:

    a) $K_C = [NO_2]^4[O_2]/[N_2O_5]^2$
        $K_p = P_{NO_2}^4 P_{O_2}/P_{N_2O_5}^2$

    b) $K_C = [SO_3]^2/[SO_2]^2[O_2]$

        $K_p = P_{SO_3}^2/P_{SO_2}^2 P_{O_2}$

    c) $K_C = [SO_3]/[SO_2][O_2]^{\frac{1}{2}}$

        $K_p = P_{SO_3}/P_{SO_2} P_{O_2}^{\frac{1}{2}}$

    d) $K_C = [P_4O_{10}]/[P_4][O_2]^5$

        $K_p = P_{P_4O_{10}}/P_{P_4} P_{O_2}^5$

2. a) As for Q. 1, from the equation
    $K_C = [NO]^2/[N_2][O_2] = 2.5 \times 10^{-3}$

    b) Since the concentrations cancel in the K_C expression, there are no units to K_C here.

3. a) Since the reaction as rewritten is the reverse of that stated originally, then its K_C is the inverse of that for the original (see text):
    $K = 1/0.212$ mol $L^{-1} = 4.72$ mol^{-1} L

    b) Since the reaction here is rewritten as one-half of that in part a, its K_C is the square root of that given above:
    $K = (4.72$ mol^{-1} L$)^{\frac{1}{2}} = 2.17$ mol$^{-\frac{1}{2}}$ L$^{\frac{1}{2}}$
    The factor of $\frac{1}{2}$ follows from the fact that the K_C expression here, $[NO_2]/[N_2O_4]^{\frac{1}{2}}$, is the square root of that for part a, which is $[NO_2]^2/[N_2O_4]$.

4. From the balanced equation,
    $K = [CH_3OH]/[H_2]^2[CO]$.
    Substituting the given values for the concentrations, we find that the value of the right-hand side is 100, i.e. not equal to the equilibrium constant K value of 300, and thus we deduce that the system is not at equilibrium.

203

5. For this reaction, from its balanced equation it follows that
$$K_c = [SO_3]^2/[SO_2]^2[O_2]$$
Substituting, $K_c = (0.100 \text{ M})^2/(0.010 \text{ M})^2(0.20 \text{ M}) = 500 \text{ M}^{-1}$

6. a) The reaction quotient has the same form as the K_c expression, but does not involve equilibrium concentrations:
$$Q = [NO_2]^2/[N_2O_4]$$
Thus, by substitution,
$$Q = (0.12 \text{ M})^2/(0.10 \text{ M})$$
$$= 0.14 \text{ M}$$

b) Since $Q < K_c$, the system is not at equilibrium.

c) To increase Q to K_c, $[NO_2]$ will have to increase (and $[N_2O_4]$ decrease).

d) Consider the current and equilibrium concentrations for this reaction:

	N_2O_4 $\rightleftharpoons$	$2NO_2$
	$[N_2O_4]$	$[NO_2]$
Current("initial")	0.10	0.12
Equilibrium	0.10-y	0.12+2y

Since $K_c = [NO_2]^2/[N_2O_4]$

thus

$$\frac{(0.12+2y)^2}{0.10-y} = 0.212$$

Upon multiplying both sides by (0.10-y) to eliminate the denominator, and expansion and rearrangement, we obtain an equation in the standard form for a quadratic:
$$4y^2 + 0.692y - 0.0068 = 0$$
The roots are −0.182 and +0.0093. Since the former yields a concentration for NO_2 which is negative, it is a chemically unacceptable solution. The second root yields
$$[NO_2] = 0.12 + 2y = 0.139$$
$$[N_2O_4] = 0.10 - y = 0.091$$

e) Since $K_c = [NO_2]^2/[N_2O_4]$
and $PV = nRT$,
thus $[NO_2] = n/V = p_{NO_2}/RT$

and similarly for $[N_2O_4]$. By substitution,

$$K_c = \frac{p_{NO_2}^2/(RT)^2}{p_{N_2O_4}/RT} = \frac{p_{NO_2}^2/p_{N_2O_4}}{RT}$$

but $K_p = p_{NO_2}^2/p_{N_2O_4}$

and therefore
$$K_p = RTK_c$$

$$= 0.0821 \text{ L atm mol}^{-1} \text{ K}^{-1} \times 373 \text{ K} \times 0.212 \text{ mol L}^{-1}$$
$$= 6.49 \text{ atm}$$

7. In each case, the concentration (or pressure) of the solid does not enter K_c (or K_p). Thus we obtain:

a) $K_c = [CO_2]/[O_2]$ and $K_p = P_{CO_2}/P_{O_2}$

b) $K_c = [CO_2]$ and $K_p = P_{CO_2}$

c) $K_c = [CO_2][H_2O]$ and $K_p = P_{CO_2}P_{H_2O}$

d) $K_c = [CO_2]/[CO]$ and $K_p = P_{CO_2}/P_{CO}$

e) $K_c = [H_2]^4/[H_2O]^4$ and $K_p = P_{H_2}^4/P_{H_2O}^4$

8. If K increases with temperature the equilibrium must shift to the right side. Thus "heat" must be present on the left side of the equation:

$$\text{Reactants} + \text{heat} \rightleftharpoons \text{Products}$$

Thus the reaction absorbs heat, and is endothermic.

9. The balanced equation is

$$PCl_5(g) \rightleftharpoons PCl_3(g) + Cl_2(g)$$

a) Compressing the volume favors the side with the smallest number of moles of gaseous material; thus the equilibrium here shifts to the left.

b) This is the opposite to (a), and thus the equilibrium shifts to the right.

c) Since the reaction is endothermic,

$$PCl_5 + \text{heat} \rightleftharpoons PCl_3 + Cl_2$$

thus reducing the temperature shifts the equilibrium to the left.

d) Adding Cl_2 temporarily increases the concentration of the products (right side), so the reaction will shift to the left side to achieve a new equilibrium.

10. a) From Appendix B, ΔH_f° values for NOCl(g), NO(g) and Cl_2(g) are + 51.7, 90.3, and 0.0 kJ mol^{-1} respectively. Thus upon substitution into

$$\Delta H^\circ = 2\Delta H_f^\circ(\text{NOCl,g}) - 2\Delta H_f^\circ(\text{NO,g}) = \Delta H_f^\circ(\text{Cl}_2,\text{g}) \text{ we}$$

obtain

$\Delta H^\circ = -77.2$ kJ mol^{-1}. Since the reaction is exothermic, increasing the temperature shifts the equilibrium to the left, decreasing the amount of product. Since the number of moles of gas decreases from 3 to 2 in going from reactants to products, increasing the pressure will favor the products. Thus to maximize the yield of

NOCl, the temperature should be kept low but the pressure maximized.

b) $\Delta H° = 2\Delta H_f°(SO_3,g) - 2\Delta H_f°(SO_2,g) - \Delta H_f°(O_2,g)$
$= 2 \times (-395.7) - 2 \times (-296.8) - (0.0)$
$= -197.8 \text{ kJ}$

Since the reaction is exothermic, increasing the temperature shifts the equilibrium to the left side. Since the number of moles of gas decreases, increasing the pressure favors the right side. Thus to maximize the yield of products, a high pressure but low temperature should be used.

c) $\Delta H° = 2\Delta H_f°(NH_3,g) - \Delta H_f°(N_2,g) - 3\Delta H_f°(H_2,g)$
$= -92.4$

The answers here are identical to those for (b), since the reaction is exothermic and the number of moles of gas decreases.

d) $\Delta H° = \Delta H_f°(CO_2,g) + \Delta H_f°(H_2,g) - \Delta H_f°(CO,g) - \Delta H_f°(H_2O,g)$
$= -41.2$

The reaction is exothermic, so the equilibrium shifts to the left at higher temperatures. There is no change in the number of moles of gas, so pressure has no significant effect. Thus the reaction should be carried out at as low a temperature as is consistent with a useful rate.

11. a) Since the number of gaseous molecules is smaller for the products than for the reactants, increasing the size of the container favors the side of greater volume and the equilibrium shifts to the left. Since this decreases the number of moles of SO_3, and the volume increases, its concentration decreases.

b) Since the reaction is exothermic, we have

$$2SO_2 + O_2 \rightleftharpoons 2SO_3 + \text{heat}$$

Thus increasing the temperature shifts the equilibrium to the left, and decreases $[SO_3]$.

c) Adding more O_2 temporarily increases the concentration of reactant, and thus the equilibrium shifts to the right to compensate, thereby increasing $[SO_3]$.

d) Adding an inert gas has no effect on the concentration of any substance in the reaction including $[SO_3]$.

12. All the acids and bases listed are strong electrolytes: thus the acids react with H_2O completely and the bases dissociate completely:
a) $HNO_3 + H_2O \longrightarrow NO_3^- + H_3O^+$
Thus $[NO_3^-] = [H_3O^+] = 10^{-5} \text{ M}$

b) $HCl + H_2O \longrightarrow Cl^- + H_3O^+$
Thus $[Cl^-] = [H_3O^+] = 0.0023 \text{ M}$

206

c) $HClO_4$ + H_2O $\longrightarrow$ ClO_4^- + H_3O^+
       Thus $[ClO_4^-]$ = $[H_3O^+]$ = 0.113 M

d) HBr + H_2O $\longrightarrow$ Br^- + H_3O^+
       Thus $[Br^-]$ = $[H_3O^+]$ = 0.034 M

e) $NaOH$ $\longrightarrow$ Na^+ + OH^-
       Thus $[Na^+]$ = $[OH^-]$ = 10^{-3} M

f) $Ba(OH)_2$ $\longrightarrow$ Ba^{2+} + $2OH^-$
       Thus $[Ba^{2+}]$ = 0.145 M, $[OH^-]$ = 0.290 M

13. Hydrocyanic acid, HCN, is a weak acid and thus it
    establishes an equilibrium. Let y be the concentration of
    it which dissociates (ionizes):

	HCN + H_2O $\rightleftharpoons$	CN^- +	H_3O^+
Initial	0.010 M	0	0
Equilibrium	0.010-y	y	y

By definition,

$$\frac{[CN^-][H_3O^+]}{[HCN^-]} = K_a$$

By substitution,

$$\frac{y^2}{0.010-y} = 4.9 \times 10^{-10}$$

Using the approximation 0.010 >> y and thus 0.010-y $\approx$ 0.010,

$$\frac{y^2}{0.010} = 4.9 \times 10^{-10}$$

   i.e. y^2 = 4.9×10^{-12}
Taking the square root of both sides, we find
        y = 2.2×10^{-6}
Thus $[CN^-]$ = $[H_3O^+]$ = 2.2×10^{-6} M. The extent of
dissociation, on a percentage basis, is

$$\frac{y}{0.010} \times 100\% = \frac{2.2 \times 10^{-6} \times 100\%}{0.01} = 0.022\%$$

14. Let us abbreviate lactic acid as HA. The reaction is (see
    Q. 13)

	HA + H_2O $\rightleftharpoons$	A^- +	H_3O^+
Initial	1.0×10^{-3}	0	0
Equilibrium	1.0×10^{-3}-y	y	y

$$\frac{y^2}{1.0 \times 10^{-3} - y} = 8.4 \times 10^{-4}$$

If we try the approximation here, i.e. assume 1×10^{-3} >> y,
we find
        y = 9.2×10^{-4}
which is 92% of the original acid. Thus the approximation
is invalid, and we must rearrange the original equation to a
quadratic and solve it:
        y^2 + $8.4 \times 10^{-4}y$ - 8.4×10^{-7} = 0

Thus $y = 5.88 \times 10^{-4}$ or -1.43×10^{-3}; clearly the latter solution is chemically unacceptable since concentrations cannot be negative. Thus

$$[H_3O^+] = y = 5.88 \times 10^{-4}$$
$$pH = -\log_{10}[H_3O^+]$$

$$= -\log_{10}(5.88 \times 10^{-4})$$
$$= 3.23$$

15. The reaction of ammonia, NH_3, with water is that of a weak base; thus OH^- is produced.

$$NH_3 + H_2O \rightleftharpoons NH_4^+ + OH^-$$

	NH_3	NH_4^+	OH^-
Initial	0.010	0	0
Equilibrium	0.010-y	y	y

For this reaction,

$$\frac{[NH_4^+][OH^-]}{[NH_3]} = K_b$$

Thus

$$\frac{y^2}{0.010-y} = 1.8 \times 10^{-5}$$

Approximating $0.010 \gg y$, we find
$$y = 4.2 \times 10^{-4}$$
and the approximation is valid, since this corresponds to a dissociation of

$$\frac{y}{0.010} \times 100\% = \frac{4.2 \times 10^{-4} \times 100\%}{0.010} = 4.2\%$$

From the definition here of y, it follows that
$$[OH^-] = 4.2 \times 10^{-4} \text{ M}$$

16. For solutions a-d of Q. 12, the pH can be obtained from the calculated $[H_3O^+]$; e.g.
a) Since $[H_3O^+] = 10^{-5}$ M
and $\qquad pH = -\log_{10}[H_3O^+]$
thus $\qquad pH = -\log_{10}(10^{-5}) = -(-5) = +5$
b) pH = 2.64
c) pH = 0.95
d) pH = 1.47

17. The method is identical to Q. 15, except that we first deduce K_b from pK_b

$$K_b = 10^{-pK_b} = 10^{-9.4} = 4.0 \times 10^{-10}$$

$$\frac{y^2}{0.10 - y} = 4.0 \times 10^{-10}$$

Using the approximation, we find $y = 6.3 \times 10^{-6}$
Thus $[OH^-] = 6.3 \times 10^{-6}$M, and the extent of dissociation is $(6.3 \times 10^{-6} \times 100\%/0.10) = 6.3 \times 10^{-3}\%$.

208

18. For basic solutions, we can obtain pOH from the calculated [OH$^-$], and then find the pH from the condition that
$$pH + pOH = 14 \text{ where } pH=-\log[OH^-] \text{ (see Study Guide)}$$
For e, [OH$^-$] = 10^{-3} so pOH = 3, and pH = 11
For f, [OH$^-$] = 0.290 so pOH = 0.54, and pH = 13.46.

19. In each case, a strong acid and a strong base are mixed, and react with each other. First we calculate the effect to the concentrations simply of mixing the two solutions, and then calculate the changes to these concentrations which result from the acid-base reaction. Finally, the reaction of the excess acid or base with water is considered.

a) Simply mixing two solutions has no effect upon the number of moles of a reactant; thus
$$\text{Moles after mixing} = \text{Moles before mixing}$$
but
$$\text{Moles} = \text{Molarity x Volume}$$
Thus
$$M_{after}V_{after} = M_{original}V_{original}$$
and thus
$$M_{after} = M_{original} (V_{original}/V_{after})$$
Here for the KOH, we have
$$M_{after} = 0.10 \text{ M } (25.0 \text{ mL}/75.0 \text{ mL})$$
$$= 0.033 \text{ M}$$
and for HNO$_3$
$$M_{after} = 0.080 \text{ M } (50.0 \text{ mL}/75.0 \text{ mL})$$
$$= 0.053 \text{ M}$$
Now consider the reaction of acid with base:

	HNO$_3$ +	KOH	$\longrightarrow$	KNO$_3$(aq) +	H$_2$O
Before rxn.	0.053	0.033		0	
After rxn.	0.020	0		0.033	

The excess nitric acid reacts with water:

	HNO$_3$ +	H$_2$O	$\longrightarrow$	NO$_3^-$ +	H$_3$O$^+$
Before rxn.	0.020			0	0
After rxn.	0			0.020	0.020

Thus [H$_3$O$^+$] = 0.020 M, and pH = 1.70.
(Alternatively, such problems can be done by calculating moles of each reactant rather than after-mixing concentrations, and only returning to molarity at the end of the problem.)

b) Similarly, after mixing but before reaction
$$[HCl] = 0.0542 \text{ M}$$
$$[NaOH] = 0.0700 \text{ M}$$

HCl +	NaOH	$\longrightarrow$	NaCl(aq) +	H$_2$O
0.0542	0.0700		0	
0	0.0158		0.0542	

$$NaOH \longrightarrow Na^+ + OH^-$$
So final [OH$^-$] = 0.0158 M
and pOH = 1.80 so pH = 14-1.80 = 12.20

c) Similarly, after mixing but before reaction
$[HNO_3]$ = 0.0167 M
$[NaOH]$ = 0.0167 M

$$HNO_3 + NaOH \longrightarrow NaNO_3(aq) + H_2O$$
$$0.0167 \quad 0.0167 \qquad\qquad 0$$
$$0 \qquad\quad 0 \qquad\qquad\quad 0.0167$$

Since no acid or base remains, the pH is determined solely by the self-ionization of water; hence pH = 7.00.

20. Since $K_a = 10^{-pK_a}$, the K_a values for the three acids are 1.6×10^{-5}, 1.3×10^{-3}, 5.0×10^{-2}, and 2.0×10^{-1} respectively. Since acid strength increases as K_a increases, this is the order of increasing acid strength. Each acid can for convenience be represented by HA and its reaction with water as

	HA + H₂O ⇌	A⁻	+ H₃O⁺

$$HA + H_2O \rightleftharpoons A^- + H_3O^+$$

Initial   0.10   0   0
Equilibrium   0.10-y   y   y

Thus $\dfrac{y^2}{0.10-y}$ = K_a in each case. Rearranging to

quadratic form, we obtain
$$y^2 + K_a y - 0.1K_a = 0$$
For $K_a = 1.6 \times 10^{-5}$, $y = 1.26 \times 10^{-3}$ = $[H_3O^+$ so pH = 2.90.
      = 1.3×10^{-3}, $y = 1.08 \times 10^{-2}$ = $[H_3O^+]$ so pH = 1.97.
      = 5.0×10^{-2}, $y = 0.050$ = $[H_3O^+]$ so pH = 1.30.
      = 2.0×10^{-1}, $y = 7.3 \times 10^{-2}$ = $[H_3O^+]$ so pH = 1.14.
In the first case only we could have used the solution from the approximation method.

21. Since pH = 4.2, thus we know $[H_3O^+] = 10^{-4.2} = 6.3 \times 10^{-5}$. We also know that the original concentration of HClO was 0.10 M. Let us write the reaction and incorporate this information:

$$HClO + H_2O \rightleftharpoons ClO^- + H_3O^+$$

Initial   0.10   0   0
Equilibrium   0.10-y   y   y

but $y = [H_3O^+] = 6.3 \times 10^{-5} = [ClO^-]$ from the stoichiometry.
Thus $[HClO] = 0.10 - 6.3 \times 10^{-5} \approx 0.10$
By definition $K_a = [ClO^-][H_3O^+]/[HClO]$
$$= (6.3 \times 10^{-5})^2/0.10$$
$$= 4.0 \times 10^{-8}$$

22. In water, KF exists as separated ions:
$$KF(s) \xrightarrow{H_2O} K^+ + F^-$$
Since F⁻ is the conjugate base of a weak acid (HF), it reacts with water to produce hydroxide ion:

$$F^- + H_2O \rightleftharpoons HF + OH^-$$

Initial   0.0050   0   0
Equilibrium   0.0050-y   y   y

Now $\dfrac{[HF][OH^-]}{[F^-]}$ = K_b for F^-

Since K_b for F^- is not listed in the table of K_b values, we obtain it from K_a of HF since

$$K_a(HF)K_b(F^-) = K_w$$

i.e. $K_b(F^-)$ = $10^{-14}/3.5 \times 10^{-4}$ = 2.9×10^{-11}

Thus we obtain

$$\dfrac{y^2}{0.0050-y} = 2.9 \times 10^{-11}$$

Using the approximations method, we obtain

$$y = 3.8 \times 10^{-7} = [OH^-]$$

Thus pOH = 6.42 and pH = 7.58

23. In water, NH_4Cl exists as separated ions:

$$NH_4Cl(s) \xrightarrow{\;H_2O\;} NH_4^+ + Cl^-$$

We recognize NH_4^+ as the conjugate of the weak base NH_3; thus NH_4^+ is a weak acid:

	NH_4^+	+ H_2O $\rightleftharpoons$	NH_3	+ H_3O^+
Initial	0.020		0	0
Equilibrium	0.020-y		y	y

$$\dfrac{[NH_3][H_3O^+]}{[NH_4^+]} = K_a \text{ for } NH_4^+$$

$$\dfrac{y^2}{0.020-y} = 5.6 \times 10^{-10}$$

Using the approximation method, we obtain

$$y = 3.3 \times 10^{-6}$$

Thus $[H_3O^+]$ = $[NH_3]$ = 3.3×10^{-6} M

$[NH_4^+]$ = $0.020 - 3.3 \times 10^{-6}$ $\approx$ 0.020 M

We can obtain $[OH^-]$ from the condition

$[OH^-][H_3O^+]$ = 10^{-14}

$[OH^-]$ = $10^{-14}/3.3 \times 10^{-6}$ = 3.0×10^{-9}

(We could have obtained $[OH^-]$ from pOH, which in turn would be obtained from the pH.)

24. a) Similar to Q. 13

	CH_3CO_2H	+ H_2O $\rightleftharpoons$	$CH_3CO_2^-$	+ H_3O^+
Initial	0.010		0	0
Equilibrium	0.010-y		y	y

$$\dfrac{y^2}{0.010-y} = 1.8 \times 10^{-5}$$

y = 4.2×10^{-4} = $[H_3O^+]$, so pH = 3.37

b) Similar to Q. 13 and part (a). We obtain

$[H_3O^+]$ = 5.9×10^{-3}, so pH = 2.23

c) Similar to Q. 15. We obtain
$$[OH^-] = 2.3 \times 10^{-4} \text{ so pOH} = 3.63 \text{ and pH} = 10.37$$
(Note that the percentage dissociation in both b and c slightly exceeds 5%, so in principle a slightly more accurate solution can be obtained by solving the appropriate quadratic equation.)

d) The equation for sodium acetate in water is
$$CH_3CO_2Na(s) \xrightarrow{H_2O} CH_3CO_2^- + Na^+$$
We recognize $CH_3CO_2^-$ as the conjugate base of the weak acid CH_3CO_2H, so it reacts with water as

$$
\begin{array}{ccccccc}
CH_3CO_2^- & + & H_2O & \rightleftharpoons & CH_3CO_2H & + & OH^- \\
0.10 & & & & 0 & & 0 \\
0.10-y & & & & y & & y
\end{array}
$$

$$\frac{y^2}{0.10-y} = K_b \text{ for acetate } = \frac{10^{-14}}{K_a \text{ for } CH_3CO_2H} = \frac{10^{-14}}{1.8 \times 10^{-5}}$$
$$= 5.6 \times 10^{-10}$$
Using the approximate method, $y = 7.5 \times 10^{-6} = [OH^-]$, so pOH = 5.13 and thus pH = 8.87.

e) Similar to Q. 23. We obtain
$$[H_3O^+] = 1.1 \times 10^{-5} , \text{ so pH} = 4.98.$$

25. a) Ammonium nitrate is NH_4NO_3, i.e. a combination of NH_4^+ and NO_3^- ions. Since NH_4^+ is the conjugate of NH_3 and NO_3^- that of HNO_3, the appropriate reaction is a proton transfer between them:
$$NH_3 + HNO_3 \longrightarrow NH_4^+ + NO_3^-$$
Of the two ions, only NH_4^+ is the conjugate of a <u>weak</u> substance, so only it will react with water. Since NH_4^+ is an acid, the solution will be acidic.

b) Similarly with part (a), the reaction is
$$NH_3 + HCl \longrightarrow NH_4^+ + Cl^-$$
and the solution is acidic.

c) Calcium sulfate is $CaSO_4$, i.e. a combination of Ca^{2+} and SO_4^{2-}. The calcium ion Ca^{2+} occurs in the base $Ca(OH)_2$ and SO_4^{2-} occurs in the acid H_2SO_4; thus the reaction is
$$Ca(OH)_2 + H_2SO_4 \longrightarrow 2H_2O + Ca^{2+} + SO_4^{2-}$$
Since it is almost insoluble in water, most of the $CaSO_4$ will precipitate, and the solution will have pH close to 7.
d) Acetate is the conjugate base of acetic acid. Thus potassium acetate can be prepared by reacting acetic acid with potassium hydroxide:
$$CH_3CO_2H + KOH \longrightarrow CH_3CO_2K + H_2O$$
A 0.1 M solution will be basic due to the reaction of the weak base $CH_3CO_2^-$ with water:
$$CH_3CO_2^- + H_2O \rightleftharpoons CH_3CO_2H + OH^-$$

212

e) Aluminum chloride can be prepared by adding aqueous HCl
to aluminum hydroxide:
$$Al(OH)_3 + 3HCl \longrightarrow AlCl_3 + 3H_2O$$
A 0.1 M solution will be acidic due to the acidic behaviour
of the hydrated aluminum cation:
$$Al(H_2O)_6^{3+} + H_2O \rightleftharpoons H_3O^+ + Al(OH)(H_2O)_5^{2+}$$
f) LiI can be made by combining LiOH and HI; both these
substances are strong so a 0.1 M aqueous solution is
neutral since neither Li^+ or I^- will react with water.
$$LiOH + HI \longrightarrow LiI + H_2O$$

26. In each case the compound is an ionic solid, so the initial
process is dissociation. Each anion subsequently reacts
with water to produce hydroxide ion, since each is a strong
base:
a)
$$Na_2O(s) \xrightarrow{\text{water}} 2Na^+ + O^{2-}$$
$$O^{2-} + H_2O \longrightarrow 2OH^-$$
Thus the overall reaction is
$$Na_2O + H_2O \longrightarrow 2Na^+ + 2OH^- \quad (i.e.\ 2NaOH)$$

b)
$$K_2S(s) \longrightarrow 2K^+ + S^{2-}$$
$$S^{2-} + H_2O \rightleftharpoons HS^- + OH^-$$
Since S^{2-} is a weak base, this only occurs to a slight
extent, so the best overall reaction is just the first
equation.

c)
$$NaNH_2(s) \longrightarrow Na^+ + NH_2^-$$
$$NH_2^- + H_2O \longrightarrow NH_3 + OH^- \text{ since } NH_2^- \text{ is a strong}$$
base. The overall reaction is
$$NaNH_2 + H_2O \longrightarrow NH_3 + Na^+ + OH^-$$

27. The acid-base reaction for the indicator is
$$HIn + H_2O \rightleftharpoons In^- + H_3O^+$$
so $K_{In} = [In^-][H_3O^+]/[HIn]$
Since pKa = 4.2, thus Ka = 6.3×10^{-5}, and by rearrangement
we can solve for $[H_3O^+]$ in terms of the HIn/In$^-$ ratio:
$$[H_3O^+] = 6.3 \times 10^{-5}[HIn]/[In^-]$$
a) Since In$^-$/HIn = 5:1, thus [HIn]/[In$^-$] = 1/5 and
$[H_3O^+] = 6.3 \times 10^{-5} \times 1/5 = 1.3 \times 10^{-5}$, pH = 4.9

b) Similarly, for 1:1, pH = 4.2

c) Similarly, for 1:5, pH = 3.5

28. According to Table 14.8, methyl red is yellow for pH > 5.0,
and bromothymol blue is yellow when pH < 7.1. Thus the pH
of the solution is 6 ± 1.

29. According to Table 14.8, phenolphthalein is colorless for
pH < 9.5, and bromothymol blue is blue for pH > 7.1. Thus
the pH of the solution is 8.3 ± 1.2.

30. The visible color change for an indicator occurs approximately over the range of pH = $pK_a(HIn) \pm 1$, according to the text. From the information given in the question, the pH range for thymol blue is only 1.5, not 2.0 pH units, but we expect its pK_a to be mid-way in this range. Thus $pK_a \approx 8.6$ for thymol blue.

31. First we write any dissociation reactions that are the result of dissolving an ionic solid in water. In this case, ammonium chloride, NH_4Cl, gives ammonium and chloride ion:

$$NH_4Cl(s) \xrightarrow{\text{water}} NH_4^+ + Cl^-$$

Thus in solution we have $[NH_3] = 0.30$ M and $[NH_4^+] = 0.25$ M. The reaction involving this conjugate pair is

	NH_3	+	H_2O	$\rightleftharpoons$	NH_4^+	+	OH^-
Initial	0.30				0.25		0
Equilibrium	0.30-y				0.25+y		y

Thus $\dfrac{(0.25+y)y}{0.30-y}$ = K_b for NH_3

Approximating $y \ll 0.25$ and 0.30, and rearranging, we have

$$y = \frac{0.30}{0.25} \times 1.8 \times 10^{-5} = 2.2 \times 10^{-5}$$

Thus $[OH^-] = 2.2 \times 10^{-5}$ M, pOH = 4.66, and pH = 9.34.

32. After mixing, $[HCN] = 0.05$ M $= [NaCN]$
The cyanide salt dissociates to give $[CN^-] = 0.05$ M:
$$NaCN \longrightarrow Na^+ + CN^-$$
The equilibrium of concern is

	HCN	+	H_2O	$\rightleftharpoons$	CN^-	+	H_3O^+
Initial	0.05				0.05		0
Equilibrium	0.05-y				0.05+y		y

Approximating that $0.05 \gg y$, then
$$0.05y/0.05 = 4.9 \times 10^{-10}$$
$$y = [H_3O^+] = 4.9 \times 10^{-10}, \text{ so pH} = 9.31.$$

33. Call m_b the mass of ammonia and m_a the mass of ammonium chloride which are required. All equilibrium calculations involve concentrations, so we first convert these masses to molarities, using V as the volume of solution:
$[NH_3]$ = (m_b/molar mass of NH_3)/V
       = (m_b/17.04)/V
       = 0.05869 m_b/V
$[NH_4Cl]$ = (m_a/53.50)/V = 0.01869 m_a/V
Thus $[NH_4^+]$ = 0.01869 m_a/V (see Q. 31)
The equilibrium is

$$NH_3 + H_2O \rightleftharpoons NH_4^+ + OH^-$$

Since the amount y of dissociation will be small, we can rearrange the K_b expression

214

$$\frac{[NH_4^+][OH^-]}{[NH_3]} = K_b$$

to the form

$$\frac{[NH_3]}{[NH_4^+]} = \frac{[OH^-]}{K_b}$$

Now since pH = 9.0, pOH = 5.0 and $[OH^-] = 1.0 \times 10^{-5}$.

By substitution,

$$\frac{0.05869 \ m_b/V}{0.01869 \ m_a/V} = \frac{1.0 \times 10^{-5}}{1.8 \times 10^{-5}}$$

$$\frac{m_b}{m_a} = 0.18$$

Thus the ratio of mass of ammonia to ammonium chloride is 0.18.

34. We first calculate the reactant concentrations which are the result of simply mixing the solutions:
   [NaOH] = 0.10 M x (25 mL/75 mL) = 0.033 M
   $[CH_3CO_2H]$ = 0.10 M x (50 mL/75 mL) = 0.067 M
   The NaOH exists as separated ions, so
   $[Na^+]$ = $[OH^-]$ = 0.033 M
   The OH^- reacts with the acetic acid, since they are respectively a base and an acid:

$$OH^- \ + \ CH_3CO_2H \ \longrightarrow \ H_2O \ + \ CH_3CO_2^-$$
   0.033   0.067   0
   0   0.034   0.033

   We now consider the equilibrium involving the weak acid and its conjugate base:

	CH_3CO_2H + H_2O $\rightleftharpoons$	$CH_3CO_2^-$ + H_3O^+
Initial	0.034	0.033 0
Equilibrium	0.034-y	0.033-y y

   As in Q. 32, we neglect y relative to 0.033 or 0.034, and obtain
        y = (0.034/0.033) x 1.8×10^{-5} = 1.8×10^{-5}
   so   pH = 4.74.

35. As a result simply of mixing, we have
   $[NH_3]$ = 0.010 M x (15 mL/40 mL) = 0.00375 M
   $[NH_4Cl]$ = 0.010 M x (25 mL/40 mL) = 0.00625 M = $[NH_4^+]$
   The rest of the problem is identical to Q. 31:
   $[OH^-]$ = (0.00375 M/0.00625 M) x 1.8×10^{-5}
             = 1.1×10^{-5}
   pOH = 4.96, so pH = 9.04.

36. The pH of the buffer solution before addition of NaOH can be calculated as in Q. 31 (though no mixing occurs):
   $[OH^-]$ = (0.18 M/0.10 M) x 1.8×10^{-5} = 3.24×10^{-5},
   so pOH = 4.49.
   When 1 mL of the NaOH solution is added, then due to mixing we have

$$[NaOH] = 1 \times (1.00 \text{ mL}/101 \text{ mL}) = 0.0099 \text{ M}$$
$$[NH_3] = 0.18 (100 \text{ mL}/101 \text{ mL}) = 0.18 \text{ M}$$
$$[NH_4Cl] = 0.10 (100 \text{ mL}/101 \text{ mL}) = 0.10 \text{ M}$$

The reaction is
$$OH^- + NH_4^+ \longrightarrow NH_3 + H_2O$$

Before	0.0099	0.10	0.18
After	0	0.09	0.19

Thus $[OH^-] = (0.19 \text{ M}/0.09 \text{ M}) \times 1.8 \times 10^{-5} = 3.8 \times 10^{-5}$
so pOH $= 4.42$ and $\Delta pOH = -0.07$, so $\Delta pH = +0.07$.

37.   The Henderson-Hassalbalch equation is

$$pH = pKa + \log [base]/[acid]$$

For acetic acid, pKa $= 4.7$ (from Table 14.3) so for pH $= 4.50$,
$$\log [base]/[acid] = 4.50 - 4.7 = -0.2$$
Raising each side to the power of 10 (i.e. taking the antilog),
$$[base]/[acid] = 0.63$$
Thus the ratio of acetate to acid is 0.63, so the ratio of moles of acetic acid to moles of acetate that must be added to the same volume of water is 1.6.

38.   We first deduce molar concentrations for the salts:
$$[KH_2PO_4] = (3.40/136.09)/1.00 = 0.0250 \text{ M}$$
$$[NaH_2PO_4] = (3.55/141.96)/1.00 = 0.0250 \text{ M}$$
pH = pKa + log [base]/[acid] = 7.21 + log 1 = 7.21

39.   a) Here we have 0.010 M HOCl with no base added. The only reaction is

$$HOCl + H_2O \rightleftharpoons OCl^- + H_3O^+$$

0.010	0	0
0.010-y	y	y

Hence $\dfrac{y^2}{0.010-y} = 3.1 \times 10^{-8}$

Using the approximation, we find $y = [H_3O^+] = 1.8 \times 10^{-5}$, so pH = 4.75.

b) Here and in the remaining parts to this question, some KOH has been added. In all cases it ionizes to K^+ and OH^-. We first calculate the effect of mixing the solutions, then of the reaction of the acid HOCl with the base OH^-, and finally consider the equilibrium involving HOCl and/or OCl^-.

216

$$[HOCl] = 0.010 \text{ M} \times (10.0 \text{ mL}/11.0 \text{ mL}) = 0.0091 \text{ M}$$
$$[OH^-] = 0.010 \text{ M} \times (1.0 \text{ mL}/11.0 \text{ mL}) = 0.0009 \text{ M}$$

	HOCl	+ OH$^-$	$\longrightarrow$	OCl$^-$	+ H$_2$O
Initial	0.0091	0.0009		0	
Final	0.0082	0		0.0009	

Since both HOCl and OCl$^-$ are present, we could consider the reaction of either with H$_2$O in calculating the pH:

	HOCl	+ H$_2$O	$\rightleftharpoons$	OCl$^-$	+ H$_3$O$^+$
Initial	0.0082			0.0009	0
Equilibrium	0.0082-y			0.0009+y	y

Using the approximation, then $0.009y/0.0082 = 3.1 \times 10^{-8}$. Thus $y = [H_3O^+] = 2.8 \times 10^{-7}$, and pH = 6.55.

c) Similarly with (b), we find pH = 7.51

d) Similarly with (b), we find pH = 9.50

e) After mixing, here [HOCl] = [OH$^-$] = 0.0050 M, so all the acid and base is converted to OCl$^-$:

	HOCl	+ OH$^-$	$\longrightarrow$	OCl$^-$	+ H$_2$O
Before	0.0050	0.0050		0	
After	0	0		0.0050	

The pH is determined by the reaction of OCl$^-$ with water:

	OCl$^-$	+ H$_2$O	$\rightleftharpoons$	HOCl	+ OH$^-$
Initial	0.0050			0	0
Equilibrium	0.0050-y			y	y

$$\frac{y^2}{0.0050-y} = K_b(OCl^-) = \frac{10^{-14}}{K_a(HOCl)} = 3.2 \times 10^{-7}$$

Thus $y = 4.0 \times 10^{-5} = [OH^-]$ here, so pOH = 4.40 and pH = 9.60.

f) Here and in part g, [OH$^-$] > [HOCl] so some is left over and determines the pH (since any extra produced via OCl$^-$ reacting with H$_2$O will be negligible):

$$[HOCl] = 0.010 \text{ M} \times (10.0 \text{ mL}/20.1 \text{ mL}) = 0.004975 \text{ M}$$
$$[OH^-] = 0.010 \text{ M} \times (10.1 \text{ mL}/20.1 \text{ mL}) = 0.005025 \text{ M}$$

	HOCl	+ OH$^-$	$\longrightarrow$	OCl$^-$	+ H$_2$O
	0.004975	0.005025		0	
	0	0.000050		0.00498	

Since excess [OH$^-$] = 0.000050 M, pOH = 4.30 and pH = 9.70. (Use of less significant figures than we here employed can lead here to erroneous results, as excess OH$^-$ is the difference between two comparable numbers.)

g) Similarly to (f), we find pH = 10.68.

40. The methodology is similar to that for Q. 39, but here the base rather than the acid is weak, and the acid is strong. The reaction is

$$HCl + NH_3 \longrightarrow Cl^- + NH_4^+$$

a) We have $[NH_3] = 0.010$ M. We obtain $y^2/(0.010-y) = 1.8 \times 10^{-5}$, so $y = 4.2 \times 10^{-4} = [OH^-]$, so pOH = 3.37 and pH = 10.63.

b) Some of the NH_3 reacts to form NH_4^+. The pOH and pH are determined by the $NH_3 + H_2O \rightleftharpoons NH_4^+ + OH^-$ reaction. As for 39(b), we obtain $0.0009y/0.0082 = 1.8 \times 10^{-5}$, so $y = 1.6 \times 10^{-4}$. Thus pOH = 3.79 and pH = 10.21.

c) Similarly with part b, we find pH = 9.26.

d) Similarly with part b, we find pH = 7.26

e) This is the end-point, and we produce $[NH_4^+] = 0.0050$ M. Reaction with H_2O gives $NH_3 + H_3O^+$, and thus $y^2/(0.0050-y) = 10^{-14}/1.8 \times 10^{-5}$, so $y = [H_3O^+] = 1.7 \times 10^{-6}$, and pH = 5.78.

f) There is excess HCl, and it reacts with H_2O to produce Cl^- and H_3O^+. $[H_3O^+] = 0.000050$ M, so pH = 4.30. (Any H_3O^+ from NH_4^+ here will be negligible.)

g) As in (f), there is excess HCl. $[H_3O^+] = 0.00048$ M, so pH = 3.32.

41. To decide which indicator is suitable, we must first calculate the pH at the end-point of the titration. At that point, all concentrations of acid or base (before reaction) are 0.050 M (since equal volumes of the two are mixed if their initial concentrations both are 0.10 M). In all cases, the acid and base produce a 0.050 M solution of the salt at the end-point.
a) Since NaCl $\longrightarrow$ Na^+ + Cl^-, neither of which act as an acid or base, the pH at the end-point is determined by the self-ionization of water, and thus pH = 7.0. The best indicator would be bromothymol blue, since according to Table 14.8 it changes color in the pH 6.0-7.8 range, whereas all others listed change before 7 or after 7.

b) At equilibrium, $[K^+] = [CH_3CO_2^-] = 0.050$ M. The acetate reacts with water since it is a base:

	$CH_3CO_2^-$	+ H_2O $\rightleftharpoons$	CH_3CO_2H	+ H_3O^+
Initial	0.050 M		0	0
Equilibrium	0.050-y		y	y

Thus $\dfrac{y^2}{0.050-y} = K_b(CH_3CO_2^-) + \dfrac{10^{-14}}{K_a(CH_3CO_2H)}$

or $\dfrac{y^2}{0.050-y} = 5.6 \times 10^{-10}$

We obtain $y = 5.3 \times 10^{-5} = [OH^-]$, so pOH = 5.28 and pH = 8.72. Thus either thymol blue or phenolphthalein would be suitable, since 8.7 lies within the range in which each changes its color.

c) The salt produced here is NH_4Cl, so $[NH_4^+] = [Cl^-] = 0.050$ M. The weak acid NH_4^+ will react with water:

$$NH_4^+ + H_2O \rightleftharpoons NH_3 + OH^-$$

Thus $\dfrac{y^2}{0.050-y} = K_a(NH_4^+) = 5.6 \times 10^{-10}$

We obtain $y = 5.3 \times 10^{-6}$, so pH = 5.28. Thus methyl red is the best indicator here, since its color change region incorporates pH = 5.28 whereas that is not true for any other indicator listed.

42. In water, Na_2CO_3 exists as separated Na^+ and CO_3^{2-} ions:

$$Na_2CO_3(s) \xrightarrow{\text{water}} 2Na^+ + CO_3^{2-}$$

The carbonate ion is the conjugate of HCO_3^-, and acts as a weak base:

	CO_3^{2-}	+ H_2O $\rightleftharpoons$	HCO_3^-	+ OH^-
Initial	0.20 M		0	0
Equilibrium	0.20-y		y	y

Thus $\dfrac{y^2}{0.20-y} = 2.1 \times 10^{-4}$

Using the approximation, then $y = 6.5 \times 10^{-3}$. Thus at equilibrium

$$[HCO_3^-] = [OH^-] = y = 6.5 \times 10^{-3} \text{ M}$$
$$[CO_3^{2-}] = 0.20-y = 0.194 \text{ M}$$
$$[H_3O^+] = 10^{-14}/[OH^-] = 1.5 \times 10^{-12} \text{ M}$$

43. a) As a result of mixing the solutions,
$$[HCl] = 0.112 \text{ M} \times (25.00 \text{ mL}/50.00 \text{ mL}) = 0.0560 \text{ M}$$
(NaCl does ionize but does not react, so can be ignored.)
$$HCl + H_2O \longrightarrow Cl^- + H_3O^+$$
As a result of the reaction of the strong acid HCl with water,
$$[H_3O^+] = 0.0560 \text{ M and pH} = 1.25$$

b) As a result solely of mixing,
$$[NaOH] = 0.00857 \text{ M}$$
$$[H_2SO_4] = 0.004285 \text{ M}$$
The NaOH ionizes to Na^+ and OH^-, and the base OH^- reacts with the strong acid H_2SO_4:

	$2OH^-$	+ H_2SO_4 $\longrightarrow$	$2H_2O$ +	SO_4^{2-}
	$[OH^-]$	$[H_2SO_4]$		$[SO_4^{2-}]$
Initial	0.00857 M	0.004285 M		0
Final	0	0		0.004285 M

We shall ignore any reaction of SO_4^{2-} with water. Since all the acid and base has reacted, pH = 7 since it is controlled by the self-ionization of water.

c) As a result solely of mixing,
$$[HCl] = 0.0827 \text{ M} \qquad [NH_3] = 0.0280 \text{ M}$$
The acid and base react:

	HCl	+	NH_3	$\longrightarrow$	Cl^-	+	NH_4^+
	0.0827 M		0.0280 M		0		0
	0.0547 M		0		0.0280 M		0.0280 M

The pH will be determined by the reaction of the excess HCl with water:

	HCl	+	H_2O	$\longrightarrow$	Cl^-	+	H_3O^+
	0.0547						0
	0						0.0547

Thus $[H_3O^+] = 0.0547$ M, and thus pH = 1.26. (The reaction of NH_4^+ with H_2O produces a negligible additional amount of H_3O^+ here.)

44. In each case, identify the reaction(s) with water and calculate pH from the OH^- or H_3O^+ which results.
a) KOH is a strong base, and dissolves to give separated ions. Thus $[OH^-] = 0.010$ M, so pOH = 2.00, and pH = 12.0.

b) KCl is a salt of a strong acid and a strong base. Thus neither K^+ nor Cl^- react with water, and the pH of the solution is determined by self-ionization of water, so pH = 7.00.

c) NH_3 is a weak base, so it reacts with H_2O as follows:
$$NH_3 + H_2O \rightleftharpoons NH_4^+ + OH^-$$
The methodology and values are identical to Q. 15, so $[OH^-]$ = 4.2 x 10^{-4} M, and pOH = 3.38, so pH = 10.62.

d) HF is a weak acid, so it reacts with H_2O as follows:

	HF	+	H_2O	$\rightleftharpoons$	F^-	+	H_3O^+
	0.010				0		0
	0.010-y				y		y

Thus $\dfrac{y^2}{0.010-y} = 3.5 \times 10^{-4}$

Using the approximation, we find that the extent of dissociation significantly exceeds 5%, so we must solve the quadratic. Thus $y = [H_3O^+] = 1.70 \times 10^{-3}$, so pH = 2.77.

e) In water, KF yields K^+ and F^-. The latter is a weak base, since it is the conjugate of the weak acid HF:

	F^-	+	H_2O	$\rightleftharpoons$	HF	+	OH^-
Initial	0.010				0		0
Equilibrium	0.010-y				y		y

Thus $\dfrac{y^2}{0.010-y} = K_b(F^-) = \dfrac{10^{-14}}{K_a(HF)} = \dfrac{10^{-14}}{3.5 \times 10^{-4}} = 2.9 \times 10^{-11}$

220

Using the approximation, we obtain $y = [OH^-] = 5.4 \times 10^{-7}$, so pOH = 6.27 and pH = 7.73.

f) HNO_3 is a strong acid:
$$HNO_3 + H_2O \longrightarrow NO_3^- + H_3O^+$$
Thus $[H_3O^+] = 0.010$, so pH = 2.00.

45. Call aniline = B for convenience; then the salt is B^+Cl^-, and dissociates to B^+ and Cl^-. As a result solely of mixing the solutions of the aniline and its salt,
$[B] = 0.020$ M x (25.0 mL/35.0 mL) = 0.0143 M
$[BH^+] = 0.030$ M x (10.0 mL/35.0 mL) = 0.0086 M
The equilibrium is

	B	+	H_2O	$\rightleftharpoons$	BH^+	+	OH^-
Initial	0.0143				0.0086		0
Equilibrium	0.0143-y				0.0086+y		y

Approximating $y \gg 0.0143$ and 0.0086, then
$0.0086y/0.0143 = 4.3 \times 10^{-10}$
i.e. $y = 7.1 \times 10^{-10} = [OH^-]$ so pOH = 9.15 and pH = 4.85.
Now consider adding 1.0 mL of 0.040 M HNO_3; as a result of mixing,
$[HNO_3] = 0.040$ M x (1.0 mL/36.0 mL) = 0.0011 M
$[B] = 0.0143$ M x (35.0 mL/36.0 mL) = 0.0139 M
$[BH^+] = 0.0086$ M x (35.0 mL/36.0 mL) = 0.0084 M
Now the strong acid HNO_3 reacts with the base B:

	HNO_3	+	B	$\longrightarrow$	NO_3^-	+	BH^+
Before	0.0011		0.0139				0.0084
After	0		0.0128				0.0095

From the equilibrium reaction (as above),
$0.0095y/0.0128 = 4.3 \times 10^{-10}$
$y = 5.8 \times 10^{-10} = [OH^-]$, so pOH = 9.24, and pH = 4.76.
Thus from addition of HNO_3, the pH decreases by 0.09 units.
If, instead of HNO_3, a volume of 2.0 mL of 0.030 M KOH had been added to the solution, then due to mixing
$[OH^-] = 0.030$ M x (2.0 mL/37.0 mL) = 0.0016 M
$[B] = 0.0143$ M x (35.0 mL/37.0 mL) = 0.0135 M
$[BH^+] = 0.0086$ M x (35.0 mL/37.0 mL) = 0.0081 M
Since OH^- is a base, it reacts with the acid BH^+:

	OH^-	+	BH^+	$\longrightarrow$	H_2O	+	B
Before	0.0016		0.0081				0.0135
After	0		0.0065				0.0151

From the equilibrium reaction (see above),
$0.0065y/0.0151 = 4.3 \times 10^{-10}$
$y = 1.0 \times 10^{-9} = [OH^-]$, so pOH = 9.00 and pH = 5.00.
Thus from addition of KOH, the pH increases by 0.15 units.

46. To act as a buffer, an aqueous solution should contain comparable equilibrium concentrations of a weak acid-base conjugate pair. We use this criterion to decide whether

the solutions will or will not act as buffers:
a) No, since HNO_3 is a strong acid.

b) After mixing, $[CH_3CO_2H]$ = 0.050 M and $[OH^-]$ = 0.025 M, but they react with each other (one is an acid, the other a base):

$$CH_3CO_2H \ + \ OH^- \ \longrightarrow \ CH_3CO_2^- \ + \ H_2O$$

0.050 M	0.025 M	0	
0.025 M	0	0.025 M	

Thus this solution does act as a buffer.

c) As in (b), mixing gives $[CH_3CO_2H]$ = 0.050 M, $[OH^-]$ = 0.075 M. The acid and base react, and excess OH^- remains. Since no weak acid remains, the solution does not act as a buffer.

47. The methodology here is identical to that of Q. 39, and thus only a brief sketch of the solutions is given.
a) $y^2/(0.020-y) = 1.8 \times 10^{-5}$, so $y = [H_3O^+] = 6.0 \times 10^{-4}$ and pH = 3.22.

b) $[CH_3CO_2H]$ = 0.0167 M, $[OH^-]$ = 0.0083, so after reaction $[CH_3CO_2H] = [CH_3CO_2^-]$ = 0.0083. Thus $0.0083y/0.0083 = 1.8 \times 10^{-5}$, pH = 4.74.

c) $[CH_3CO_2H]$ = 0.01433 M, $[OH^-]$ = 0.01418 so after reaction $[CH_3CO_2H]$ = 0.00015, $[CH_3CO_2^-]$ = 0.01418 so $0.01418y/0.00015 = 1.8 \times 10^{-5}$, $y = 1.9 \times 10^{-7}$ and pH = 6.72.

d) $[CH_3CO_2H] = [OH^-]$ = 0.01429, so after reaction all CH_3CO_2H and OH^- has been converted to $CH_3CO_2^-$, which is present at 0.01429 M. Its reaction with H_2O leads to $y^2/(0.01429-y) = 10^{-14}/1.8 \times 10^{-5}$, so $y = [OH^-] = 2.8 \times 10^{-6}$ so pOH = 5.55 and pH = 8.45.

e) Excess $[OH^-]$ after reaction is found to be 0.00270 M, so pOH = 2.57 and pH = 11.43.

48. From the equation for the reaction, we note that H_3O^+ and $C_6H_5O^-$ are produced in equal amounts, say y, and that the equilibrium concentration of phenol will be its solubility, c, minus y:

$$C_6H_5OH \ + \ H_2O \ \rightleftharpoons \ C_6H_5O^- \ + \ H_3O^+$$

	C_6H_5OH	H_2O	$C_6H_5O^-$	H_3O^+
Initial	c		0	0
Equilibrium	c-y		y	y

But from the pH of 4.90, $[H_3O^+] = y = 1.26 \times 10^{-5}$. Thus
$$\frac{y^2}{c-y} = Ka \text{ becomes } \frac{(1.26 \times 10^{-5})^2}{c-1.26 \times 10^{-5}} = 1.6 \times 10^{-10}$$
Rearranging, we obtain c = 0.99. Thus the solubility of phenol in water is 0.99 moles per litre.

49. a) From the P,V,T information we deduce that

$$n = PV/RT = 1 \times 1/0.0821 \times 333 = 0.0366 \text{ moles}$$

Thus $n_{NO_2} + n_{N_2O_4} = 0.0366$

We know $m_{NO_2} + m_{N_2O_4} = 2.50$

and $M_{NO_2} = 46.01$ and $M_{N_2O_4} = 92.02$

so since $m = nM$,

$$46.01 \, n_{NO_2} + 92.02 \, n_{N_2O_4} = 2.50$$

Solving the simultaneous equations yields

$$n_{NO_2} = 0.0189 \quad \text{and} \quad n_{N_2O_4} = 0.0177$$

Thus for the reaction

$$N_2O_4 \rightleftharpoons 2NO_2$$

	$[N_2O_4]$	$[NO_2]$
Equilibrium	0.0177	0.0189
Initial	0.0272	0

Thus the percentage dissociation of N_2O_4 is $100 \times (0.0272 - 0.0177)/0.0272 = 35\%$.

b) For this reaction, $K_p = P_{NO_2}^2/P_{N_2O_4}$

Now $P_{NO_2} = n_{NO_2} RT/V = 0.517 \text{ atm}$

and $P_{N_2O_4} = n_{N_2O_4} RT/V = 0.484 \text{ atm}$

Thus $K_p = (0.517 \text{ atm})^2/0.484 \text{ atm} = 0.55$

50. Let the initial pressure of O_2 be P; thus that of SO_2 is 2P (since the initial mole ratio of SO_2 to O_2 is 2:1). According to the information, one-third of the SO_2 is converted to SO_3; thus the equilibrium pressure of SO_2 is $2P-2P/3 = 4P/3$. The amount of SO_3 which is produced must be $2P/3$ since SO_3 is produced in the same amount in which SO_2 reacts. The loss of O_2 must be $P/3$ since O_2 and SO_2 react in a 1:2 ratio:

$$2SO_2 + O_2 \rightleftharpoons 2SO_3$$

Thus the final pressures of SO_2, O_2, and SO_3 are $4P/3$, $2P/3$, and $2P/3$ respectively, for a total of $8P/3$. From the information supplied,

$$8P/3 = 5$$

so $P = 15/8 = 1.875$

Thus $P_{SO_3} = 1.25$, $P_{SO_2} = 2.50$, and $P_{O_2} = 1.25$ atm.

$$K_p = P_{SO_3}^2/P_{SO_2}^2 P_{O_2}$$

$$= (1.25 \text{ atm})^2/(2.50 \text{ atm})^2 \times 1.25 \text{ atm}$$

$$= 0.200 \text{ atm}^{-1}$$

1. Presumably the reactivity increases with increasing atomic number since the ionization energies (for $M \rightarrow M^+ + e^-$) decrease.

2. In reactions with non-metals, lithium forms the +1 ion and calcium the +2 ion. As anions, bromine forms Br^-, sulfur forms S^{2-} and nitrogen forms N^{3-}. The formula for each compound can be deduced from the condition that the sum of the positive charges must equal the sum of the negative charges. All ionic salts are solids at room temperature. Thus:

   a) $2Li(s) + Br_2(\ell) \longrightarrow 2LiBr(s)$
   $Ca(s) + Br_2(\ell) \longrightarrow CaBr_2(s)$.

   b) $2Li(s) + S(s) \longrightarrow Li_2S(s)$
   $Ca(s) + S(s) \longrightarrow CaS(s)$.

   c) $6Li(s) + N_2(g) \longrightarrow 2Li_3N(s)$
   $3Ca(s) + N_2(g) \longrightarrow Ca_3N_2(s)$.

3. In all cases, the metal is an alkali and thus its charge is +1. In (a)-(d), the metal combines with a non-metal which forms an anion, to yield a solid ionic compound.

   a) $2K(s) + Br_2(\ell) \longrightarrow 2KBr(s)$.
   The formula of the product is KBr, since the anion is Br^-.

   b) $4Li(s) + O_2(g) \longrightarrow 2Li_2O(s)$.
   Since the charge on oxide is −2, two Li^+ ions are required per O^{2-}.

   c) $2Na(s) + H_2(g) \longrightarrow 2NaH(s)$.
   The hydride charge is −1, so the formula is NaH.

   d) $6Li(s) + N_2(g) \longrightarrow 2Li_3N(s)$.
   The nitride charge is −3, so to balance charge we need three Li^+ per N^{3-}.

   e) LiH is an ionic solid, Li^+H^-. In water, H^- acts as a strong base, liberating H_2:
   $$LiH(s) \longrightarrow Li^+ + H^-$$
   $$H^- + H_2O \longrightarrow H_2 + OH^-$$
   _____
   Net $\quad LiH(s) + H_2O(\ell) \longrightarrow H_2 + Li^+ + OH^-$ (i.e. LiOH).

f) Li_3N is an ionic solid, $(Li^+)_3N^{3-}$. In water, N^{3-} acts as a strong base, liberating ammonia:

$$Li_3N(s) \longrightarrow 3Li^+ + N^{3-}$$
$$N^{3-} + 3H_2O \longrightarrow NH_3 + 3OH^-$$

$$\text{Net } Li_3N(s) + 3H_2O(\ell) \longrightarrow NH_3 + 3Li^+ + 3OH^- \text{ (i.e. } 3LiOH)$$

g) Potassium reacts with water to replace one hydrogen and release it as hydrogen:
$$2K(s) + 2H_2O(\ell) \longrightarrow H_2(g) + 2K^+ + 2OH^- \text{ (i.e. } 2KOH)$$

4. A buffer solution must contain a weak acid to react with any strong base that may be added, and a weak base to react with added strong acid. The hydrogen carbonate ion HCO_3^- can act either as a weak acid or as a weak base, depending upon what is added to it:

$$\underset{\text{acid}}{HCO_3^-} + \underset{\text{base}}{OH^-} \longrightarrow CO_3^{2-} + H_2O$$

$$\underset{\text{base}}{HCO_3^-} + \underset{\text{acid}}{H_3O^+} \longrightarrow H_2CO_3 + H_2O (\longrightarrow CO_2 + H_2O).$$

Thus a solution of sodium hydrogen carbonate can act as a buffer, since in water it exists as Na^+ and HCO_3^-. The common name for sodium hydrogen carbonate is "bicarbonate of soda".

5. Lime is $CaO(s)$. When water is added, calcium hydroxide is formed:
$$CaO(s) + H_2O(\ell) \longrightarrow Ca(OH)_2(s).$$
Lime is an important industrial chemical because it is a relatively inexpensive base and is readily available; it is used in making glass, cement and for removing acidic impurities in metallurgical processes.

6. Using reasoning similar to that for calcium in Q. 2, then:
a) $2Mg(s) + O_2 \longrightarrow 2MgO(s)$.

b) $Mg(s) + S \longrightarrow MgS(s)$.

c) $3Mg(s) + N_2 \longrightarrow Mg_3N_2(s)$.

7. The first ionizations occur from the 3s level, and that for Mg is greater since its core charge is +2 whereas that for Na is only +1. The second ionization for Mg also occurs from the 3s level, but for Na it must come from the very stable 2p level; thus the second ionization energy for Na > Mg.

8. In all cases, the cation of the solids is Na^+, and this does not react with water and thus does not give a different ion.
a) No reaction here, as Cl^- does not react with water (since it is the conjugate of a strong acid).

b) H^- is a strong base and reacts with water:
$$H^- + H_2O \longrightarrow H_2 + OH^-.$$

Thus overall we have
$$NaH + H_2O \longrightarrow H_2 + Na^+ + OH^- \text{ (or NaOH)}.$$

c) No reaction, as $OH^- + H_2O$ does not give a net reaction.

d) O^{2-} is a strong base and reacts with water:
$$O^{2-} + H_2O \longrightarrow 2OH^-.$$
Thus overall we have
$$Na_2O + H_2O \longrightarrow 2Na^+ + 2OH^- \text{ (or 2NaOH)}.$$

e) $SO_4{}^{2-}$ is the conjugate base of the weak acid $HSO_4{}^-$; thus to a slight extent, the following reaction occurs:
$$SO_4{}^{2-} + H_2O \rightleftarrows HSO_4{}^- + OH^-$$

f) Similarly, $CO_3{}^{2-}$ is the conjugate base of the weak acid $HCO_3{}^-$, and thus the following reaction occurs:
$$CO_3{}^{2-} + H_2O \rightleftarrows HCO_3{}^- + OH^-$$

9. All the products here are ionic so they are solid. All the metals are from Group II, and thus form +2 ions.
   a) $Mg(s) + Cl_2(g) \longrightarrow MgCl_2(s)$.

   b) $2Ca(s) + O_2(g) \longrightarrow 2CaO(s)$.

   c) $Sr(s) + H_2(g) \longrightarrow SrH_2(s)$.

   d) $3Mg(s) + N_2(g) \longrightarrow Mg_3N_2(s)$.

   e) $Ca(s) + 2H_2O(\ell) \longrightarrow H_2(g) + Ca^{2+} + 2OH^-$ (i.e $Ca(OH)_2$).

10. Based upon the trend for $Mg(OH)_2$ and $Ca(OH)_2$, we deduce that the solubilities of hydroxides increase as we go down the group. As stated in the text, the solubilities of the sulfates decrease as we go down the group.

11. The drops of water hanging from the roofs of caves are saturated aqueous $Ca(HCO_3)_2$ solutions. Upon evaporation of some of the water and loss of CO_2, the equilibrium in the reaction
$$Ca(HCO_3)_2(aq) \rightleftarrows H_2O(\ell) + CO_2(aq) + CaCO_3(s)$$
then shifts to the right, and solid $CaCO_3$ is deposited. If this process occurs always at the same place in the cave, stalactites and stalagmites are formed.

12. All the reactions here are discussed in the text.
    a) $CaCO_3(s) \longrightarrow CaO(s) + CO_2(g)$.

    b) $Ca(OH)_2(s) \longrightarrow CaO(s) + H_2O(g)$

    c) $2NaHCO_3(s) \longrightarrow Na_2CO_3(s) + H_2O + CO_2$

226

d) $MgCl_2 \cdot 6H_2O(s) \longrightarrow MgO(s) + 2HCl(s) + 5H_2O(g)$.

13. As a result of heating, the $CaCO_3$ and $Ca(HCO_3)_2$ decompose:
$$CaCO_3 \longrightarrow CaO + CO_2$$
$$Ca(HCO_3)_2 \longrightarrow CO_2 + H_2O + CaCO_3$$
but the $CaCO_3$ here also decomposes (see first equation), to give overall the reaction
$$Ca(HCO_3)_2 \longrightarrow 2CO_2 + H_2O + CaO.$$
Since H_2O is produced only from this reaction, we can deduce from it the original mass of $Ca(HCO_3)_2$:

$$0.200 \text{ g } H_2O \times \frac{1 \text{ mole } H_2O}{18.02 \text{ g } H_2O} \times \frac{1 \text{ mole } Ca(HCO_3)_2}{1 \text{ mole } H_2O}$$
$$= 0.0111 \text{ mole } Ca(HCO_3)_2.$$

Since the molar mass of $Ca(HCO_3)_2$ is 162.12 g, the mass of $Ca(HCO_3)_2$ was 1.80 g and it constituted 18.0% of the original sample.
    The CO_2 mass of 1.500 g, or 0.0341 moles, is the sum of contributions from $Ca(HCO_3)_2$ and the original $CaCO_3$. Since 1 mole $Ca(HCO_3)_2$ yields 2 moles CO_2, and since from the H_2O results we deduced that 0.0111 mole $Ca(HCO_3)_2$ was present, therefore
    Moles $CaCO_3$ = 0.0341 - 2 x 0.0111 = 0.0119.
Thus the mass of $CaCO_3$ originally was 0.0119 moles x 100.09 g/mole = 1.19 g, i.e. 11.9%. Thus we can deduce that the mass of the original CaO was
10.00 - 1.19 - 1.80 = 7.01 g, i.e. 70.1% of the sample.

14. Since H^- reacts with water as
$$H^- + H_2O \longrightarrow H_2 + OH^-$$
the overall reaction of CaH_2 with water will be
$$CaH_2 + 2H_2O \longrightarrow 2H_2 + Ca(OH)_2.$$
The mass of CaH_2 can be converted to moles CaH_2, then via the coefficients in the balanced equation to moles H_2, and then to volume H_2 given the STP molar volume of 22.4 L:

$$2.00 \text{ g } CaH_2 \times \frac{1 \text{ mole } CaH_2}{42.10 \text{ g } CaH_2} \times \frac{2 \text{ moles } H_2}{1 \text{ mole } CaH_2} \times \frac{22.4 \text{ L } H_2}{1 \text{ mole } H_2} = 2.13 \text{ L}$$

15. We begin using the information for the product, Mg, and work back to volume of water. First we convert from mass of Mg extracted to that theoretically available from the water, i.e.

$$100 \text{ g available} \equiv 70 \text{ g extracted}$$

$$1 \times 10^6 \text{ g Mg extracted} \times \frac{100 \text{ g Mg available}}{70 \text{ g Mg extracted}} \times \frac{1 \text{ mole Mg}}{24.31 \text{ g Mg}}$$

$$\times \frac{1 \text{ L}}{0.05 \text{ mole Mg}} = 1.2 \times 10^6 \text{ L of seawater.}$$

16. According to the text, the appropriate reaction is
$$2 Na_5(CO_3)_2(HCO_3) \cdot 2H_2O \longrightarrow 5Na_2CO_3 + CO_2 + 5H_2O$$
and then $5[Na_2CO_3 + 10 H_2O \longrightarrow Na_2CO_3 \cdot 10 H_2O]$.
Thus 2 moles trona yields 5 moles washing soda:

$$1 \times 10^6 \text{ g trona} \times \frac{1 \text{ mole trona}}{332.03 \text{ g trona}} \times \frac{5 \text{ moles soda}}{2 \text{ moles trona}}$$

$$\times \frac{286.2 \text{ g soda}}{1 \text{ mole soda}} = 2 \times 10^6 \text{ g washing soda.}$$

17. All reactions are discussed in the text:
a) $O^{2-} + H_2O \longrightarrow 2OH^-$.

b) $H^- + H_2O \longrightarrow H_2 + OH^-$.

c) $N^{3-} + 3H_2O \longrightarrow NH_3 + 3OH^-$.

d) $CO_3^{2-} + H_2O \longrightarrow HCO_3^- + OH^-$.

18. a) Sulfates generally are soluble, but that of Pb^{2+} is an exception: $PbSO_4$ is insoluble.

b) Iodides generally are soluble, but that of Ag^+ is an exception: AgI is insoluble.

c) Salts of Group I cations are soluble, so Na_2CO_3 is soluble, although in general, carbonates are insoluble.

d) Sulfides generally are insoluble and that of Fe^{2+} is not an exception: FeS is insoluble.

e) Nitrates are soluble: $AgNO_3$ is soluble.

f) Oxides generally are insoluble unless the O^{2-} ion reacts with water: CuO is insoluble.

19. a) Since chlorides generally are soluble, $AlCl_3$ is predicted to be soluble.

b) Sulfates generally are soluble; in fact $CaSO_4$ is a borderline case.

c) Sulfates generally are soluble: $CuSO_4$ is predicted to be soluble.

d) Hydroxides generally are insoluble, but those of Group I cations are exceptions; thus $LiOH$ is predicted to be soluble.

e) Since carbonates generally are insoluble, $BaCO_3$ should be insoluble.

228

f) Although sulfides generally are insoluble, those of Group I cations are soluble so Na_2S is soluble.

20. In each case, we combine the cation of the first reactant with the anion of the second, and also vice-versa, and use the solubility rules (see logic of Q. 18 and 19) to predict whether each of these two potential product salts is insoluble.

a) Products are $CaCO_3$, which should be insoluble and thus precipiate, and NaCl which is soluble:
$$Na_2CO_3 + CaCl_2 \longrightarrow CaCO_3(s) + 2NaCl(aq).$$

b) Neither potential product, $Ca(NO_3)_2$ and NaBr, is insoluble so no precipitation will occur.

c) Since AgI should be insoluble, it will precipitate:
$$AgNO_3 + NaI \longrightarrow NaNO_3(aq) + AgI(s).$$

d) Since $BaSO_4$ is insoluble, it will precipitate:
$$BaCl_2 + MgSO_4 \longrightarrow MgCl_2(aq) + BaSO_4(s).$$

e) Since $PbCl_2$ is only sparingly soluble, it will likely precipitate:
$$2HCl + Pb(NO_3)_2 \longrightarrow PbCl_2(s) + 2HNO_3(aq).$$

21. Logic used here is the same as for Q. 20.
a) $Fe(OH)_3$ is insoluble and will precipitate:
$$FeCl_3 + 3NaOH \longrightarrow 3NaCl(aq) + Fe(OH)_3(s).$$

b) Neither potential product, $AgClO_4$ and $NaNO_3$, is insoluble so no precipitate is predicted to form.

c) Since both $Ba(OH)_2$ and KCl are soluble, no precipitate should form.

d) Since $PbSO_4$ is insoluble, it will precipitate:
$$Pb(NO_3)_2 + H_2SO_4 \longrightarrow 2HNO_3(aq) + PbSO_4(s).$$

e) Since Ag_2S is insoluble, it will precipitate:
$$2AgNO_3 + Na_2S \longrightarrow 2NaNO_3(aq) + Ag_2S(s).$$

22. For $Fe(OH)_3$ the reaction is $Fe(OH)_3 \rightleftarrows Fe^{3+} + 3OH^-$
Thus $K_{sp} = [Fe^{3+}][OH^-]^3$.

For $Ca_3(PO_4)_2$ the reaction is $Ca_3(PO_4)_2 \rightleftarrows 3Ca^{2+} + 2PO_4^{3-}$
Thus $K_{sp} = [Ca^{2+}]^3[PO_4^{3-}]^2$
In each case we raise the concentration of each ion to a power equal to its coefficient in the ionization reaction.

23. Similar to Q. 22. Answers are:
a) $[Ag^+][Cl^-]$ b) $[Ba^{2+}][F^-]^2$

c) $[Cr^{3+}][OH^-]^3$ d) $[Bi^{3+}]^2[S^{2-}]^3$

229

24. The common ions for these metals should be known, and are Ag^+, Ca^{2+}, Pb^{2+}, Mg^{2+}, Al^{3+}, and Sr^{2+} and those for the anions are F, OH^-, and SO_4^{2-}. Thus the formulas for the compounds are AgF, CuF_2, PbF_2, $AgOH$, $Mg(OH)_2$, $Al(OH)_3$, Ag_2SO_4 and $SrSO_4$. It follows that K_{sp} expressions (see Q. 22) are $K_{sp} = [Ag^+][F^-]$, $[Ca^{2+}][F]^{-2}$, $[Pb^{2+}][F^-]^2$, $[Ag^+][OH^-]$, $[Mg^{2+}][OH^-]^2$, $[Al^{3+}][OH^-]^3$, $[Ag^+]^2[SO_4^{2-}]$, and $[Sr^{2+}][SO_4^{2-}]$.

25. Since K_{sp} is defined in terms of moles per litre, we first convert mass $PbSO_4$ to moles:

$$0.060 \text{ g } PbSO_4 \times \frac{1 \text{ mole } PbSO_4}{303.25 \text{ g } PbSO_4} = 0.00020 \text{ moles } PbSO_4.$$

In solution, 1 mole dissolved $PbSO_4$ yields 1 mole each of Pb^{2+} and SO_4^{2-}; thus in this case
$[Pb^{2+}] = [SO_4^{2-}] = 0.00020 \text{ moles}/2 \text{ L} = 0.00010 \text{ M}$.
Since $K_{sp} = [Pb^{2+}][SO_4^{2-}]$
therefore $K_{sp} = (0.00010)^2 = 1.0 \times 10^{-8}$.

26. Since 0.0012 moles MgF_2 dissolves per litre, the concentration of ions produced by

$$MgF_2(s) \rightleftharpoons Mg^{2+} + 2F^-$$

is $[Mg^{2+}] = 0.0012$ M
$[F^-] = 0.0024$ M.
Since $K_{sp} = [Mg^{2+}][F^-]^2$
therefore $K_{sp} = (0.0012)(0.0024)^2 = 6.9 \times 10^{-9}$.

27. Method of solution is identical to Q. 25 and Q. 26, noting that 1 pg $= 10^{-12}$ g, 1 mg $= 10^{-3}$ g, 1 μg $= 10^{-6}$ g, and K_{sp}'s are $[Pb^{2+}][S^{2-}]$, $[Ca^{2+}][F^-]^2$, and $[Cr^{3+}][OH^-]^3$. Final answers:
For PbS, 3.4×10^{-28}
For CaF_2, 4.0×10^{-11}
For $Cr(OH)_3$, 2.4×10^{-28}.

28. a) First we write the reaction that occurs in solution – i.e. the production of two ions in aqueous solution from the ionic solid:

$$MgCO_3(s) \rightleftharpoons Mg^{2+}(aq) + CO_3^{2-}(aq).$$

If the solubility of $MgCO_3$ is S moles per litre of solution, the equilibrium concentrations of Mg^{2+} and CO_3^{2-} are each equal to S also. Now the solubility product expression for $MgCO_3$ is
$[Mg^{2+}][CO_3^{2-}] = K_{sp}$
thus $S^2 = 1 \times 10^{-15}$.
Taking the square root of each side, then
$$S = 3.2 \times 10^{-8}.$$
Thus the solubility of $MgCO_3$ is 3.2×10^{-8} moles per litre. This value can be converted to grams $MgCO_3$ per litre by

$$\frac{3.2 \times 10^{-8} \text{ moles MgCO}_3}{1 \text{ L solution}} \times \frac{84.32 \text{ g MgCO}_3}{1 \text{ mole MgCO}_3}$$

$\frac{2.7 \times 10^{-6} \text{ g MgCO}_3}{L}$ or 3×10^{-6} g L^{-1} to 1 significant figure

b) Identical to Q. 29; see that question for solution; answer is 1.9×10^{-3} g L^{-1}.

c) The reaction is $Al(OH)_3 \rightleftharpoons Al^{3+} + 3OH^-$.
If the solubility is defined as S, the molar concentrations will be $[Al^{3+}] = S$, $[OH^-] = 3S$.
Now $K_{sp} = [Al^{3+}][OH^-]^3 = 5 \times 10^{-33}$
Therefore $S(3S)^3 = 5 \times 10^{-33}$
    i.e. $27S^4 = 5 \times 10^{-33}$.
        Thus $S = 3.7 \times 10^{-9}$ M.
In g/L, the solubility is 3.7×10^{-9} moles/L x 78.01 g/mole $= 2.9 \times 10^{-7}$ g/L; the answer is 3×10^{-7} g/L.

d) Similar to part (c); answer is 1.3×10^{-3} M, i.e. 0.59 g/L.

e) Similar to part (c); since it dissociates to $3Ag^+$ and PO_4^{3-}; answer is 1.6×10^{-5} M, i.e. 0.0067 g/L, since the molar mass of Ag_3PO_4 is 418.58 g.

29. The reaction here is

$$AgCl(s) \rightleftharpoons Ag^+ + Cl^-$$
Thus $[Ag^+] = [Cl^-]$
Now $K_{sp} = [Ag^+][Cl^-]$.
By substitution, $[Ag^+]^2 = K_{sp}$
                        $= 1.7 \times 10^{-10}$
        thus $[Ag^+] = 1.3 \times 10^{-5}$ M.
Since all Ag^+ comes from the AgCl which dissolves, this also is the molar solubility of AgCl, i.e. 1.3×10^{-5}. Converting to grams, the solubility is

$$1.3 \times 10^{-5} \text{ moles AgCl/L} \times \frac{143.32 \text{ g AgCl}}{1 \text{ mole AgCl}}$$
$$= 1.9 \times 10^{-3} \text{ g AgCl/L.}$$

In 250 mL, the solubility is one-quarter this amount, i.e. 4.8×10^{-4} g.

30. Method is identical to Q. 44. If solubility of $Pb(OH)_2$ and $[Pb^{2+}]$ are S, then $[OH^-] = 2S$, so since
$[Pb^{2+}][OH^-]^2 = 4.2 \times 10^{-15}$
$S(2S)^2 = 4.2 \times 10^{-15}$
$S = 1.0 \times 10^{-5}$.
Thus the Pb^{2+} concentration is 1.0×10^{-5} M.

31. First recalculate the concentrations to allow for the fact that two solutions are mixed; since the moles of each reactant are constant, therefore the new molarity and volume is related to the original "old" values for each solution by

$$M_{new}V_{new} = M_{old}V_{old}$$

Hence $[Pb^{2+}]$ = 0.10 M x (50 mL/150 mL) = 0.033 M
and $[Cl^-]$ = 0.05 M x (100 mL/150mL) = 0.033 M.

In the present solution, the ion product $[Pb^{2+}][Cl^-]^2$ has the value $(0.033)^3$ = 3.6×10^{-5}. Since this value is greater than the K_{sp} of 1.7×10^{-5} for $PbCl_2$, some precipitate _will_ form.

32. As in No. 28, the solubilities can be found to be
    S = 7.7×10^{-6} M, i.e. 6.9×10^{-4} g L^{-1}, for $Fe(OH)_2$
and S = 1.4×10^{-10} M, i.e 1.5×10^{-8} g L^{-1}, for $Fe(OH)_3$.
Thus $Fe(OH)_3$ is the least soluble, both on a molar and a mass basis.

33. In each case we should first deduce the salt concentrations after mixing, then see what ion concentrations are present, and compare the ion products Q of the potential product salts with their K_{sp} values.
    a) After mixing, $[KOH]$ = 1.0 M x (50 mL/100 mL) = 0.50 M
    $$[BaCl_2] = 0.001 \text{ M x (50 mL/100 mL)}$$
    $$= 0.00050 \text{ M.}$$
    Thus the concentrations of the ions associated with the only potential product which is insoluble, $Ba(OH)_2$), are
    $[OH^-]$ = 0.50 M $[Ba^{2+}]$ = 0.00050 M.
    If $Ba(OH)_2$ precipitates, the equilibrium will be

    $$Ba(OH)_2(s) \rightleftharpoons Ba^{2+} + 2OH^-$$
    so the ion product Q is $[Ba^{2+}][OH^-]^2$,
    which here is $(0.0005)(0.5)^2$ = 1.2×10^{-4}.
    Since K_{sp} for $Ba(OH)_2$ is listed as 5.0×10^{-3}, then Q < K_{sp} and no precipitate will form.

    b) Similarly to part a), $[OH^-]$ = 0.50 M and $[Ba^{2+}]$ = 0.50 M so Q = $[Ba^{2+}][OH^-]^2$ = 1.2×10^{-1}, and precipitate will form.

34. Methodology is similar to Q. 35.
    After mixing, $[NaCl]$ = 1.00 M and $[AgNO_3]$ = 0.010 M, so $[Na^+]$ = $[Cl^-]$ = 1.00 M, $[Ag^+]$ = $[NO_3^-]$ = 0.010 M.
    The ion product for AgCl, 1.00 x 0.01 = 0.01, exceeds its K_{sp} of 1.7×10^{-10} so precipitation will occur. At equilibrium, if p moles/L of Ag^+ and Cl^- precipitate,
    $$[Cl^-] = 1.00 - p \approx 1.00$$
    $$[Ag^+] = 0.01 - p$$
    $$[Ag^+][Cl^-] = 1.7 \times 10^{-10}$$
    $$(0.01 - p)(1.00) = 1.7 \times 10^{-10}$$
    $$p = 0.01 - 1.7 \times 10^{-10} \approx 0.01$$

232

a) Since 100mL of solution was used, the moles of $AgCl$ formed is $0.01 \times 0.1 = 0.001$, i.e 0.001 moles $\times$ 143.32 g/mole $= 0.14$ g $AgCl$.

b) The $[Ag^+]$ value is obtained from
$$[Ag^+] = K_{sp}/[Cl^-] = 1.7 \times 10^{-10}/(1.00 - 0.01)$$
$$= 1.7 \times 10^{-10} \text{ M}.$$

35. After mixing, $[Pb(NO_3)_2] = 1.00$ M and $[NaI] = 2.00 \times 10^{-3}$ M. The potential precipitates are PbI_2 and $NaNO_3$; the latter is unlikely since nitrates are soluble. For PbI_2, the equilibrium would be

$$PbI_2(s) \rightleftharpoons Pb^{2+} + 2I^-$$

so the ion product Q is $[Pb^{2+}][I^-]^2$. Since without precipitation, $Q = 1.00 \times (2.00 \times 10^{-3})^2 = 4.00 \times 10^{-6}$ and since $K_{sp} = 8.3 \times 10^{-9}$, precipitation will occur.

Let us define the number of moles per litre of Pb^{2+} which precipitates as p; thus I^- is reduced by 2p. At equilibrium
$$[Pb^{2+}] = 1.00 - p$$
$$[I^-] = 2.00 \times 10^{-3} - 2p.$$
Since $p < 1 \times 10^{-3}$ by necessity, thus $1.00 - p \approx 1.00$. The equilibrium will be in effect after precipitation occurs, so we know
$$[Pb^{2+}]_e[I^-]_e^2 = 8.3 \times 10^{-9}$$
$$(1.00)(2.00 \times 10^{-3} - 2p)^2 = 8.3 \times 10^{-9}$$
i.e.
$$2.00 \times 10^{-3} - 2p = 9.1 \times 10^{-5}$$
$$2p = 1.9 \times 10^{-3}.$$
Since only 100 mL solution is available, the moles of PbI_2 obtained is $1.0 \times 10^{-3} \times 0.1 = 1.0 \times 10^{-4}$. The final ion concentrations are
$$[Pb^{2+}] = 1.00 - 1.0 \times 10^{-3} = 0.999 \text{ M}$$
$$[I^-] = 9 \times 10^{-5} \text{ M}$$
$$[Na^+] = 2.00 \times 10^{-3} \text{ M} (= [NaI] \text{ after mixing})$$
$$[NO_3^-] = 2.00 \text{ M} (= 2[Pb(NO_3)_2] \text{ after mixing}).$$

36. a) Method same as for Q. 28 and Q. 29. Answer is 2.0×10^{-4} M, i.e. 0.016 g/L.

b) $$CaCl_2 \longrightarrow Ca^{2+} + 2Cl^-.$$
Thus from this source $[Ca^{2+}] = 0.010$ M.
For the slightly-soluble salt,

$$CaF_2(g) \rightleftharpoons Ca^{2+} + 2F^-$$

	$[Ca^{2+}]$	$[F^-]$
Initial	0.010	0
Final	0.010+S	2S

Thus $(0.010+S)(2S)^2 = 3.4 \times 10^{-11}$
Since $0.010 \gg S$, $0.10+S \approx 0.10$
Thus $0.01 \times 4S^2 = 3.4 \times 10^{-11}$
$$S = 2.9 \times 10^{-5} \text{ M, i.e. } 2.3 \times 10^{-3} \text{ g/L}.$$

233

c)
$$NaF \longrightarrow Na^+ + F^-$$
Thus from this source, $[F^-] = 0.10$

$$CaF_2(s) \rightleftharpoons Ca^{2+} + 2F^-$$

	$[Ca^{2+}]$	$[F^-]$
Initial	0	0.10
Final	S	0.10+2S

Thus $S(0.10+2S)^2 = 3.4 \times 10^{-11}$. Approximating $0.10+2S \simeq 0.10$, then $0.10^2 S = 3.4 \times 10^{-11}$

$S = 3.4 \times 10^{-9}$ M, i.e. 2.7×10^{-7} g/L.

37. Calculations are similar to Q. 36b.
Thus $(0.20+S)(2S)^2 = 2.4 \times 10^{-5}$, and if follows that $S = 5.5 \times 10^{-3}$ M; for 500 mL, the solubility then is 2.7×10^{-3} moles, i.e. 0.48 g.

38. Before any $MgCl_2$ is added,
$$[Mg^{2+}] = [CO_3^{2-}] = 5.0 \times 10^{-9} \text{ M}$$
and since $[CO_3^{2-}]$ is unchanged by addition of $MgCl_2$. then just at the point of precipitation since
$$[Mg^{2+}][CO_3^{2-}] = 1.0 \times 10^{-15} \text{ (the } K_{sp} \text{ for } MgCO_3)$$
thus
$$[Mg^{2+}] = 1.0 \times 10^{-15}/[CO_3^{2-}]$$
$$= 1.0 \times 10^{-15}/5.0 \times 10^{-9}$$
$$= 2.0 \times 10^{-7} \text{ M.}$$
Thus the moles of $MgCl_2$ which can be added is
$$2.0 \times 10^{-7} - 5.0 \times 10^{-9} = 1.95 \times 10^{-7}.$$

39. The equilibrium is

$$Fe(OH)_3(s) \rightleftharpoons Fe^{3+} + 3OH^-.$$
To deduce the effect on $Fe(OH)_3$ solubility, we must consider if the equilibrium is upset by addition of the other chemicals:
a) Since addition of KOH instantaneously increases the OH^- concentration, by Le Chatelier's Principle the new equilibrium will be shifted to the left; thus the amount of solid $Fe(OH)_3$ will increase.

b) In solution, HCl exists as H_3O^+ and Cl^-. The H_3O^+ will react with OH^- from $Fe(OH)_3$, and thereby shift the equilibrium to the right; thus the amount of solid $Fe(OH)_3$ will decrease.

40. The equilibrium reaction is

$$Ca_3(PO_4)_2(s) \rightleftharpoons 3Ca^{2+} + 2PO_4^{3-}.$$
If the solubility of the salt is S, the $[Ca^{2+}]$ from the source is 3S and the $[PO_4^{3-}]$ concentration is 2S. From the K_{sp} table,
$$[Ca^{2+}]^3[PO_4^{3-}]^2 = 1.3 \times 10^{-32}.$$
a) From the reaction $CaCl_2 \longrightarrow Ca^{2+} + 2Cl^-$, the calcium concentration increases by 0.10 M, reching a total of 3S + 0.10. Since S is very small,
$$[Ca^{2+}] \simeq 0.10.$$
Thus we obtain the equation

$$(0.10)^3(2S)^2 = 1.3 \times 10^{-32}$$
$$\text{i.e. } S = 1.8 \times 10^{-15}.$$

Thus the solubility is 5.7×10^{-16} M, i.e 5.6×10^{-13} g L^{-1}, since the molar mass of calcium phosphate is 310.18 g.

b) The dissociation of 0.10 M Na_3PO_4 gives us a contribution to $[PO_4^{3-}]$ of 0.10 M; thus the total phosphate concentration is $2S + 0.10$ which in value will be close to 0.10. Thus

$$(3S)^3 \times (0.10)^2 = 1.3 \times 10^{-32}$$
$$S = 3.6 \times 10^{-11}.$$

Thus the solubility is 3.6×10^{-11} M, or 1.1×10^{-8} g L^{-1}.

c) For pure water we have
$$(3S)^3(2S)^2 = 1.3 \times 10^{-32}$$
$$\text{i.e. } 108S^5 = 1.3 \times 10^{-32}$$
$$S = 1.6 \times 10^{-7}$$

The solubility in water is 1.6×10^{-7} M, or 3.2×10^{-5} g L^{-1}.

41. Just at the point of precipitation of the first salt,
$$[F^-] = 0.0010 \text{ M}$$
and $[CO_3^{2-}] = 0.010$ M.
The possible products are MgF_2 and $MgCO_3$. For each we can write the K_{sp} expression that will be valid once some of the corresponding solid is present:
$$[Mg^{2+}][F^-]^2 = 8 \times 10^{-8}$$
$$[Mg^{2+}][CO_3^{2-}] = 1 \times 10^{-15}.$$
We can calculate $[Mg^{2+}]$ at the point of precipitation for each salt, since we know the anion concentration just before precipitation,
$$[Mg^{2+}] = 8 \times 10^{-8}/[F^-]^2 = 8 \times 10^{-8}/(0.0010)^2$$
$$= 8 \times 10^{-2}$$
$$[Mg^{2+}] = 1 \times 10^{-15}/[CO_3^{2-}] = 1 \times 10^{-15}/0.010$$
$$= 1 \times 10^{-13}.$$
Since $[Mg^{2+}]$ is much smaller for $MgCO_3$ than for MgF_2 precipitation, it will precipitate first.

42. For the first part, method is similar to that for Q. 41.
$$[Pb^{2+}] = 4 \times 10^{-8}/(0.10)^2 = 4 \times 10^{-6} \text{ for } PbF_2$$
$$[Pb^{2+}] = 1.3 \times 10^{-8}/0.10 = 1.3 \times 10^{-7} \text{ for } PbSO_4.$$
Thus $PbSO_4$ precipitates before PbF_2. The second salt, PbF_2, begins to precipitate when $[Pb^{2+}] = 4 \times 10^{-6}$. We can deduce the sulfate concentration at this point, since
$$[Pb^{2+}][SO_4^{2-}] = 1.3 \times 10^{-8}$$
$$[SO_4^{2-}] = 1.3 \times 10^{-8}/4 \times 10^{-6} = 3.2 \times 10^{-3} \text{ M}.$$

This level of sulfate is $\dfrac{3.2 \times 10^{-3}}{0.10} \times 100\% = 3.2\%$ of

that present initially; thus 3.2% of the sulfate is left when PbF_2 begins to precipitate.

43. When the precipitate just starts to form, almost all the Fe^{2+} is still in solution, so
$$[Fe^{2+}] = 0.005.$$
At this point the solution is just saturated; thus
$$[Fe^{2+}][OH^-]^2 = K_{sp}$$
$$= 1.8 \times 10^{-15}.$$
Therefore $[OH^-]^2 = 1.8 \times 10^{-15}/0.005$
$$[OH^-] = 6 \times 10^{-7} \text{ M}$$
$pOH = 6.22$ and thus $pH = 7.78$.

44. The equilibrium is $Mg(OH)_2(s) \rightleftharpoons Mg^{2+} + 2OH^-$
Let S = molar solubility; then $[Mg^{2+}] = S$
and $[OH^-] = 2S$
Thus $S(2S)^2 = 8.9 \times 10^{-12}$
$$S = 1.3 \times 10^{-4} \text{ M}$$
and $[OH^-] = 2S = 2.6 \times 10^{-4} \text{ M}.$
Thus $pOH = 3.59$ and $pH = 10.41$.

45. Solubility will increase as the pH is decreased only if one of the ions of the salt will react with H_3O^+, and thereby have its concentration diminished so that the solubility equilibrium shifts to the right. Thus we search the formula for ions that react with H_3O^+:
a) Here $S^{2-} + H_3O^+ \longrightarrow HS^- + H_2O$
   so decreasing the pH increases the solubility of CuS:
$$CuS(s) \rightleftharpoons Cu^{2+} + S^{2-}.$$

b) No effect, as I^- has no basic properties.

c) Decreasing pH will increase $MgCO_3$ solubility, since
$$CO_3^{2-} + H_3O^+ \longrightarrow HCO_3^- + H_2O.$$

d) Since H_3O^+ reacts with OH^- ($\longrightarrow 2H_2O$), decreasing pH will increase the solubility of $Cu(OH)_2$.

e) Since
$$F^- + H_3O \longrightarrow HF + H_2O$$
decreasing pH increases the solubility of CaF_2.

f) There is a slight increase in solubility, since to a small extent
$$SO_4^{2-} + H_3O^+ \rightleftharpoons HSO_4^- + H_2O.$$

46. Since the solution is buffered to $pH = 8.0$, thus $pOH = 6.0$ and the hydroxide concentration is
$$[OH^-] = 1.0 \times 10^{-6}.$$
For $Pb(OH)_2$,
$$[Pb^{2+}][OH^-]^2 = 4.2 \times 10^{-15}$$
$$[Pb^{2+}] = 4.2 \times 10^{-15}/[OH^-]^2$$
$$= 4.2 \times 10^{-3}.$$
Thus the solubility of $Pb(OH)_2$ here is 4.2×10^{-3} M, i.e. 1.0 g L^{-1}.

47. Since pH = 8.0, pOH = 6.0 and $[OH^-] = 1.0 \times 10^{-6}$ M.
In the saturated solution,
$$[Ni^{2+}] = 0.0020 \text{ M}.$$
From the equilibrium

$$Ni(OH)_2(s) \rightleftharpoons Ni^{2+} + 2OH^-$$

$$K_{sp} = [Ni^{2+}][OH^-]^2.$$

By substitution,
$$K_{sp} = 2.0 \times 10^{-15}.$$
The solubility at pH = 7 can be found by substituting
$[OH^-] = 1.0 \times 10^{-7}$ M:
$$[Ni^{2+}] = 2.0 \times 10^{-15}/(1.0 \times 10^{-7})^2$$
$$= 0.20 \text{ M}.$$

48. The solubilities can be calculated by the same methodology as used for Q. 46; since pH = 5.5, pOH = 8.5 and $[OH^-] = 3.2 \times 10^{-9}$ M.
For $Cu(OH)_2$, $[Cu^{2+}] = 1.6 \times 10^{-19} (3.2 \times 10^{-9})^2$
$$= 1.6 \times 10^{-2} \text{ M}.$$
For $Pb(OH)_2$, $[Pb^{2+}] = 4.2 \times 10^{-15} (3.2 \times 10^{-9})^2$
$$= 4.1 \times 10^2 \text{ M}.$$
Yes, they can be separated since most Cu^{2+} in a concentrated solution will precipitate, but $Pb(OH)_2$ will not.

49. For the equilibrium

$$H_2S + 2H_2O \rightleftharpoons 2H_3O^+ + S^{2-}$$

we have $\dfrac{[H_3O^+]^2[S^{2-}]}{[H_2O} = 1.0 \times 10^{-19}.$

We are told
$$[H_2S] = 0.10 \text{ M}$$
and $[H_3O^+] = 1.0 \times 10^{-4}$ (since pH = 4.00).
Thus we can solve for the sulfide concentration in this solution:
$$[S^{2-}] = 1.0 \times 10^{-19} \times 0.10/(1.0 \times 10^{-4})^2$$
$$= 1.0 \times 10^{-12}.$$
Each of the cations Cu^{2+}, Fe^{2+}, Pb^{2+}, and Ag^+ has an insoluble sulfide: CuS, FeS, PbS, Ag_2S. We can find the maximum ion concentrations by determining $[Cu^{2+}]$, etc. just at the point of precipitation, i.e. when
$$[Cu^{2+}][S^-] = K_{sp}$$
$$[Cu^{2+}] = 8 \times 10^{-37}/1.0 \times 10^{-12} = 8.0 \times 10^{-25} \text{ M}$$
$$[Fe^{2+}] = 6.3 \times 10^{-18}/1.0 \times 10^{-12} = 6.3 \times 10^{-6} \text{ M}$$
$$[Pb^{2+}] = 7 \times 10^{-29}/1.0 \times 10^{-12} = 7.0 \times 10^{-17} \text{ M}$$
while for Ag_2S, since
$$[Ag^+]^2[S^{2-}] = K_{sp}$$
$$[Ag^+]^2 = 5.5 \times 10^{-51}/1.0 \times 10^{-12}$$
so $[Ag^+] = 7.4 \times 10^{-20}$ M.

CHAPTER 16

1. Electrolysis is a process in which electrical energy is used to produce a chemical change. An electrolyte is a substance which, when melted or dissolved in a solvent, will carry an electrical current. In ionic conduction, the electrical current is carried by ions whereas in electronic conduction it is carried by electrons.

2. In each case, we first write the balanced half-reaction, and thereby deduce the moles of electrons from the moles of chemicals; the latter is transformed to coulombs by the conversion factor
   1 mole electrons = 96,500 C.

a) $Cu^{2+} + 2e^- \longrightarrow Cu$

$$1 \text{ mole } Cu^{2+} \times \frac{2 \text{ moles } e^-}{1 \text{ mole } Cu^{2+}} \times \frac{96,500 \text{ C}}{1 \text{ mole } e^-} = 1.93 \times 10^5 \text{ C.}$$

b) $Fe^{3+} + e^- \longrightarrow Fe^{2+}$
Similarly to (a), we obtain 96,500 C.

c) $MnO_4^- + 8H^+ + 5e^- \longrightarrow Mn^{2+} + 4H_2O$
Similarly to (a), we obtain 4.83×10^5 C.

d) $ClO_3^- + 6H^+ + 6e^- \longrightarrow Cl^- + 3H_2O$
Similarly to (a), we obtain 5.79×10^5 C.

3. The methodology is the same as in Q. 2.
a) $2H_2O \longrightarrow O_2 + 4H^+ + 4e^-$

$$1 \text{ mole } H_2O \times \frac{4 \text{ moles } e^-}{2 \text{ moles } H_2O} \times \frac{96,500 \text{ C}}{1 \text{ mole } e^-} = 1.93 \times 10^5 \text{ C.}$$

b) $Cl_2 + 6H_2O \longrightarrow 2ClO_3^- + 12H^+ + 10e^-$.
Similarly to part (a), we obtain 9.65×10^5 C.

c) $Pb + 2H_2O \longrightarrow PbO_2 + 4H^+ + 4e^-$
Similarly to part (a), we obtain 3.86×10^5 C.

d) $2FeO + H_2O \longrightarrow Fe_2O_3 + 2H^+ + 2e^-$
We obtain 9.65×10^4 C.

4. In each case we must first identify the half-reaction which involves the product whose amount is specified, balance it, deduce the moles of product from the mass or volume given, and relate it to the moles and coulombs of electrons.

a) At STP, 1 mole of gas = 22.4 L.
Thus we can convert volume O_2 to moles O_2:

$$50.0 \text{ mL } O_2 \times \frac{1 \text{ L } O_2}{1000 \text{ mL } O_2} \times \frac{1 \text{ mole } O_2}{22.4 \text{ L } O_2} = 0.00223 \text{ moles } O_2.$$

In $Na_2SO_4(aq)$, according to the text H_2O is electrolyzed. Thus the half-reaction is
$$2H_2O \longrightarrow O_2 + 4H^+ + 4e^-$$

$$0.00223 \text{ moles } O_2 \times \frac{4 \text{ moles } e^-}{1 \text{ mole } O_2} \times \frac{96,500 \text{ C}}{1 \text{ mole } e^-} = 861 \text{ C.}$$

b) $Al^{3+} + 3e^- \longrightarrow Al$

$$50,000 \text{ g Al} \times \frac{1 \text{ mole Al}}{26.98 \text{ g Al}} \times \frac{3 \text{ moles } e^-}{1 \text{ mole Al}} \times \frac{96,500 \text{ C}}{1 \text{ mole } e^-}$$

$$= 5.37 \times 10^8 \text{ C.}$$

c) $Ca^{2+} + 2e^- \longrightarrow Ca$
Similarly to part (b), we obtain 9.63×10^4 C.

d) $Ag^+ + e^- \longrightarrow Ag$
Similarly to part (b), we obtain 4470 C.

5. From the balanced half-reaction, we first deduce the moles of electrons, and then transform this to coulombs and ultimately to seconds since for a current of 2.00 A,
     2.00 coulomb ≡ 1 second
$Ni^{2+} + 2e^- \longrightarrow Ni.$

$$1000 \text{ g Ni} \times \frac{1 \text{ mole Ni}}{58.71 \text{ g Ni}} \times \frac{2 \text{ moles } e^-}{1 \text{ mole Ni}} \times \frac{96,500 \text{ C}}{1 \text{ mole } e^-} \times \frac{\text{second}}{2 \text{ C}}$$

$$= 1.64 \times 10^6 \text{ s (i.e 19 days).}$$

6. Here we require the balanced equations for both oxidation and reduction:
     $2 Cl^- \longrightarrow Cl_2 + 2e^-$
     $2H_2O + 2e^- \longrightarrow 2OH^- + H_2.$
The coulombs of charge, and thus the moles of electrons, can be obtained from the current and time (in seconds):

$$\frac{0.200 \text{ C}}{1 \text{ s}} \times 3.00 \text{ h} \times \frac{60 \text{ min}}{1 \text{ h}} \times \frac{60 \text{ s}}{1 \text{ min}} \times \frac{1 \text{ moles } e^-}{96,500 \text{ C}} = 0.0224 \text{ moles } e^-.$$

The amount of chemicals can be obtained from moles of e^-:

$$0.0224 \text{ moles } e^- \times \frac{1 \text{ mole } Cl_2}{2 \text{ moles } e^-} \times \frac{70.90 \text{ g } Cl_2}{1 \text{ mole } Cl_2} = 0.794 \text{ g } Cl_2.$$

Similarly since 1 mole OH^- yields 1 mole NaOH, we obtain 0.896 g NaOH.

239

7. From the time and current, we can deduce the moles of e^-; from the half-reactions this can be used to deduce moles of H_2 and O_2, and using the ideal gas law their volumes can be computed:

$$\frac{4.00\ C}{1\ s} \times 30\ min \times \frac{60\ s}{1\ min} \times \frac{1\ mole\ e^-}{96,500\ C} = 0.0746\ moles\ e^-.$$

$$2H_2O \longrightarrow O_2 + 4H^+ + 4e^-$$
$$2H_2O + 2e^- \longrightarrow H_2 + 2OH^-$$

$$0.0746\ moles\ e^- \times \frac{1\ mole\ O_2}{4\ moles\ e^-} = 0.0187\ moles\ O_2.$$

Similarly, we obtain 0.0373 moles H_2.
Since $PV = nRT$, $V = nRT/P$.
Thus for O_2, $V = 0.0187 \times 0.0821 \times 300/(740/760) = 0.473$ L and similarly for H_2, $V = 0.944$ L.

8. We convert mass Ag to moles Ag and then to moles e^- since the half-reaction is $Ag^+ + e^- \longrightarrow Ag$. We then obtain coulombs of charge and ultimately seconds of reaction, since according to the current, 6.00 C = 1 second:

$$16.0\ g\ Ag \times \frac{1\ mole\ Ag}{107.87\ g\ Ag} \times \frac{1\ mole\ e^-}{1\ mole\ Ag} \times \frac{96,500\ C}{1\ mole\ e^-} \times \frac{1\ s}{6.00\ C}$$

$$= 2390\ s.$$

9. First calculate the mass of Ag needed, remembering that the tray has two sides:
$V = 0.002\ cm \times 24\ cm \times 12\ cm = 0.576\ cm^3$ per side.
We then obtain the mass of Ag from the total volume of $2 \times 0.576 = 1.15\ cm^3$ and the density:

$$1.15\ cm^3 \times \frac{10.54\ g}{1\ cm^3} = 12.1\ g.$$

We then convert mass Ag to moles Ag and moles e^- given that the half-reaction is $Ag^+ + e^- \longrightarrow Ag$, and then to coulombs and finally time:

$$12.1\ g\ Ag \times \frac{1\ moles\ Ag}{107.87\ g\ Ag} \times \frac{1\ mole\ e^-}{1\ mole\ Ag} \times \frac{96,500\ C}{1\ mole\ e^-} \times \frac{1\ s}{7.65\ C}$$

$$= 1410\ s.$$

10. The reaction is $Cr^{3+} + 3e^- \longrightarrow Cr$.
The volume of Cr, in cm^3, is
$(100\ cm)^2 \times 0.01\ cm = 100\ cm^3$
and thus the mass of Cr required is

$$100\ cm^3 \times \frac{7.1\ g}{1\ cm^3} = 710\ g.$$

240

We convert mass Cr to moles Cr and then to moles e (using the chemical equation) and charge:

$$710 \text{ g Cr} \times \frac{1 \text{ mole Cr}}{52.00 \text{ g Cr}} \times \frac{3 \text{ moles e}^-}{1 \text{ mole Cr}} \times \frac{96,500 \text{ C}}{1 \text{ mole e}^-} = 3.95 \times 10^6 \text{ C}$$

Given that the current is 1.5 A = 1.5 C/s, then the time is

$$3.95 \times 10^6 \text{ C} \times \frac{1 \text{ s}}{1.5 \text{ C}} = 2.63 \times 10^6 \text{ s}.$$

Thus 2.63×10^6 seconds, i.e. 30 days, are required.

11. First we write the half-reactions:
$$Cu^{2+} + 2e^- \longrightarrow Cu$$
$$Ni^{2+} + 2e^- \longrightarrow Ni.$$
Thus the moles of Cu and Ni are identical, and we can calculate the latter from the former:

$$10.0 \text{ g Cu} \times \frac{1 \text{ mole Cu}}{63.54 \text{ g Cu}} \times \frac{1 \text{ mole Ni}}{1 \text{ mole Cu}} \times \frac{58.71 \text{ g Ni}}{1 \text{ mole Ni}}$$

$$= 9.24 \text{ g Ni}.$$

12. a) In a molten salt, the cation of the salt gives electrons and its anion loses electrons:
$$Al^{3+} + 3e^- \longrightarrow Al$$
$$2Cl^- \longrightarrow Cl_2 + 2e^-.$$

   b) In aqueous solutions, we must consider the possibility that H_2O rather than the ions is oxidized and/or reduced. Since Al^{3+} is less easily reduced than H_2O, the reduction reaction will be
$$2H_2O + 2e^- \longrightarrow H_2 + 2OH^-.$$
If the solution is concentrated, Cl^- will be oxidized to Cl_2 as we find for NaCl(aq); otherwise H_2O will be oxidized to O_2.

13. a) See the logic in Q. 12(a). We obtain Mg and Br_2.

   b) See the logic in Q. 12(b). Since Cu^{2+} is more easily reduced than H_2O, but NO_3^- is less readily oxidized, we obtain Cu and O_2.

   c) See the logic for Q. 12(b). We obtain H_2 and I_2.

   d) See the logic for Q. 12(a). We obtain Fe and Cl_2.

14. In aqueous solution, HBr dissociates to H^+ (or H_3O^+) and Br^-. Thus the reduction is
$$2H^+ + 2e^- \longrightarrow H_2(g).$$
The oxidation will be either that of Br^- or of H_2O. Since Br^- is more easily oxidized than is H_2O, the oxidation is
$$2Br^- \longrightarrow Br_2(\ell) + 2e^-.$$

Br⁻ ions move to the anode, and H^+ (or H_3O^+) to the cathode. Your diagram should be like Fig. 16.4 of the text, with Br⁻ replacing Cl⁻ and H^+ replacing Na^+.

15. In aqueous solution, $CuSO_4$ exists as Cu^{2+} and SO_4^{2-}. Since Cu^{2+} is more easily reduced than water, the reduction half-reaction is
$$Cu^{2+} + 2e^- \longrightarrow Cu.$$
Since sulfate is less easily oxidized than water, the oxidation half-reaction is
$$2H_2O \longrightarrow O_2(g) + 4H^+ + 4e^-.$$
In your diagram (see Fig. 16.5 of text), the Cu^{2+} should move to the cathode, and sulfate to the anode.

16. From the current and time, the amount of electricity can be calculated:

$$3601.5 \text{ s} \times \frac{1.487 \text{ C}}{1 \text{ s}} = 5355 \text{ C}.$$

The moles of I_2 and moles e^- can be obtained from the balanced reaction $2I^- \longrightarrow I_2 + 2e^-$ and the mass of I_2:

$$7.2428 \text{ g } I_2 \times \frac{1 \text{ mole } I_2}{253.81 \text{ } I_2} \times \frac{2 \text{ moles } e^-}{1 \text{ mole } I_2} = 0.05707 \text{ moles } e^-.$$

Thus the value for the Faraday constant is

$$\frac{5355 \text{ C}}{0.05707 \text{ moles } e^-} = 93830 \text{ C/mole}.$$

The accepted value listed in the text is 96485.

17. The balanced half-reactions are
$$Al^{3+} + 3e^- \longrightarrow Al$$
$$C + 2O^{2-} \longrightarrow CO_2 + 4e^-.$$
The current is 1.30×10^5 C/s; thus for 1 minute we obtain:

$$\frac{60 \text{ s}}{1 \text{ m}} \times \frac{1.30 \times 10^5 \text{ C}}{1 \text{ s}} \times \frac{1 \text{ mole } e^-}{96,500 \text{ C}}$$

$$= 8.08 \times 10^3 \text{ moles } e^-, \text{ i.e. } 8.08 \times 10^1 \text{ F}.$$

We now transform to masses of products, using the balanced equations:

$$8.08 \times 10^1 \text{ moles } e^- \times \frac{1 \text{ mole Al}}{3 \text{ moles } e^-} \times \frac{26.98 \text{ g Al}}{1 \text{ mole Al}} = 7.27 \times 10^7 \text{ g Al}$$

$$8.08 \times 10^1 \text{ moles } e^- \times \frac{1 \text{ mole C}}{4 \text{ moles } e^-} \times \frac{12.01 \text{ g C}}{1 \text{ mole C}} = 2.43 \times 10^2 \text{ g C}.$$

Converting to 100 such cells, and transforming to a complete day basis, we obtain 1.05×10^8 g Al and 3.51×10^7 g C.

18. From the current, time and balanced equation we can deduce the moles of metal:

$$M^{2+} + 2e^- \longrightarrow M$$

$$2\ h \times \frac{3600\ s}{1\ h} \times \frac{0.500\ C}{1\ s} \times \frac{1\ mole\ e^-}{96,500\ C} \quad \frac{1\ mole\ M}{2\ moles\ e^-}$$

$$= 0.0187\ moles\ M.$$

Thus the atomic mass is 1.98 g/0.0187 moles = 106 g/mole, and thus the metal is palladium since only it has an atomic mass of 106.

19. To decide whether or not a given redox reaction proceeds to a significant extent, we compare the positions of the two half-reactions (written as reductions) in Table 16.1. The one lying lower in the Table proceeds as a reduction, but the higher one is reversed. In the present example, a reaction will "go" if $Cr_2O_7^{2-}$ is reduced to Cr^{3+}; that is, if it is the $Cr_2O_7^{2-}$ half-reaction which proceeds as a reduction, and therefore the other half-reaction lies <u>above</u> it in the Table. For example, since F^- lies <u>below</u> $Cr_2O_7^{2-}$ (i.e. in the $F_2 \rightarrow F^-$ reaction) clearly $Cr_2O_7^{2-}$ will not oxidize F^- to F_2, and similarly for Cl^-. However since the reduction $Br_2 \rightarrow 2Br^-$ lies above the $Cr_2O_7^{2-}$ reduction, we conclude $Cr_2O_7^{2-}$ will oxidize Br^-. Similarly we obtain: $Cr_2O_7^{2-}$ will oxidize Br^-, I^-, Hg_2^{2+}, Fe^{2+} and H_2S.

20. For each reaction, we can calculate the potential of the corresponding cell from the values in Table 16.1.

   a) The unbalanced half-cell reactions are

   $$H_2O_2 \longrightarrow O_2$$
   $$Cu^{2+} \longrightarrow Cu$$

   which after balancing become

   From Table 16.1

   $$H_2O_2 \longrightarrow O_2 + 2H^+ + 2e^- \quad E^\circ_{ox} = -E^\circ_{red} = -0.68\ V$$
   $$Cu^{2+} + 2e^- \longrightarrow Cu \qquad\qquad\qquad E^\circ_{red} = +0.34\ V$$
   $$\overline{\qquad\qquad\qquad\qquad\qquad\qquad E^\circ_{cell} = -0.34\ V}$$

   Since E°_{cell} is negative, this reaction does <u>not</u> proceed as written, which in full was
   $$H_2O_2 + Cu^{2+} \longrightarrow O_2 + 2H^+ + Cu.$$

b) The half-reactions (balanced) are

   $$Ag^+ + e^- \longrightarrow Ag \qquad\qquad\qquad E^\circ_{red} = +0.80\ V$$
   $$Fe^{2+} \longrightarrow Fe^{3+} + e^- \quad E^\circ_{ox} = -E^\circ_{red} = -0.77\ V$$
   $$\overline{\qquad\qquad\qquad\qquad\qquad\qquad E^\circ_{cell} = +0.03\ V}$$

   Thus the overall reaction $Ag^+ + Fe^{2+} \longrightarrow Ag + Fe^{3+}$ will proceed as written.

c) Similarly to parts a) and b),

$$2I^- \rightarrow I_2 + 2e^- \qquad E^\circ_{ox} = -E^\circ_{red} = -0.54 \text{ V}$$
$$4H^+ + 3e^- + NO_3^- \rightarrow NO + 2e^- \qquad \underline{E^\circ_{red} = +0.97 \text{ V}}$$
$$E^\circ_{cell} = +0.43 \text{ V}$$

The overall reaction,
$$6I^- + 8H^+ + 2NO_3^- \longrightarrow 3I_2 + 2NO + 4H_2O$$
therefore does proceed as written.

21. Methodology is similar to that for Q. 19. Since the $Cr_2O_7^{2-}$ reduction lies below that for O_2 to H_2O, $Cr_2O_7^{2-}$ can oxidize H_2O to O_2. Solutions of $Cr_2O_7^{2-}$ are stable presumably because the E°_{cell} value while positive is small and because the reaction is very slow.

22. In each case, we calculate the cell potential for the reaction as written in order to decide if the reaction is spontaneous.

    a) The half-reactions and their potentials are

$$Mg \longrightarrow Mg^{2+} + 2e^- \qquad E^\circ_{ox} = -E^\circ_{red} = +2.36 \text{ V}$$
$$Cr^{3+} + 3e^- \longrightarrow Cr \qquad \underline{E^\circ_{red} = -0.74 \text{ V}}$$
$$E^\circ_{cell} = +1.62 \text{ V}$$

Thus the overall reaction given below (and obtained by forcing the electrons on the two sides to balance) is spontaneous:
$$3Mg + 2Cr^{3+} \longrightarrow 3Mg^{2+} + 2Cr.$$

    b) The half-reactions and their potentials are

$$I_2(s) + 2e^- \longrightarrow 2I^- \qquad E^\circ_{red} = +0.54 \text{ V}$$
$$H_2(g) \longrightarrow 2H^+ + 2e^- \qquad E^\circ_{ox} = -E^\circ_{red} = 0$$
$$E^\circ_{cell} = +0.54 \text{ V}$$

Thus the overall reaction is spontaneous:
$$H_2(g) + I_2(g) \longrightarrow 2H^+ + 2I^-.$$

    c) The unbalanced half-reactions are $Cu \longrightarrow Cu^{2+}$ and $NO_3^- \longrightarrow N_2O_4$ (used since $NO_3^- \rightarrow NO_2$ is not in the Table). Upon balancing (acid solution) we obtain

$$Cu \rightarrow Cu^{2+} + 2e^- \qquad E^\circ_{ox} = -E^\circ_{red} = -0.34 \text{ V}$$
$$2NO_3^- + 4H^+ + 2e^- \rightarrow N_2O_4 + 2H_2O \qquad \underline{E^\circ_{red} = +0.80 \text{ V}}$$
$$E^\circ_{cell} = +0.46 \text{ V}$$

Thus the overall reaction shown below is spontaneous:
$$Cu + 2NO_3^- + 4H^+ \longrightarrow Cu^{2+} + N_2O_4 + 2H_2O.$$

23. The order will be that given in Table 16.1 for these metals, since that of the lower half-reaction will always occur as written, i.e. the lower metal will be produced in

244

its elemental form. Thus magnesium will dissolve and produce any of the other metals, Al will displace any but Mg, etc.

$$Mg \; > \; Al \; > \; Zn \; > \; Fe \; > \; Cu.$$

24. If Fe^{2+} is to reduce a substance, it will yield an electron and form Fe^{3+}. Thus we want the $Fe^{3+} + e^- \longrightarrow Fe^{2+}$ reduction to be reversed; this will occur with any material for which the half-reaction lies below that for Fe^{3+} in Table 16.1. Thus Fe^{2+} will reduce Ag^+, Br_2 and MnO_4^- only in the list given.

25. Since the MnO_2 reaction in Table 16.1 lies lower than do the reduction reactions for all the ions mentioned, i.e. since their E°_{red} values are less positive than that for MnO_2, we conclude that all four ions are oxidized by MnO_2.

26. a) The reduction of Fe^{3+} to Fe^{2+} lies below the reduction of I_2 to I^- in Table 16.1; thus Fe^{3+} oxidizes I^- to I_2.

    b) The reduction of Ag^+ to Ag lies below that of Cu^{2+} to Cu (or Cu^+ to Cu) in Table 16.1; thus Ag^+ oxidizes Cu.

    c) Fe^{3+} will not oxidize Br^- to Br_2, since the reduction of Br_2 to Br^- lies lower in the Table than the reduction of Fe^{3+} to Fe^{2+}. No reaction will occur.

    d) As in (c), no reaction will occur, for the same reason.

    e) The reduction of Br_2 to Br^- lies lower than the reduction of Fe^{3+} to Fe^{2+}; thus the reaction $Br_2 + 2Fe^{2+} \longrightarrow 2Br^- + 2Fe^{3+}$ will occur.

27. The method is similar to that for Q. 19,20; the data in Table 16.1 is appropriate to 1 M solutions.

    a) The balanced half-reactions are
    $$Mn^{2+} + 4H_2O \longrightarrow MnO_4^- + 8H^+ + 5e^-$$
    $$Cr_2O_7^{2-} + 14H^+ + 6e^- \longrightarrow 2Cr^{3+} + 7H_2O.$$

    For the Mn^{2+} oxidation, $E^\circ_{ox} = - E^\circ_{red} = - 1.49$ V
    $Cr_2O_7^{2-}$ reduction, $\underline{\hspace{2.5cm} E^\circ_{red} = + 1.33 \text{ V}}$
    $E^\circ_{cell} = - 0.16$ V.

    Thus the balanced reaction (see below) will <u>not</u> occur.
    $$6Mn^{2+} + 5Cr_2O_7^{2-} + 22H^+ \longrightarrow 6MnO_4^- \; 10Cr^{3+} + 11H_2O.$$

    b) Presumably here the O_2 is reduced to H_2O; thus the half-reactions are

    $O_2 + 4H^+ + 4e^- \longrightarrow H_2O$ $\qquad E^\circ_{red} = + 1.23$ V
    $2Br^- \longrightarrow Br_2 + 2e^-$ $\quad \underline{E^\circ_{ox} = - E^\circ_{red} = - 1.09 \text{ V}}$
    $E^\circ_{cell} = + 0.14$ V.

The balanced overall reaction, which will proceed, is
$$O_2 + 4Br^- + 4H^+ \longrightarrow 2H_2O + Br_2$$

c) The half-reactions are

$$Au \longrightarrow Au^{3+} + 3e^- \qquad E^\circ_{ox} = -E^\circ_{red} = -1.50 \text{ V}$$
$$2e^- + Cl_2 \longrightarrow 2Cl^- \qquad \qquad \underline{E^\circ_{red} = +1.36 \text{ V}}$$
$$E^\circ_{cell} = -0.14 \text{ V}.$$

Thus the overall reaction (below) will <u>not</u> proceed:
$$2Au + 3Cl_2 \longrightarrow 2Au^{3+} + 6Cl^-$$

28. a) The half-reactions are
$$Zn \longrightarrow Zn^{2+} + 2e^- \qquad \text{oxidation; anode}$$
$$e^- + Ag^+ \longrightarrow Ag \qquad \qquad \text{reduction; cathode.}$$

Your cell diagram should show Zn as the anode and Ag as the cathode, with electrons moving externally from Zn to Ag. The current within the cell is carried by movement of Ag^+ ions toward the Ag electrode, and anions (not specified) toward the Zn electrode.

b)
$$Zn \longrightarrow Zn^{2+} + 2e^- \qquad E^\circ_{ox} = -E^\circ_{red} = 0.76 \text{ V}$$
$$e^- + Ag^+ \longrightarrow Ag \qquad \qquad E^\circ_{red} = +0.80 \text{ V}.$$

Thus $E^\circ_{cell} = 1.56$ V.

29. a) The reaction of the electrode dipping into $KMnO_4$ (which dissociates to K^+ and MnO_4^-) is (see Table 16.1)
$$MnO_4^- + 8H^+ + 5e^- \longrightarrow Mn^{2+} + 4H_2O \qquad E^\circ_{red} = +1.49 \text{ V}.$$
This is the cathode, since it occurs as a reduction (see full equation given in the question). The other reaction must be the oxidation of Fe^{2+} to Fe^{3+}:
$$Fe^{2+} \longrightarrow Fe^{3+} + e^- \qquad E^\circ_{ox} = -E^\circ_{red} = -0.77 \text{ V}.$$
Since it is an oxidation, the Pt electrode dipping in the $FeSO_4$ is the anode.

b) The electrons move from the Pt electrode in $FeSO_4$ to that dipping into MnO_4^-, since Fe^{2+} releases electrons and MnO_4^- uses them.

c) The Fe^{2+} ions move toward the anode and the MnO_4^- to the cathode.

d) $E^\circ_{cell} = E^\circ_{red} + E^\circ_{ox} = +1.49 - 0.77 = +0.72$ V.

30. a) The possible reduction half-reactions are

$$Pb^{2+} + 2e^- \longrightarrow Pb \qquad E^\circ_{red} = -0.13 \text{ V}$$
$$Cu^{2+} + 2e^- \longrightarrow Cu \qquad E^\circ_{red} = +0.34 \text{ V}.$$

Since Cu lies lower in the table, the copper electrode will be the cathode and the Pb the anode, at which Pb $\longrightarrow Pb^{2+} + 2e^-$ will occur. $E^\circ_{cell} = E^\circ_{red} +$

E°_{ox} = + 0.34 + 0.13 = + 0.47 V. Electrons will flow from Pb to Cu externally in the circuit in your diagram.

b) $Cl_2 + 2e^- \longrightarrow 2Cl^-$ E°_{red} = + 1.36 V
    $AgCl(s) + e^- \longrightarrow Ag + Cl^-$ E°_{red} = + 0.22 V.

Since the Cl_2 reaction lies lower, the platinum wire will be the cathode at which Cl_2 reduction will occur, and the silver wire will be the anode, at which the reaction is $Ag + Cl^- \longrightarrow AgCl + e^-$. The cell potential is 1.236 – 0.22 = 1.14 V, and electrons flow externally from the Ag electrode to the Pt.

c) The potential reaction here is
      $2HI \longrightarrow H_2 + I_2$
which in aqueous solution would proceed via

   $2H^+ + 2e^- \longrightarrow H_2$ E°_{red} = 0
   $2I^- \longrightarrow I_2 + 2e^-$ $E^{\circ}_{ox} = - E^{\circ}_{red}$ = – 0.54 V

Overall E°_{cell} = – 0.54 V and the reaction will not proceed as written. Since no I_2 is available, the reverse reactionn cannot occur.

31. According to Le Chatelier's Principle as applied to this reaction, increasing $[I^-]$ will shift the equilibrium to the right; i.e. it will make the cell potential more positive, or less negative.

32. The unbalanced half-reactions are
         $Cl_2 \longrightarrow HOCl$ for which E°_{ox} = +1.63 V.
and $Cl_2 \longrightarrow Cl^-$
Upon balancing, we obtain

$Cl_2 + 2H_2O \longrightarrow$
   $2HOCl + 2H^+ + 2e^-$ $E^{\circ}_{ox} = - E^{\circ}_{red}$ = – 1.63 V
and
$Cl_2 + 2e^- \longrightarrow 2Cl^-$ E°_{red} = + 1.36 V

Thus the overall reaction is
    $2Cl_2 + 2H_2O \longrightarrow 2HOCl + 2H^+ + 2Cl^-$
for which E°_{cell} = 1.36 – 1.63 = – 0.27 V.
We can obtain K from E°_{cell} via the equation (from the text)
     $\ln K = nE^{\circ}/0.0257$.
Here n = 2 (since two electrons are involved in the reaction), so
     $\ln K$ = 2 x (– 0.27)/0.0257 = – 21.
Thus   K = 7.6 x 10^{-10}.

33. Since for

$Sn^{2+} + 2e^- \longrightarrow Sn$ E°_{red} = – 0.16 V
      $Pb \longrightarrow Pb^{2+} + 2e^-$ $E^{\circ}_{ox} = - E^{\circ}_{red}$ = + 0.13 V

thus $E^{\circ}_{cell} = -0.03$ V. Under non-standard conditions,
$$E = E^{\circ} - (RT/nF) \ln Q.$$

Here n $= 2$, we take T $= 298$ K, F $= 96,500$ C and R
$= 8.314$ J K^{-1}, so
$$E = E^{\circ} - 0.0128 \ln Q$$
Since $E^{\circ} = -0.03$ V but E $= +0.22$ V, thus
$$0.22 = -0.03 - 0.0128 \ln Q$$
i.e. $Q = 3.3 \times 10^{-9}$.
Since here $Q = [Pb^{2+}]/[Sn^{2+}]$
but we are told $[Sn^{2+}] = 1$ M, thus
$$3.3 \times 10^{-9} = [Pb^{2+}]/1$$
i.e. $[Pb^{2+}] = 3.3 \times 10^{-9}$ M.

Now for $PbSO_4(s) \rightleftharpoons Pb^{2+} + SO_4{}^{2-}$
it follows that
$$K_{sp} = [Pb^{2+}][SO_4{}^{2-}]$$
then by substitution
$$K_{sp} = 3.3 \times 10^{-9} \times 1$$
i.e. $K_{sp} = 3.3 \times 10^{-9}$.

34. The possible reduction half-reactions are
$$Fe^{2+} + 2e^- \longrightarrow Fe$$
$$Cu^{2+} + 2e^- \longrightarrow Cu$$
Since the Cu reduction lies lower in Table 16.1, it will
proceed as written and iron will be oxidized, not reduced.
The correct reactions and cell potentials are

$$Fe \longrightarrow Fe^{2+} + 2e^- \qquad E^{\circ}_{ox} = -E^{\circ}_{red} = +0.44 \text{ V}$$
$$Cu^{2+} + 2e^- \longrightarrow Cu \qquad \qquad E^{\circ}_{red} = +0.34 \text{ V}$$
$$E^{\circ}_{cell} = +0.78 \text{ V}.$$

Thus the iron will dissolve, and the copper electrode will
increase in mass. The initial cell potential will be 0.78
V, i.e. when the ion concentrations are at their standard
1 M values. As the reaction proceeds toward equilibrium,
this potential will decrease eventually to zero; the Cu^{2+}
solution will become less concentrated and the Fe^{2+}
solution will become more concentrated.

35. We write first the half-reaction for oxidation of C_2H_6 to
CO_2:
$$C_2H_6 \longrightarrow 2CO_2.$$
Balancing in acidic solutions we obtain
$$C_2H_6 + 4H_2O \longrightarrow 2CO_2 + 14H^+ + 14e^-.$$
The reaction for O_2 produces H_2O (see Table 16.1):
$$O_2 + 4H^+ + 4e^- \longrightarrow 2H_2O.$$
When combined to eliminate electrons, we obtain
$$2C_2H_6 + 7O_2 \longrightarrow 4CO_2 + 6H_2O$$
in a process which involves 28 electrons.
From the current of 0.50 A and the time of 6.0 h, we
obtain the charge in coulombs and then moles:

$$6.0 \text{ h} \times \frac{3600 \text{ s}}{1 \text{ h}} \times \frac{0.50 \text{ C}}{1 \text{ s}} \times \frac{1 \text{ mole e}^-}{96,500 \text{ C}} = 0.11 \text{ mole e}^-.$$

Converting to moles C_2H_6 and then to volume, we obtain

$$0.11 \text{ moles e}^- \times \frac{2 \text{ moles } C_2H_6}{28 \text{ moles e}^-} \times \frac{22.4 \text{ L } C_2H_6}{1 \text{ mole } C_2H_6} = 0.18 \text{ L } C_2H_6.$$

The volume of O_2 needed is 7/2 times as great (see balanced equation), i.e. 0.63 L O_2.

36. a) The half-reactions are (see Table 16.1)
$Zn \rightarrow Zn^{2+} + 2e^-$ anode (since it is oxidized)
$O_2 + 4H^+ + 4e^- \rightarrow 2H_2O$ cathode (reduction).

b) Under standard conditions, since $E°_{red} = -0.76$ V for the Zn reaction, $E°_{ox} = +0.76$ V. For the O_2 reduction under standard conditions, $E°_{red} = +1.23$ V. Thus the standard cell potential is 1.99 V. Thus if concentrations and potential measures near standard were used, a cell potential of 2 V would be obtained.

c) We can deduce the total electrical charge associated with a 5.0 g Zn electrode as follows:

$$5.0 \text{ g Zn} \times \frac{1 \text{ mole Zn}}{65.37 \text{ Zn}} \times \frac{2 \text{ moles e}^-}{1 \text{ mole Zn}} \times \frac{96,500 \text{ C}}{1 \text{ mole e}^-} = 1.5 \times 10^4 \text{ C}.$$

This value can be converted to time by using a unit factor based upon the current of 40 microamperes:

$$1.50 \times 10^4 \text{ C} \times \frac{1s}{40 \times 10^{-6} \text{ C}} = 3.8 \times 10^8 \text{ s}.$$

Upon conversion, this is found to be about 12 years.

249

CHAPTER 17

1. a) HNO_3.

    c) KNO_2 since nitrite is NO_2^-.

    e) N_2O_5.

    g) NaN_3.

    b) HNO_2.

    d) NO.

    f) N_2H_4.

    h) NH_2OH.

2. a) O_3.

    b) Na_2O_2 since peroxide ion is O_2^{2-}.

    c) BaO_2.

    d) KO_2.

3. a) Sodium nitrate, since NO_3^- is nitrate.

    b) Potassium nitrite, since NO_2^- is nitrite.

    c) Dinitrogen tetraoxide.

    d) Hydrazoic acid.

    e) Hydroxylamine.

    f) Barium peroxide.

    g) Potassium superoxide.

    h) Hydrazine.

    i) Lithium azide, since N_3^- is the azide ion.

    j) Lithium nitride, since N^{3-} is the nitride ion.

4. The anhydride of an acid is the oxide for which the atoms have the same oxidation states as they do in the acid; thus the acid can be obtained from the anhydride by an acid-base reaction with water.

    a) N_2O_5, since nitrogen is +5 in both N_2O_5 and HNO_3.

    b) N_2O_3.

    c) P_2O_3.

    d) Cl_2O_7.

    e) B_2O_3.

    f) SO_3.

    g) CO_2.

5. a) The unbalanced reaction is
    $$NH_3 + CuO \longrightarrow N_2 + H_2O + Cu.$$
    The half-reactions (unbalanced) clearly are
    $$NH_3 \longrightarrow N_2$$
    and $CuO \longrightarrow Cu$.

Using the techniques developed previously, we obtain balanced half-reactions (for alkaline solution since NH_3 is a base):

$$2NH_3 + 6OH^- \longrightarrow N_2 + 6H_2O + 6e^-$$
$$H_2O + CuO + 2e^- \longrightarrow Cu + 2OH^-.$$

Clearly the NH_3 is oxidized and the CuO is reduced, and the overall reaction is (after balancing electrons)

$$2NH_3 + 3CuO \longrightarrow N_2 + 3Cu + 3H_2O.$$

b) The unbalanced reaction is

$$NaNO_2 + NH_4Cl \longrightarrow N_2 + NaCl.$$

The Na^+ and Cl^- are not affected; thus the half-reactions both must give N_2 as product:

$$NO_2^- \longrightarrow N_2$$
$$NH_4^+ \longrightarrow N_2.$$

Upon balancing (in acid) we obtain

$$2NO_2^- + 8H^+ + 6e^- \longrightarrow N_2 + 4H_2O$$
$$2NH_4^+ \longrightarrow N_2 + 8H^+ + 6e^-.$$

Thus the nitrite is reduced and the ammonium is oxidized, and the overall balanced ionic reaction is

$$2NO_2^- + 2NH_4^+ \longrightarrow 2N_2 + 4H_2O.$$

In terms of compounds, the balanced reaction is

$$NaNO_2 + NH_4Cl \longrightarrow N_2 + 2H_2O + NaCl.$$

c) The unbalanced reaction is

$$NO + NH_3 \longrightarrow N_2 + H_2O.$$

By reasoning similar to part (b), we obtain

$$4e^- + 2NO + 4H^+ \longrightarrow N_2 + 2H_2O$$
$$2NH_3 \longrightarrow N_2 + 6H^+ + 6e^-.$$

Thus NO is reduced and NH_3 is oxidized. The overall equation is

$$6NO + 4NH_3 \longrightarrow 5N_2 + 6H_2O.$$

d) $(NH_4)_2Cr_2O_7 \longrightarrow Cr_2O_3 + N_2 + H_2O.$

The reactant can be rewritten in terms of ions, NH_4^+ and $Cr_2O_7^{2-}$, each of which is the reactant in a half-reaction; upon balancing,

$$2NH_4^+ \longrightarrow N_2 + 8H^+ + 6e^-$$
$$8H^+ + Cr_2O_7^{2-} + 6e^- \longrightarrow Cr_2O_3 + 4H_2O.$$

Thus the NH_4^+ is oxidized and the $Cr_2O_7^{2-}$ is reduced. In the form of compounds,

$$(NH_4)_2Cr_2O_7 \longrightarrow N_2 + Cr_2O_3 + 4H_2O.$$

6. a) $2KNO_3 \longrightarrow 2KNO_2 + O_2.$ In KNO_2, nitrogen is +3.

b) $NH_4NO_3 \longrightarrow N_2O + 2H_2O.$
In N_2O, the (average) oxidation number of nitrogen is +1 since oxygen is -2.

c) From Section 17.1,

$$2Pb(NO_3)_2 \longrightarrow 2PbO + 4NO_2 + O_2.$$

In NO_2, nitrogen has an oxidation number of +4 (since each oxygen is -2).

251

7. a) The unbalanced reaction is
$$HNO_2 \longrightarrow HNO_3 + NO.$$
Clearly HNO_2 must be the reactant in both half-reactions:
$$HNO_2 \longrightarrow HNO_3$$
$$HNO_2 \longrightarrow NO.$$
Upon balancing, we obtain
$$HNO_2 + H_2O \longrightarrow HNO_3 + 2H^+ + 2e^-$$
$$HNO_2 + H^+ + e^- \longrightarrow NO + H_2O.$$
Upon balancing electrons, we obtain
$$3HNO_2 \longrightarrow HNO_3 + 2NO + H_2O.$$

b) The unbalanced reaction is
$$HNO_3 \longrightarrow NO_2 + O_2.$$
Since nitrogen is present in only one reactant and one product, HNO_3 cannot be the reactant in both half-reactions. Since O_2 is produced, H_2O must then be the missing reactant.
$$HNO_3 \longrightarrow NO_2$$
$$H_2O \longrightarrow O_2.$$
Upon balancing, we obtain
$$HNO_3 + H^+ + e^- \longrightarrow NO_2 + H_2O$$
$$2H_2O \longrightarrow O_2 + 4H^+ + 4e^-.$$
Upon balancing electrons, we obtain
$$4HNO_3 \longrightarrow 4NO_2 + 2H_2O + O_2.$$

c) The unbalanced reaction, as stated in the problem, is
$$C_6H_6 + H_2SO_4 + HNO_3 \longrightarrow C_6H_5NO_2.$$
Since there is no sulfur in a product, we must assume the H_2SO_4 is present only to remove water. Thus the reaction is
$$C_6H_6 + HNO_3 \longrightarrow C_6H_5NO_2.$$
One cannot write this in half-reactions unless the product is written as a sum of separate ions, e.g. $C_6H_5^+$ and NO_2^-. Then
$$C_6H_6 \longrightarrow C_6H_5^+ + H^+ + 2e^-$$
$$H^+ + 2e^- + HNO_3 \longrightarrow NO_2^- + H_2O.$$
Adding, we obtain $C_6H_6 + HNO_3 \longrightarrow C_6H_5^+NO_2^- + H_2O.$

8. Recall that HNO_3 can act as an oxidizing agent or as an acid, depending upon its concentration and the chemical nature of the other reactant.

a) Cu cannot act as a base but can be oxidized, to Cu^{2+}. As discussed in the text, either (or both) NO_2 or NO can be produced depending upon concentration. For dilute acid,
$$3Cu + 8HNO_3 \longrightarrow 3Cu(NO_3)_2 + 2NO + 4H_2O$$

b) P_4O_{10} contains phosphorus in a fully-oxidized state, so it cannot be oxidized by HNO_3. However P_4O_{10} is a good dehydrating agent.

c) $HNO_3 + 2H_2SO_4 \longrightarrow NO_2^+ + H_3O^+ + 2HSO_4^-.$

252

d) Since NH_3 is a base, HNO_3 will act as an acid:
$$NH_3 + HNO_3 \longrightarrow NH_4NO_3(aq)$$

e) Since $Mg(OH)_2$ is a base with two OH^- ions, two moles of HNO_3 are required to react:
$$2HNO_3 + Mg(OH)_2 \longrightarrow Mg(NO_3)_2 + 2H_2O.$$

9. In an acid-base reaction, H^+ is transferred from one species to another. Thus we inspect each reaction in turn to see if such a process occurs. If not, then we test to see if it is an oxidation-reduction reaction, by either searching for a change in oxidation number or/and trying to split the overall reaction into two half-reactions which involve e^-.

a) According to the text, Section 17.2, this reaction produces $NaHSO_4$ and HNO_3:
$$NaNO_3 + H_2SO_4 \longrightarrow NaHSO_4 + HNO_3.$$
Since H^+ is transferred from H_2SO_4 (the acid) to the NO_3^- ion (the base) of $NaNO_3$, it is an acid-base reaction.

b) Again from Section 17.2,
$$4HNO_3 \xrightarrow{\;h\nu\;} 4NO_2 + O_2 + 2H_2O.$$

Clearly this is an oxidation-reduction, since nitrogen in the +5 and oxygen in the −2 yields nitrogen as +4 and some oxygen in the zero state. Thus the N in HNO_3 is reduced and some oxygen is oxidized.

c) From Section 17.1,
$$2Pb(NO_3)_2 \longrightarrow 2PbO + 4NO_2 + O_2.$$
As in (b), the nitrogen is reduced and some oxygen is oxidized in this oxidation-reduction process.

d) From Section 17.2,
$$HNO_3 + H_2SO_4 \longrightarrow H_2NO_3^+ + HSO_4^-.$$
Since H^+ is transferred from H_2SO_4 (the acid) to HNO_3 (here the base), the process is an acid-base reaction. Subsequently, $H_2NO_3^+$ is dehydrated by H_2SO_4, producing NO_2^+, overall we obtain
$$HNO_3 + 2H_2SO_4 \longrightarrow NO_2^+ + H_3O^+ + 2HSO_4^-$$

e) Since HNO_2 is a weak acid, H_2O will act as the base in this acid-base reaction:
$$HNO_2 + H_2O \rightleftarrows NO_2^- + H_3O^+.$$

f) From Section 17.3,
$$2NH_3 + OCl^- \longrightarrow N_2H_4 + H_2O + Cl^-.$$
Since the Cl oxidation number changes from +1 to −1, it is reduced and the nitrogen in ammonia (which changes from −3 to −2) is oxidized.

253

g) From Section 17.5,
$$2H_2O_2 \longrightarrow 2H_2O + O_2.$$
Here some of the oxygen (O.N. = -1 in H_2O_2) is oxidized (to O_2) and some is reduced (to H_2O) in this oxidation-reduction reaction.

h) From Section 17.5,
$$BaO_2 + H_2SO_4 \longrightarrow BaSO_4 + H_2O_2.$$
This is an acid-base reaction, since both H^+ from H_2SO_4 (the acid) are transferred to the O_2^{2-} ion (the base).

10. See Section 17.2 of the text for details. The equations are
$$4NH_3 + 5O_2 \longrightarrow 4NO + 6H_2O$$
$$2NO + O_2 \longrightarrow 2NO_2$$
$$3NO_2 + H_2O \longrightarrow 2HNO_3 + NO.$$

11. Barium nitrate is $Ba(NO_3)_2$, and gives Ba^{2+} and NO_3^- ions. Barium sulfate, $BaSO_4$, is insoluble and probably is the precipitate. Thus SO_2 must be oxidized to SO_4^{2-} in the reaction:
$$SO_2 + 2H_2O \longrightarrow SO_4^{2-} + 4H^+ + 2e^-.$$
The oxidizing agent presumably is the nitrate ion, with NO presumably the product (although it is not mentioned):
$$NO_3^- + 4H^+ + 3e^- \longrightarrow NO + 2H_2O.$$
Overall the balanced reaction is
$$3SO_2 + 2NO_3^- + 2H_2O \longrightarrow 3SO_4^{2-} + 2NO + 4H^+.$$

12. In all cases, we use the Lewis structure procedures developed in Chapter 8.

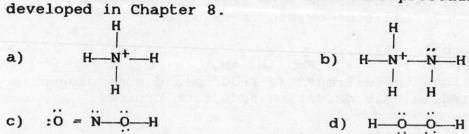

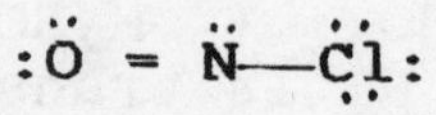

13. Note that lone pairs on oxygen are not shown here for reasons of clarity. Each neutral O has 2 such pairs, and each O^- has three.

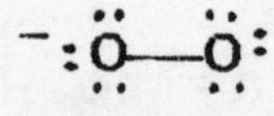

a)

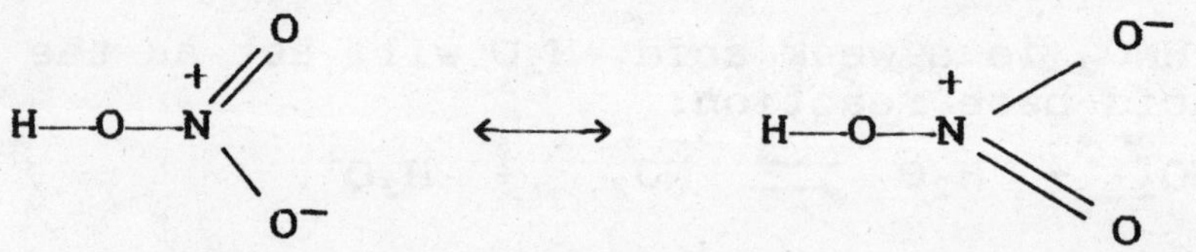

Two structures are required, since the double bond to oxygen can be drawn to either one of the two equilavent oxygens.

b)

$$^-O-\overset{+}{N}{=}O \;\; (\text{with } O \text{ above and } O^- \text{ below}) \longleftrightarrow \;\; ^-O-\overset{+}{N} \;\; (\text{with } O^- \text{ above and } O \text{ below}) \longleftrightarrow \;\; O{=}\overset{+}{N} \;\; (\text{with } O^- \text{ above and } O^- \text{ below})$$

All three oxygens are equivalent here, so three structures are required.

c) $H-O-N{=}O$

d) $^-O-N{=}O \longleftrightarrow O{=}N-O^-$

e) $:N{=}O: \longleftrightarrow :N{=}O:^+$
The first structure is more important (see text).

f)

$$\overset{^-O}{\diagup}\overset{+}{N}{-}\overset{+}{N}\overset{O^-}{\diagdown} \longleftrightarrow \overset{O}{\diagup}\overset{+}{N}{-}\overset{+}{N}\overset{O}{\diagdown}$$

$$\longleftrightarrow \overset{^-O}{\diagup}\overset{+}{N}{-}\overset{+}{N}\overset{O}{\diagdown} \longleftrightarrow \overset{O}{\diagup}\overset{+}{N}{-}\overset{+}{N}\overset{O^-}{\diagdown}$$

g)

$$\overset{^-O}{\diagup}\overset{+}{N}{-}O{-}\overset{+}{N}\overset{O^-}{\diagdown} \longleftrightarrow \overset{O}{\diagup}\overset{+}{N}{-}O{-}\overset{+}{N}\overset{O}{\diagdown}$$

$$\longleftrightarrow \overset{O}{\diagup}\overset{+}{N}{-}O{-}\overset{+}{N}\overset{O^-}{\diagdown} \longleftrightarrow \overset{^-O}{\diagup}\overset{+}{N}{-}O{-}\overset{+}{N}\overset{O}{\diagdown}$$

14. For each example, we first deduce the Lewis structure (see Chapter 8 for details), and from it determine the values of n and m. In most diagrams below, the only lone pairs shown are those on the central nitrogen.

    a) $O{=}\overset{..}{N}{-}\overset{.}{\underset{..}{O}}:$ Odd number of electrons, thus not classifiable.

    b) $O{=}\overset{+}{N}{=}O$ Since each double bond counts only as one X, this is an AX_2 species which therefore should be linear.

    c) $^-O-\overset{..}{N}{=}O$ AX_2E, therefore angular.

d) 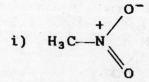 AX$_3$, therefore triangular planar.

e) $\overline{}$N = N = O AX$_2$, therefore linear.

f) O = N̈—Cl AX$_2$E, therefore angular.

g) F—N̈—F AX$_3$E, therefore pyramidal.
     |
     F

h) O = N̈—OH AX$_2$E, therefore angular.

i) H$_3$C—N (with O$^-$ and =O) AX$_3$, therefore triangular planar.

15. a) The anhydride is N$_2$O$_5$, for which the Lewis structure is given in the answer to Q. 13(g).

   b) The anhydride is N$_2$O$_3$, for which the Lewis structure is
      :O̤ = N̈—O̤—N̈ = O̤:

   c) The anhydride is P$_4$O$_{10}$, for which the Lewis structure is

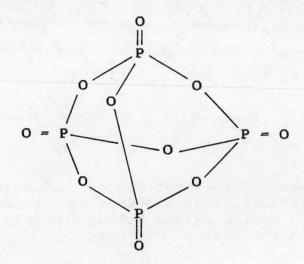

Each oxygen possesses two lone pairs (not shown).

d) The anhydride is SO_3, for which the Lewis structure is

$$\ddot{O} \backslash\!\!\backslash \quad S = \ddot{O}: \quad /\!\!/ \quad :\ddot{O}$$

16. In most cases we first deduce the Lewis structure, and from it and VSEPR theory determine the geometry (see Q. 14). Then we determine if the dipoles add vectorially to zero or not, i.e. if the center of the δ^- and the δ^+ charges coincide.

a) There will be a dipole moment for this molecule since there is but one pair of atoms and its bond is polar.

b) See Section 17.1 for a discussion of the geometry, which is angular. Clearly the dipoles do not cancel, and the molecule has a dipole moment.

c) Zero dipole moment, since the (only) bond is purely covalent.

d) The Lewis structures for O_3 are $^-O\!\!-\!\!\overset{+}{\ddot{O}} = O$ and $O = \overset{+}{\ddot{O}} - O^-$. Since the central atom is AX_2E, it is angular. Since the two atoms in each OO bond are nonequivalent, there could be some polarity to them and the molecule will therefore have some dipole moment.

e) See 14(e); the structure is linear $^-N = \overset{+}{N} = O$. The molecule will have a dipole moment since the bonds are nonequivalent, and the dipoles do not cancel.

f) One Lewis structure is

$$^-O \qquad O^- \\ \backslash \; \overset{+}{}\; \overset{+}{} \; / \\ N\!\!-\!\!N \\ /\!\!/ \qquad \backslash\!\!\backslash \\ O \qquad\qquad O$$

, and thus the

molecule is planar at each AX_3 nitrogen. The centers of partial negative charges (on each oxygen) and positive charges (on each nitrogen) must both be at the NN bond midpoint, so the molecule has a zero dipole moment.

g) $H\!\!-\!\!\ddot{O}\!\!-\!\!\ddot{O}\!\!-\!\!H$ The geometry is AX_2E_2, therefore angular, about each oxygen. If the conformation were to be fixed as planar trans, there would be no dipole moment as the centers of positive and negative partial charge would both be the OO bond midpoint, but since it

261

is not fixed, the centers do not coincide and the molecule does have a dipole moment.

h) $H_2N\text{——}NH_2$ The geometry is AX_3E, therefore pyramidal about each nitrogen. As in (g), rotation about the NN single bond means that the molecule spends most of its time in conformations with a dipole moment, rather than all the time in the only zero-dipole geometry, i.e. with the HNH planes trans to each other, and therefore the molecule does have a dipole moment.

i) See Q. 14(d) for the structure. The polarity of the O——H bond gives the molecule a nonzero dipole moment even in the (unlikely) circumstance that all three NO bonds are of equal polarity.

17. NO_2^+, N_2O, N_3^- all have 22 electrons total, as does CO_2.

18. Ozone is not given a Lewis structure containing three equivalent single bonds, because experimentally one OO distance is much longer than are the other two – so long in fact that there can be no bond between two of the oxygen atoms; rather there is a double bond in the molecule:

$$^-\overset{..}{O}\text{——}\overset{+}{\overset{..}{O}} = O \longleftrightarrow O = \overset{+}{\overset{..}{O}}\text{——}O^-.$$

19. a) To use % by mass information, it is simplest to take 100 g of the solution; thus we have 65.3 g HNO_3 and $100.0 - 65.3 = 34.7$ g H_2O (since all solutions are assumed to be aqueous unless specified otherwise). The molarity of the solution is the ratio of moles HNO_3 to volume of solution. We obtain these two parameters individually.

$$65.3 \text{ g } HNO_3 \times \frac{1 \text{ mole } HNO_3}{63.02 \text{ g } HNO_3} = 1.04 \text{ moles } HNO_3$$

$$100 \text{ g solution} \times \frac{1 \text{ mL}}{1.40 \text{ g solution}} = 71.4 \text{ mL solution.}$$

Hence the molarity is 1.04 moles/0.0714 L = 14.6 M.

b) Here we are told the final volume, and thus must deduce the moles HNO_3. Let us deduce the moles of HNO_3. Since 100 g of solution are specified in the problem, the mass of HNO_3 is 24.84 g.

$$24.86 \text{ g } HNO_3 \times \frac{1 \text{ mole } HNO_3}{63.02 \text{ g } HNO_3} = 0.3942 \text{ moles } HNO_3.$$

Hence molarity = moles HNO_3/volume solution
= 0.3942 moles/0.500 L
= 0.7884 M.

20. The reaction is
$$NH_4NO_2 \longrightarrow N_2 + 2H_2O.$$
The moles of N_2 obtained is given by

$$10.0 \text{ g } NH_4NO_2 \times \frac{1 \text{ mole } NH_4NO_2}{64.06 \text{ g } NH_4NO_2} \times \frac{1 \text{ mole } N_2}{1 \text{ mole } NH_4NO_2}$$
= 0.156 moles N_2.

From the Ideal Gas Equation PV = nRT, then
V = nRT/P = 0.156 x 0.0821 x 333/(750/760)
= 4.32 L.

21. The reaction of the base NH_3 with the acid HNO_3 is
$$HNO_3 + NH_3 \longrightarrow NH_4^+NO_3^-.$$
Thus 1 mole of NH_3 reacts with 1 mole HNO_3:

$$1.00 \times 10^6 \text{ g } HNO_3 \times \frac{1 \text{ mole } HNO_3}{63.02 \text{ g } HNO_3} \times \frac{1 \text{ mole } NH_3}{1 \text{ mole } HNO_3} \times \frac{17.04 \text{ g } NH_3}{1 \text{ mole } NH_3}$$
= 2.70×10^5 g, i.e. 0.27 metric ton.

22. Sufficient information is given to calculate the moles of
O_2, and then the moles and mass of $NaNO_3$ since the reaction
is
$$2NaNO_3 \longrightarrow 2NaNO_2 + O_2.$$
The purity of the sample can then be computed by comparing
this mass of $NaNO_3$ to the mass of the impure sample.
$$p_{O_2} = P_{total} - p_{H_2O} = 760 - 20.8 = 739 \text{ mm Hg}$$
Since $p_{O_2} V = n_{O_2} RT$, thus
$$n_{O_2} = p_{O_2} V/RT = (739/760) \times 0.1318/0.0821 \times 298$$
= 0.00524 moles O_2.

$$0.00524 \text{ moles } O_2 \times \frac{2 \text{ moles } NaNO_3}{1 \text{ mole } O_2} \times \frac{85.00 \text{ g } NaNO_3}{1 \text{ mole } NaNO_3}$$
= 0.891 g $NaNO_3$.

Thus the percent purity of the sample is $\frac{0.891 \text{ g}}{1.354 \text{ g}} \times 100\%$ = 65.8%.

23. The balanced reaction is (see text)
$$2NO_2(g) \rightleftarrows N_2O_4(g) \qquad \Delta H° < 0.$$

a) Increasing the total pressure by adding an inert gas
has no effect, as the concentrations and partial
pressures of NO_2 and N_2O_4 are not affected.

b) If the volume is increased, the equilibrium shifts to the left side since it involves more moles of (gaseous) molecules than does the right side.

c) Decreasing the temperature shifts the equilibrium to the right side, according to Le Chatelier's Principle, since the reaction can be rewritten as

$$2NO_2 \rightleftharpoons N_2O_4 + heat$$

and a temperature decrease is equivalent to removing "heat".

24. For nitrous acid, $K_a = 7.2 \times 10^{-4}$; thus for nitrite, $K_b = 10^{-4}/7.2 \times 10^{-4} = 1.4 \times 10^{-11}$

a)

	HNO_2	$+ H_2O \rightleftharpoons$	NO_2^-	$+ H_3O^+$
Initial	0.02		0	0
Equilibrium	0.02-X		X	X

$$\frac{X^2}{0.02-X} = 7.2 \times 10^{-4}.$$

Trying the approximate method, we obtain $X \approx 3.8 \times 10^{-3} = [H_3O^+]$, which gives pH = 2.42. (Since the dissociation is estimated to be 19%, the approximate method is not completely satisfactory here. Solving the quadratic gives $X = 3.45 \times 10^{-3}$, and pH = 2.46.)

b) Since $NaNO_2 \longrightarrow Na^+ + NO_2^-$, the relevant reaction is

	NO_2^-	$+ H_2O \rightleftharpoons$	HNO_2	$+ OH^-$
Initial	0.02		0	0
Equilibrium	0.02-X		X	X

Thus $\frac{X^2}{0.02-X} = K_b = 1.4 \times 10^{-11}$.

The approximate method gives $X = [OH^-] = 5.3 \times 10^{-7}$, so pOH = 6.28 and pH = 7.72.

c)

	HNO_2	$+ H_2O \longleftarrow$	NO_2^-	$+ H_3O^+$
Initial	0.01		0.01	0
Equilibrium	0.01-X		0.01+X	X

Thus $\frac{(0.01+X)X}{0.01-X} = 7.2 \times 10^{-4}.$

Using the approximation, $X = 7.2 \times 10^{-4}$, so pH = 3.14.

25. For the reaction,
$$\Delta H^\circ = 4\Delta H_f^\circ(NO,g) + 6\Delta H_f^\circ(H_2O,g) - 4\Delta H_f^\circ(NH_3,g) - 5\Delta H_f^\circ(O_2,g)$$
$$= 4 \times (+ 90.3) + 6 \times (- 241.8) - 4 \times (- 46.2) - 5 \times (0)$$
$$= - 904.8 \text{ kJ}.$$

26. The total bond energy in O_3 is by definition equal to ΔH° for
$$O_3(g) \longrightarrow 3\ O(g)$$
$$\Delta H^\circ = 3\Delta H_f^\circ(O,g) - \Delta H_f^\circ(O_3,g).$$
We obtain $\Delta H_f^\circ(O,g)$ from the dissociation energy for O_2:
$$O_2(g) \longrightarrow 2\ O(g)$$
$$\Delta H^\circ = 498 = 2\Delta H_f^\circ(O,g) - \Delta H_f^\circ(O_2) = 2\Delta H_f^\circ(O,g) - 0.$$
Thus $\Delta H_f^\circ(O,g) = 249$ kJ mol^{-1}
and we obtain for the first reaction
$$\Delta H^\circ = 3 \times 249 - 142 = 605.$$
Thus the average energy for each of the two OO interactions in O_3 is $605/2 = 302$ kJ mol^{-1}.

27. For the reaction,
$$\Delta H^\circ = \Delta H_f^\circ(CO_2,g) + \Delta H_f^\circ(NO,g) - \Delta H_f^\circ(CO,g) = \Delta H_f^\circ(NO_2,g)$$
$$= -393.5 + 90.3 - (-110.5) - 33.2$$
$$= -225.9 \text{ kJ mol}^{-1}.$$

28. From the solution to Q. 26, $\Delta H_f^\circ(O,g) = 249$ kJ mol^{-1}.
For the reaction $NO + O_3 \longrightarrow NO_2 + O_2$
$$\Delta H^\circ = \Delta H_f^\circ(NO_2) + \Delta H_f^\circ(O_2) - \Delta H_f^\circ(NO) - \Delta H_f^\circ(O_3)$$
$$= 33.2 + 0 - 90.3 - 142.7$$
$$= -199.8 \text{ kJ mol}^{-1}.$$
For the reaction $NO_2 + O \longrightarrow O_2 + NO$
$$\Delta H^\circ = \Delta H_f^\circ(O_2) + \Delta H_f^\circ(NO) - \Delta H_f^\circ(NO_2) - \Delta H_f^\circ(O)$$
$$= 0 + 90.3 - 33.2 - 249$$
$$= -192 \text{ kJ mol}^{-1}.$$

29. a) Since each H is +1 and the net charge is +1, the nitrogen must be -3.

b) Since each H is +1, each N is $(-4/2) = -2$.

c) Since each O is -2 and K is +1, the N is +3.

d) Since each O is -2, the N is +4.

e) Since each H is +1 and O is -2, the N is -1 if the sum is to be zero over all atoms.

f) Since O is -2, each N is +1.

g) Since each H is +1 and each O is -2, the average value for each N is $(+2/2) = +1$.

h) Since Li is +1, the average value for N is -1/3.

i) Since Li is +1, the nitrogen is -3.

j) Since each F is -1, the nitrogen is +3.

30. a) The obvious half-reactions are
$$H_2S \longrightarrow S$$
$$NO_3^- \longrightarrow NO.$$

Upon balancing each in the usual way, we obtain
$$H_2S \longrightarrow S + 2H^+ + 2e^-$$
$$NO_3^- + 4H^+ + 3e^- \longrightarrow NO + 2H_2O.$$
Multiplying the first by 3 and the second by 2 (to ensure cancellation of electrons) and adding, we obtain
$$3H_2S + 2NO_3^- + 2H^+ \longrightarrow 3S + 2NO + 4H_2O.$$

b)
$$Zn \longrightarrow Zn(OH)_2$$
$$NO_3^- \longrightarrow NH_3 \text{ (not } NH_4^+ \text{ since the solution is basic).}$$
Upon balancing, we obtain
$$Zn + 2OH^- \longrightarrow Zn(OH)_2 + 2e^-$$
$$NO_3^- + 6H_2O + 8e^- \longrightarrow NH_3 + 9OH^-.$$
Combining (after multiplying the first by four) gives
$$4Zn + NO_3^- + 6H_2O \longrightarrow 4Zn(OH)_2 + NH_3 + OH^-.$$

c)
$$P_4 \longrightarrow H_3PO_4$$
$$NO_3^- \longrightarrow NO.$$
Upon balancing each, we obtain
$$P_4 + 16H_2O \longrightarrow 4H_3PO_4 + 20 H^+ + 20e^-$$
$$NO_3^- + 4H^+ + 3e^- \longrightarrow NO + 2H_2O.$$
Combining after equating electrons yields
$$3P_4 + 20NO_3^- + 20H^+ + 8H_2O \longrightarrow 12H_3PO_4 + 20NO.$$

31. H_2O_2 can act as both an oxidizing and as a reducing agent since it contains oxygen in the -1 oxidation number; this is intermediate between two other common values, i.e. -2, eg. in H_2O, to which H_2O_2 can therefore be reduced, and zero, in O_2, to which H_2O_2 can therefore be oxidized. The corresponding half-reactions are
$$2H^+ + 2e^- + H_2O_2 \longrightarrow 2H_2O$$
$$H_2O_2 \longrightarrow O_2 + 2H^+ + 2e^-.$$

a) The half-reaction for SO_2 is
$$2H_2O + SO_2 \longrightarrow SO_4^{2-} + 4H^+ + 2e^-.$$
Thus we combine this reaction with the reduction of H_2O_2, to give
$$H_2O_2 + SO_2 \longrightarrow SO_4^{2-} + 2H^+.$$

b) The half-reaction $O_3 \longrightarrow H_2O$ upon balancing is
$$O_3 + 6H^+ + 6e^- \longrightarrow 3H_2O.$$
Upon combining with the oxidation of H_2O_2, we obtain
$$3H_2O_2 + O_3 \longrightarrow 3O_2 + 3H_2O.$$

c) The reduction half-reaction $I_2 + 2e^- \longrightarrow 2I^-$, when combined with the oxidation half-reaction above for H_2O_2, gives
$$I_2 + H_2O_2 \longrightarrow O_2 + 2H^+ + 2I^-.$$

d) The half-reaction $Cr(OH)_3 \longrightarrow CrO_4^{2-}$, when balanced for basic solution, is
$$Cr(OH)_3 + 5OH^- \longrightarrow CrO_4^{2-} + 4H_2O + 3e^-$$
whereas the reduction of H_2O_2 in base is
$$H_2O_2 + 2e^- \longrightarrow 2OH^-.$$

Combining, we obtain
$$2Cr(OH)_3 + 3H_2O_2 + 4OH^- \longrightarrow 2CrO_4^{2-} + 8H_2O.$$

e) The $NO_2^- \longrightarrow NO_3^-$ half-reaction upon balancing is
$$NO_2^- + H_2O \longrightarrow NO_3^- + 2H^+ + 2e^-.$$
Combining with the reduction (above) for H_2O_2 yields
$$H_2O_2 + NO_2^- \longrightarrow NO_3^- + H_2O.$$

1. The rate at each time interval is equal to minus the change in concentration of HCl, as measured by H^+, divided by the length Δt of the time interval:

$$\text{Rate} = -\frac{\Delta[\text{HCl}]}{\Delta t} = -\frac{\Delta[H^+]}{\Delta t} = -\frac{[H^+]_{\text{end}} - [H^+]_{\text{beginning}}}{t_{\text{end}} - t_{\text{beginning}}}$$

Here "end" and "beginning" refer to the time interval.

t	$[H^+]$	Δt	$\Delta[H^+]$	Average rate = $-\Delta[H^+]/\Delta t$
0	1.85			
		80	-0.19	0.0024
80	1.66			
		79	-0.13	0.0016
159	1.53			
		155	-0.22	0.0014
314	1.31			
		314	-0.29	0.0009
628	1.02			

2. This problem is similar to Problem 1.

t	$[SO_2Cl_2]$	Δt	$\Delta[SO_2Cl_2]$	Average rate = $-\Delta[SO_2Cl_2]\Delta t$
0	0.01000			
		20	0.00030	0.000015
20	0.00970			
		30	0.00042	0.000014
50	0.00928			
		50	0.00067	0.000013
100	0.00861			
		100	0.00120	0.000012
200	0.00741			
		200	0.00192	0.0000096
400	0.00549			
		300	0.00199	0.0000066
700	0.00350			
		300	0.00127	0.0000042
1000	0.00223			

The rates can be obtained either from a plot, or by interpolating the average rates given above.

3. In each case, the rate equals the change in product concentration (or minus reactant concentrations) with time,

divided by the coefficient in the balanced equation for that chemical.

a) Rate $= \dfrac{\Delta[H_2]}{\Delta t} = \dfrac{\Delta[I_2]}{\Delta t} = -\dfrac{1}{2}\dfrac{\Delta[HI]}{\Delta t}$

b) Rate $= \dfrac{1}{2}\dfrac{\Delta[NO]}{\Delta t} = \dfrac{\Delta[Cl_2]}{\Delta t} = -\dfrac{1}{2}\dfrac{\Delta[NOCl]}{\Delta t}$

c) Rate $= \dfrac{1}{4}\dfrac{\Delta[NO_2]}{\Delta t} = \dfrac{\Delta[O_2]}{\Delta t} = -\dfrac{1}{2}\dfrac{\Delta[N_2O_5]}{\Delta t}$

4. We are given $k = 3.7 \times 10^{-1}\ s^{-1}$ and thus if the reactant is B,
   $$\text{Rate} = 3.7 \times 10^{-1}\ s^{-1}\ [B].$$

   a) For $[B] = 0.040\ mol\ L^{-1}$, thus
   $$\begin{aligned}\text{Rate} &= 3.7 \times 10^{-1}\ s^{-1} \times 0.040\ mol\ L^{-1}\\ &= 1.5 \times 10^{-2}\ mol\ L^{-1}\ s^{-1}.\end{aligned}$$

   b) To transform the rate to an hourly basis, we use the relationship 1 hr $= 3600$ s.

   $$\text{Rate} = \dfrac{1.5 \times 10^{-2}\ mol\ L^{-1}}{1\ s} \times \dfrac{3600\ s}{1\ h}$$

   $$= 54\ mol\ L^{-1}\ h^{-1}.$$

5. The rate law is expected to be of the form
   $$\text{Rate} = k[NOBr]^x$$
   where the order x is probably a small integer or half-integer. The value of x can be determined by plotting the data for Rate against the data for $[NOBr]^x$ for various likely values of x; the plot in which a straight line is obtained must correspond to the correct value for x. By trial and error, only the plot for x=2 is found to be linear. Thus we conclude that the rate is second order in NOBr.

6. When the rates established for Problem 2 (either by drawing tangents to the concentration-versus-time curve, or by evaluating the average rate in each time interval and assuming that this corresponds to the rate for the average concentration in that interval) are plotted against the first power of the concentration, a good straight line is obtained. Thus the reaction is first-order in SO_2Cl_2. No other plot, eg. rate versus the square of the concentration, yields a straight line.

7. From the N_2 rate, we can deduce a standard reaction "rate" :
   $$\text{Rate} = \dfrac{1}{2}\dfrac{\Delta[N_2]}{\Delta t} = \dfrac{1}{2} \times 0.270\ mol\ L^{-1}\ s^{-1} = 0.135\ mol\ L^{-1}\ s^{-1}$$

265

a) In terms of $[H_2O]$, by definition

$$\text{Rate} = \frac{1}{6}\frac{\Delta[H_2O]}{\Delta t}$$

Thus $\dfrac{\Delta[H_2O]}{\Delta t}$ = 6 x Rate = 6 x 0.135 mol L^{-1} s^{-1}

$$= 0.81 \text{ mol } L^{-1} \text{ } s^{-1}.$$

b) In terms of $[NH_3]$, by definition

$$\text{Rate} = -\frac{1}{4}\frac{\Delta[NH_3]}{\Delta t}$$

Thus $\dfrac{\Delta[NH_3]}{\Delta t}$ = - 4 x Rate = - 4 x 0.135 mol^{-1} L^{-1} s^{-1}

$$= - 0.54 \text{ mol } L^{-1} \text{ } s^{-1}.$$

c) Similarly,

$$\frac{\Delta[O_2]}{\Delta t} = - 3 \text{ x Rate } = - 3 \text{ x } 0.135 \text{ mol } L^{-1} \text{ } s^{-1}$$

$$= - 0.405 \text{ mol } L^{-1} \text{ } s^{-1}.$$

8. As stated in the text (Section 18.3), the reaction rate depends upon
    i)   reactant concentrations, since this factor determines the rate at which the molecules collide with each other;
    ii) temperature, since this factor determines the distribution of energy between molecules which collide; and
    iii) the nature of the reaction, since this determines the activation energy, steric factor and the exact form of the rate law.

9. The rate of a reaction is the change with time of the concentration of reactants or products. The rate law is a mathematical statement of the dependence of rate upon concentration of (usually) the reactants. The rate constant is the proportionality constant between rate and concentration in the rate law.

10. From the information given, we conclude that in terms of the concentrations of the reactants B and C,
    Rate = $k[B]^x[C]^y$ and x + y = 2.
    Substituting [B] = [C] = 0.2 mol L^{-1} and for the rate, then

$$8.1 \text{ x } 10^{-3} \text{ mol } L^{-1} \text{ min}^{-1} = k(0.20)^x \text{ } (0.20)^y$$
$$= k(0.20)^{x+y}$$
$$= k(0.20)^2$$

266

Thus $k = \dfrac{8.1 \times 10^{-3} \text{ mol L}^{-1} \text{ min}^{-1}}{(0.20 \text{ mol L}^{-1})^2}$

$k = 0.20 \text{ mol}^{-1} \text{ L min}^{-1}$.

Finally, we transform to the desired units:

a) $k = \dfrac{0.20 \text{ mol}^{-1} \text{ L}}{1 \text{ min}} \times \dfrac{1 \text{ min}}{60 \text{ s}} = 0.0033 \text{ mol}^{-1} \text{ L s}^{-1}$

b) $k = \dfrac{0.20 \text{ L min}^{-1}}{1 \text{ mol}} \times \dfrac{1 \text{ mol}}{6.022 \times 10^{23} \text{ molecules}} \times \dfrac{1000 \text{ mL}}{1 \text{ L}}$

$= 3.3 \times 10^{-22} \text{ molecule}^{-1} \text{ mL min}^{-1}$.

11. Since doubling $[Cl_2]$ alone doubles the rate, the reaction must be first order in Cl_2. Thus when both NO and Cl_2 are doubled, we expect a doubling of rate from the change in $[Cl_2]$; since the rate increases by a factor of 8, the effect of doubling [NO] must be therefore an increase by a factor of 4 (= 8/2). Thus the reaction is second-order in [NO]. The overall reaction order is three (= 2+1).

12. The rate law is expected to be of the form
    $R = k[E]^x$ where E stands for ethanal.
    For two experiments 1 and 2,

    $$\dfrac{\text{Rate 2}}{\text{Rate 1}} = \dfrac{k[E]_2{}^x}{k[E]_1{}^x} = \left(\dfrac{[E]_2}{[E]_1}\right)^x$$

    From the information given, Rate 2/Rate 1 = 2.83
    and $[E]_2/[E]_1 = 2.00$.

    Thus $2.00^x = 2.83$.

    This equation can be solved for x by taking the $\ln$ of both sides:

    $x \ln 2.00 = \ln 2.83$
    $x = 1.040/0.693 = 1.50$.
    Thus the reaction is 3/2 order in ethanol.

13. Comparing the first two experiments (i.e. the first two rows of data), we see that if [NO] is doubled but $[H_2]$ remains constant, the rate increases by a factor of 4; thus the reaction is second order in NO. To obtain the order in H_2, we compare two experiments in which [NO] is the same but $[H_2]$ differs - i.e. the first and third rows. Since doubling $[H_2]$ doubles the rate, the reaction is first-order in H_2.
    $Rate = k[NO]^2[H_2]$.
    The rate constant k can be evaluated using any one row of data; eg.

$$k = \frac{\text{Rate}}{[NO]^2[H_2]} = \frac{0.500 \text{ mol L}^{-1} \text{ min}^{-1}}{(0.15 \text{ mol L}^{-1})^2(0.80 \text{ mol L}^{-1})}$$

$$= 28 \text{ mol}^{-2} \text{ L}^2 \text{ min}^{-1}.$$

14. Since doubling $[H_2]$ doubles the rate, the reaction is first-order in it. Tripling $[Br_2]$ gives a rate increase of 1.73, which is the square root of 3; thus the order is one-half in $[Br_2]$. (If this is not obvious, the method of problem 12 can be used instead.) The reaction cannot proceed by a one-step bimolecular reaction since if it did, the rate would be first-order in both $[H_2]$ and $[Br_2]$.

15. Since the reaction is first-order, one-half the remaining reactant disappears in each half-life time period.

    a) Since 1 half-life is 17.0 min, then 51.0 min represents (51.0/17.0) = 3 half-life periods. The fraction of reactant left then is $(1/2)^3$, i.e. one-eighth.

    b) The fraction remaining after 10 half-life periods is $(1/2)^{10}$, i.e. 1/1024 or 0.00098.

16. When one-quarter the reactant remains, the reaction must have proceeded for 2 half-life periods; thus each half-life is (8.0 min/2) = 4.0 minutes. The concentration will reach 1/32 of its initial value after a total elapsed time of 5 half-life periods, i.e. 20 minutes, since $(1/2)^5$ = 1/32. Since in the experiment discussed, two half-life periods had passed, it will take 3 more half-life periods, i.e. 12.0 more minutes, for the reactant concentration to reach 1/32 of its initial value.

17. Upon direct substitution of the values into the rate law, we obtain
    Rate = $4.0 \times 10^{-3} \text{ M}^{-2} \text{ s}^{-1}$ $(0.01 \text{ M})^2$ (0.01 M)
    = $4.0 \times 10^{-9} \text{ M s}^{-1}$.

18. From the chemical equation, we expect a rate law of the form
    Rate = $k[A]^x[B]^y$.
    Comparing the rates for experiments 1 and 2, we see that in the rate ratio expression, both k and $[A]^x$ will cancel since they are the same in the two cases; thus

    $$\frac{\text{Rate 2}}{\text{Rate 1}} = \frac{[B]_2^y}{[B]_1^y} = \left(\frac{[B]_2}{[B]_1}\right)^y$$

    or

    $$\frac{0.01020}{0.00340} = \left(\frac{0.30}{0.10}\right)^y$$

    i.e. $3 = 3^y$
    so $y = 1$.

268

The order with respect to A can be obtained similarly by comparing the rates of two experiments in which B is constant but A varies, i.e. experiments 2 and 3. Thus the orders are 2 and 1 respectively. We obtain the value of k from the data from any one experiment, i.e.

$$k = \text{Rate}/[A]^2[B]^1$$
$$= 0.00340 \text{ M s}^{-1}/(0.20 \text{ M})^2 (0.10 \text{ M})$$
$$= 0.85 \text{ M}^{-2} \text{ s}^{-1}.$$

Thus the complete rate law is
$$\text{Rate} = 0.85 [A]^2[B]$$
from which the rate for [A] = [B] = 0.50 M is calculated to be 0.11 M s^{-1}.

19. If the reaction is first-order in SO_2Cl_2, a plot of $\ln[SO_2Cl_2]$ versus t would be linear; if it is second-order, a plot of $1/[SO_2Cl_2]$ versus t would be linear. If you construct these plots, it is clear that only that for $\ln[SO_2Cl_2]$ is linear; thus the reaction is first-order in SO_2Cl_2. Thus
$$\text{Rate} = k[SO_2Cl_2]$$
and $\ln[SO_2Cl_2]_t = - kt + \ln[SO_2Cl_2]_0.$
Since the slope of the straight line is $- 0.0015$, thus
$$k = 0.0015 \text{ min}^{-1}.$$

20. Since $KMnO_4$ oxidizes the H_2O_2 which had remained unreacted, it follows that the volume of $KMnO_4$ used is proportional to $[H_2O_2]$ at time t. Since a plot of $\ln[H_2O_2]$ versus time is linear for a first order reaction, a plot of $\ln V(KMnO_4)$ versus time will also be linear. Such a plot is indeed linear, and has a slope of -0.050. The rate constant and half-life cannot be determined, however, since 0.050 equals the rate constant times the proportionality constant between $[H_2O_2]$ and $KMnO_4$ volume.

21. The Arrhenius equation is

$$\ln \frac{k_2}{k_1} = \frac{Ea}{R} \left(\frac{1}{T_1} - \frac{1}{T_2} \right)$$

We can use any two temperatures as t_1 and t_2 and obtain Ea. If we choose t_1 = 302°C and t_2 = 356°C, thus T_1 = 575 K and T_2 = 629 K. Thus

$$\ln \frac{3.33 \times 10^{-5}}{1.18 \times 10^{-6}} = \frac{Ea}{8.314 \text{ JK}^{-1} \text{ mol}^{-1}} \left(\frac{1}{575 \text{ K}} - \frac{1}{629 \text{ K}} \right)$$

$$3.34 = 0.1203 \text{ Ea} (0.001739 - 0.001590)$$
and thus
$$Ea = 186,000 \text{ J mol}^{-1} = 186 \text{ kJ mol}^{-1}.$$

We can obtain the rate constant at 400°C, i.e. 673 K, by using this temperature as t_2 instead of 356°C:

$$\ln(k_2/k_1) = \frac{Ea}{R}\left(\frac{1}{T_1} - \frac{1}{T_2}\right)$$

$$= \frac{186{,}000}{8.314}\left(\frac{1}{575} - \frac{1}{673}\right)$$

$$\ln(k_2/k_1) = 5.666$$

i.e. $\dfrac{k_2}{k_1} = 288.8$

and since $k_1 = 1.18 \times 10^{-6}$ mol L s^{-1}
thus $k_2 = 3.41 \times 10^{-4}$ mol L s^{-1}.

22. The Arrhenius equation relates rate constant k to Kelvin temperature T:

$$\ln \frac{k_2}{k_1} = \frac{Ea}{R}\left(\frac{1}{T_1} - \frac{1}{T_2}\right)$$

Since the final rate is to be ten times the initial rate, and since presumably this is to be achieved by a ten-fold increase in rate constant, then

$$\frac{k_2}{k_1} = 10$$

We are given that $Ea = 80$ kJ mol^{-1} = 80,000 J mol^{-1}
and $T_1 = 0 + 273 = 273$ K.
Thus upon substitution we have

$$\ln(10) = \frac{80{,}000 \text{ J mol}^{-1}}{8.314 \text{ JK}^{-1} \text{ mol}^{-1}}\left(\frac{1}{273 \text{ K}} - \frac{1}{T_2}\right)$$

This leads to
$$2.303 = 9622 (0.003663 - T_2^{-1})$$
$$= 35.245 - 9622\, T_2^{-1}$$
$$9622\, T_2^{-1} = 32.942$$
$$T_2^{-1} = 0.0034236$$
and $T_2 = 292.$
Thus $t_2 = T_2 - 273 = 19°C.$

23. This problem is virtually identical to Problem 22, with changes in data. We eventually obtain

$$\ln(2) = \frac{100{,}000}{8.314}\left(\frac{1}{300} - \frac{1}{T_2}\right)$$

from which
$$T_2 = 305 \text{ K} \quad \text{and} \quad t_2 = 32°C.$$

24. The Arrhenius equation is

$$\ln \frac{k_2}{k_1} = \frac{Ea}{R}\left(\frac{1}{T_1} - \frac{1}{T_2}\right)$$

which upon rearrangement to solve for Ea yields

$$E_a = R \ln(k_2/k_1) / \left(\frac{1}{T_1} - \frac{1}{T_2}\right)$$

If $k_2/k_1 = 3$ (since the rate is three times as large and no change has occurred in concentration), and given $T_1 = 298$ K and $T_2 = 323$

$$\begin{aligned} E_a &= 8.314 \ \ln(3)/(0.0033557 - 0.0030960) \\ &= 35,170 \text{ K mol}^{-1} \\ &= 35.2 \text{ kJ mol}^{-1}. \end{aligned}$$

25. This problem is very similar to Problem 21, except that the temperatures are given directly on the Kelvin scale. Thus

$$\ln \frac{28.2}{3.16} = \frac{Ea}{8.314} \left(\frac{1}{650} - \frac{1}{730}\right)$$

$2.189 = 0.0000203 \ E_a$, so $E_a = 108$ kJ mol^{-1}. Use of any other pair of temperatures will give this $E_a \pm 15$ kJ mol^{-1}.

26. Recall that

$$\ln (k_2/k_1) = \frac{Ea}{R} \left(\frac{1}{T_1} - \frac{1}{T_2}\right)$$

By substitution, we obtain

$$\ln (0.050/0.040) = \frac{E_a}{8.314} \left(\frac{1}{295} - \frac{1}{303}\right)$$

$E_a = 20700$ J mol^{-1}, i.e. 20.7 kJ mol^{-1}.
At 40°C, T = 313

$$\ln (k_3/k_1) = \frac{20700}{8.314} \left(\frac{1}{295} - \frac{1}{313}\right)$$

$$\begin{aligned} &= 0.485 \\ k_3/k_1 &= 1.625 \end{aligned}$$
and since $\quad k_1 = 0.040$, thus $k_3 = 0.065$.

27. As in the previous problem,

$$\ln (6/1) = \frac{E_a}{8.314} \left(\frac{1}{263} - \frac{1}{323}\right)$$

so $\quad E_a = 21100$ J mol^{-1}, or 21.1 kJ mol^{-1}.
We can find T_3, the temperature at which the rate is double its - 10°C value, from

$$\ln (k_3/k_1) = \frac{21100}{8.314} \left(\frac{1}{263} - \frac{1}{T_3}\right)$$

where $k_3/k_1 = 2.0$. Thus

271

$$3.80 \times 10^{-3} - T_3^{-1} = 2.73 \times 10^{-4}$$
or
$$T_3^{-1} = 3.53 \times 10^{-3}$$
so
$$T_3 = 283 \text{ K}$$
and the required temperature therefore is + 10°C.

28. The slow step is listed as
$$Br + H_2 \longrightarrow HBr + H.$$
Thus the rate law is
$$Rate = k_2[Br][H_2].$$
However since Br is an intermediate, we must attempt to eliminate it from the rate law. From the equilibrium in step 1,

i.e. $Br_2 \rightleftharpoons 2Br$

it follows that
$$K_1 = [Br]^2/[Br_2]$$
i.e. $[Br]^2 = K_1[Br_2].$
Thus $[Br] = K_1^{1/2}[Br_2]^{1/2}.$
Upon substitution, we obtain
$$Rate = k_2 K_1^{1/2}[H_2][Br_2]^{1/2}.$$

29. The slow (rate-limiting step) here is the third, i.e.
$$COCl + Cl_2 \longrightarrow COCl_2 + Cl$$
and thus it follows that the rate law is
$$Rate = k_3[COCl][Cl_2].$$

Since COCl is an intermediate, we must try to eliminate it from the rate law. From the equilibrium in the second step, it follows that
$$K_2 = [COCl]/[Cl][CO]$$
i.e. $[COCl] = K_2[Cl][CO].$
Thus the rate law becomes
$$Rate = k_3 K_2[Cl][CO][Cl_2].$$

Since Cl also is an intermediate, we need to eliminate it; from the equilibrium in the first step it follows that
$$[Cl] = K_1^{1/2}[Cl_2]^{1/2}.$$
Thus our final rate law is

$$Rate = k_3 K_2 K_1^{1/2}[CO][Cl_2]^{3/2} = k[CO][Cl_2]^{3/2}.$$

30. The rate law for the overall process is the rate law for the slow step. Thus for the two-step mechanism, the rate law would be
$$Rate = k_1[NO_2]^2$$
since the reactants in the slow step are two molecules of NO_2. If the reaction occurred in a single step, by definition it would be the slow step and the rate law would be
$$Rate = k[NO_2][CO].$$

31. The rate law for the overall reaction is that for the slow step; since one atom of O and one molecule of O_3 are the reactants in the step, the rate law is

$$\text{Rate} = k_2[O][O_3].$$

Since O is an intermediate, we must develop sufficient algebra to substitute for [O]. From the equilibrium in the first step,

$$K_1 = \frac{[O_2][O]}{[O_3]}$$

Solving for [O] we obtain
$$[O] = K_1[O_3]/[O_2].$$
By substitution we obtain
$$\text{Rate} = k_2K_1[O_3]^2/[O_2]$$
i.e. $\quad \text{Rate} = k_2K_1[O_3]^2[O_2]^{-1}.$

The rate decreases as $[O_2]$ increases since by Le Chatelier's Principle any increase in O_2 results in a shift in the equilibrium (of the first step) such that [O] is decreased; this results in a decrease in the rate of the second step (and the overall reaction) since atomic O is a reactant in this step.

32. The overall rate law is second order in NO and first order in O_2. Thus the slow step, if it does not involve 2NO and O_2, must involve one or two of these three molecules and an intermediate whose equilibrium concentration is proportional to the molecules "missing" from 2NO + 1 O_2. One possibility is that two NO molecules combine in a fast equilibrium to form an intermediate, N_2O_2, which collides with O_2 in the slow step:

$$\begin{array}{lll} 2NO & \rightleftharpoons \quad N_2O_2 & \text{fast equilibrium} \\ N_2O_2 + O_2 & \longrightarrow \quad 2NO_2 & \text{slow} \end{array}$$

Since $\quad \text{Rate} = k_2[N_2O_2][O_2]$

but $\quad K_1 = [N_2O_2]/[NO]^2$

upon substitution
$$\text{Rate} = k_2K_1[NO]^2[O_2].$$

Another possibility is that one NO and one O_2 molecule combine in a fast equilibrium, and that the resulting intermediate, NO_3, collides with the other NO molecule in the slow step:

$$\begin{array}{lll} NO + O_2 & \rightleftharpoons \quad NO_3 & \text{fast equilibrium} \\ NO_3 + NO & \longrightarrow \quad 2NO_2 & \text{slow} \end{array}$$

This mechanism leads to
$$\text{Rate} = k_2K_1[NO]^2[O_2].$$
Another mechanism which is less likely on energetic grounds (since a stable molecule is decomposed) is

$$\begin{array}{lll} O_2 & \rightleftharpoons \quad 2\,O & \text{fast equilibrium} \\ O + NO & \longrightarrow \quad NO_2 & \text{slow.} \end{array}$$

273

Note however that this mechanism leads to the rate law

$$\text{Rate} = k_2 K_1{}^{1/2}[NO][O_2]^{1/2}$$

which is <u>not</u> the experimental law. Thus this last mechanism must be rejected. The only mechanism involving atomic O which does yield the correct rate law has as the slow step

$$2NO + 2O \longrightarrow 2NO_2$$

but this also is unacceptable since it involves a step in which four molecules collide simultaneously. A similar but acceptable mechanism would have as the slow step

$$2O + N_2O_2 \longrightarrow 2NO_2$$

which would require, as previous equilibria, not only

$$O_2 \rightleftharpoons 2O$$

but also

$$2NO \rightleftharpoons N_2O_2.$$

Thus except on energetic grounds, the mechanism

$$O_2 \rightleftharpoons 2O \qquad\qquad \text{fast equilibrim}$$

$$2NO \rightleftharpoons N_2O_2 \qquad\qquad \text{fast equilibrium}$$
$$2O + N_2O_2 \longrightarrow 2NO_2 \qquad\qquad \text{slow}$$

is also acceptable.

33. Visible light is unable to dissociate H_2 molecules into H atoms since the energy of 1 photon of such light is less than the H——H bond energy. Thus the effect of UV light on the $H_2 + I_2$ mixture cannot be to produce H atoms directly.

34. a) The oxidation here is $2Br^- \longrightarrow Br_2 + 2e^-$ and thus H_2O_2 is reduced, presumably to water
   $$H_2O_2 \longrightarrow H_2O \qquad\qquad \text{(unbalanced)}.$$
   Upon balancing this half-reaction, we obtain
   $$2H^+ + H_2O_2 + 2e^- \longrightarrow 2H_2O.$$
   Thus the overall reaction is
   $$2Br^- + H_2O_2 + 2H^+ \longrightarrow Br_2 + 2H_2O.$$

   b) For this reaction, the rate law is expected to have the form
   $$\text{Rate} = k[Br^-]^x[H_2O_2]^y[H^+]^z.$$
   Since doubling either Br^- or H_2O_2 doubles the rate, then $x = y = 1$, i.e. the reaction is first-order both in Br^- and in H_2O_2.
   To obtain the order in $[H^+]$, we must translate the rate-versus-pH information into rate-versus-concentration terms. If the original pH is b, the new pH is b − 0.60. Thus

   $$\frac{[H^+]_{new}}{[H^+]_{old}} = \frac{10^{-b+0.60}}{10^{-b}} = 10^{0.60} = 3.98.$$

274

Thus decreasing the pH by 0.60 units is equivalent to increasing $[H^+]$ by a factor of 4; since the rate also increases by this factor of 4, we conclude that the reaction also is first-order in $[H^+]$. Overall then
Rate $= k[Br^-][H_2O_2][H^+]$.

c) From the balanced equation for the overall reaction,

$$Rate = \frac{\Delta[Br_2]}{\Delta t} = -\frac{1}{2}\frac{\Delta[Br^-]}{\Delta t} = -\frac{\Delta[H_2O_2]}{\Delta t} = -\frac{1}{2}\frac{\Delta[H^+]}{\Delta t}$$

Thus if $\quad \frac{\Delta[Br^-]}{\Delta t} = -7.2 \times 10^{-3}$ mol L^{-1} s^{-1},

then $\quad \frac{\Delta[H_2O_2]}{\Delta t} = -3.6 \times 10^{-3}$ mol L^{-1} s^{-1}

and $\quad \frac{\Delta[Br_2]}{\Delta t} = +3.6 \times 10^{-3}$ mol L^{-1} s^{-1}

d) There is no effect on k of changing the pH, since k is independent of concentration.

e) There is no effect on k of doubling the solution's volume, since this would simply halve the initial concentration of each reactant, and k is independent of concentration. However, the rate itself would be reduced to $(1/2)(1/2)(1/2) = 1/8$ of its previous value, since the reaction is first-order in each of these species whose rates would each be halved.

f) Since the orders in the rate law do not equal the coefficients in the overall equation, the reaction cannot proceed by a one-step mechanism; thus we must try to devise a multistep mechanism. From the orders of 1,1,1 for Br^-, H_2O_2, and H^+ we deduce that the slow step must involve one Br^-, one H_2O_2, and one H^+, or perhaps an intermediate instead. One possibility for the slow step then is
$Br^- + H_2O_2 + H^+ \longrightarrow$?.
We know that Br atoms could combine quickly to form Br_2, and similarly for OH to form H_2O_2, so the products could be Br, OH and H_2O:

$$Br^- + H_2O_2 + H^+ \longrightarrow Br + OH + H_2O \quad \text{slow}$$
$$2Br \longrightarrow Br_2 \quad \text{fast}$$
$$2OH \longrightarrow H_2O_2 \quad \text{fast.}$$

If the slow step occurs twice as often as do each of the fast steps, the net reaction is equivalent to the overall reaction given.
The above mechanism is somewhat unrealistic since in the slow step two free radicals are formed; instead one HOBr could be produced which upon collision with

another could yield Br_2 and H_2O_2. Thus an alternative mechanism is

$$Br^- + H_2O_2 + H^+ \longrightarrow HOBr + H_2O \qquad \text{slow}$$
$$2HOBr \longrightarrow Br_2 + H_2O_2 \qquad \text{fast.}$$

Both above mechanisms suffer from the problem that they involve termolecular steps. It is more likely that two bimolecular steps would occur instead, with the net result being equivalent to the termolecular step. For example

$$H_2O_2 + H^+ \rightleftharpoons H_3O_2^+ \qquad \text{fast equilibrium}$$
$$H_3O_2^+ + Br^- \longrightarrow HOBr + H_2O \qquad \text{slow}$$
$$2HOBr \longrightarrow Br_2 + H_2O_2 \qquad \text{fast.}$$

Since $K_1 = [H_3O_2^+]/[H_2O_2][H^+]$
and thus $[H_3O_2^+] = K_1[H_2O_2][H^+]$
the rate law for the slow step here,
    i.e.   Rate $= k_2[H_3O_2^+][Br^-]$
after substitution is first order in each of H_2O_2, Br^-, and H^+:

$$\text{Rate} = k_2K_1[H_2O_2][H^+][Br^-].$$

Similar mechanisms can also be generated by combining H^+ and Br^- or H_2O_2 and Br^- in the first, fast equilibrium but the products involved (HBr and H_2O_2Br) are unlikely to exist in this undissociated form in aqueous solution.

35. The overall rate is equal to that of the slow step, which has as its only reactant $NHNO_2^-$; thus

$$\text{Rate} = k_2[NHNO_2^-].$$

Since $NHNO_2^-$ is an intermediate, we use the equilibrium constant expression from the previous equilibrium step to eliminate it:

$$K_1 = [NHNO_2^-][H^+]/[NH_2NO_2].$$
Thus
$$[NHNO_2^-] = K_1[NH_2NO_2]/[H^+]$$
and after substitution of this into the rate law, we obtain
$$\text{Rate} = k_2K_1[NH_2NO_2]/[H^+].$$

This is identical with the rate law given in the problem if we identify k with k_2K_1.
If $[H^+]$ is decreased, the equilibrium in the first step is displaced to the right, thus increasing the concentration of $NHNO_2^-$ and thus speeding up the rate of the second, and rate-determining, step.

36. The step $Br_2 \longrightarrow 2Br$ is a chain initiator since it produces free radical intermediates, i.e. Br atoms, from stable, non-radical molecules. The step $2Br \longrightarrow Br_2$ is a chain termination step since it decreases the number of free radical intermediates. Both the second and third steps are propagation steps since the number of radicals is not changed by them but reactants (CH_4, Br_2) are converted to products (CH_3Br, HBr).

CHAPTER 19

1. a) 2-methyl-1-propanol since the longest chain has 3
        carbons. (2-methyl-3-propanol involves a substituent
        number greater than the correct answer.) The -ol
        ending, instead of -ane, indicates that the substituent
        at the 1 position is an -OH group.

    b) 1-chloro-2-propanol.

    c) 2,2-dimethyl-3-pentanol.

    d) 2,4-pentanediol.

2. a) $CH_3-\overset{\displaystyle OH}{\underset{\displaystyle CH_3}{C}}-CH_2-CH_3$ since both substituents are on
        carbon 2.

    b) $CH_3-\overset{\displaystyle OH}{CH}-CH_2-CH_2-\overset{\displaystyle CH_3}{CH}-CH_3$

    c) $\overset{\displaystyle O}{\underset{\displaystyle H}{C}}-\overset{\displaystyle Cl}{CH}-CH_3$ The -al ending signifies an
        aldehyde.

    d) Presumably the -OH group is in the 1-position.

3. a) Primary since the carbon is —CH_2OH, i.e. bonded to
        only 1 C.

    b) Tertiary since the carbon is $\supset$C—OH, i.e. bonded to 3
        carbons.

    c) Secondary since the carbon is —CHOH, i.e. bonded to 2
        carbons.

d) Secondary since the carbon is —CHOH.

4. a) 1-propanal since -al is the ending for an aldehyde,
       i.e. the CHO group. (Propanal would be sufficient as
       the aldehyde group must be on a terminal carbon.)

   b) 2-methyl-butanal.

   c) 2-butanone (or simply butanone since 1-butanone is
       impossible).

   d) 2-methyl-3-pentanone.

5. a)
$$
\begin{array}{c}
\quad\;\; O \\
\quad\;\; \| \\
H\!-\!CCH_2CH_2CH_3 .
\end{array}
$$

   b)
$$
\begin{array}{c}
\quad\quad O \\
\quad\quad \| \\
CH_3CCH_2CH_2CH_3 .
\end{array}
$$ The -one signifies it is a ketone.

   c)
$$
\begin{array}{c}
\quad\quad\;\; O \\
\quad\quad\;\; \| \\
CH_3CHCCH_3 \\
\;\;| \\
\;\;CH_3
\end{array}
$$

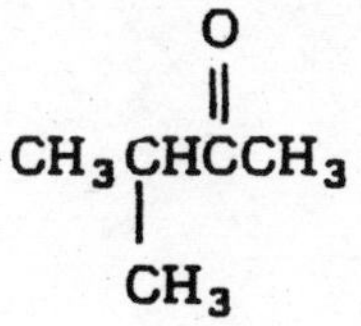

   d)

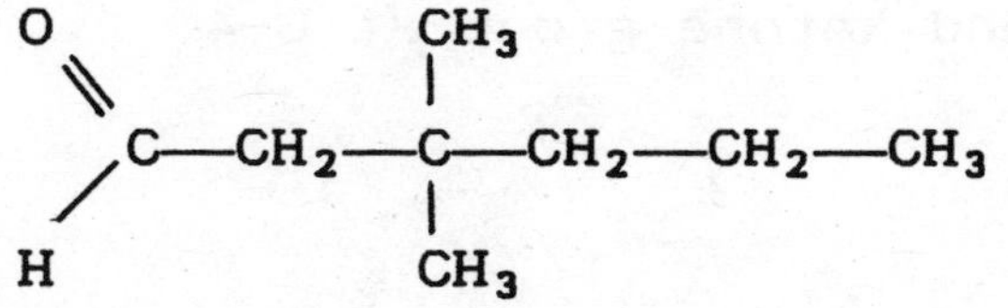

6. a) $CH_2Cl\!-\!CCl_2\!-\!CH_2\!-\!CH_3 .$

   b)

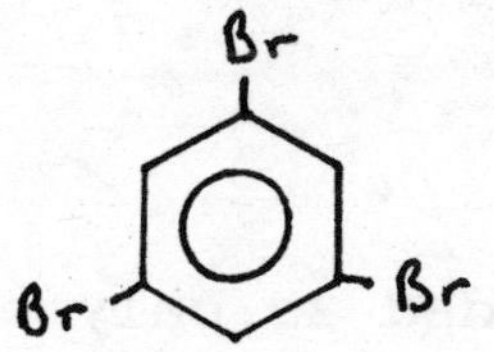

   c)

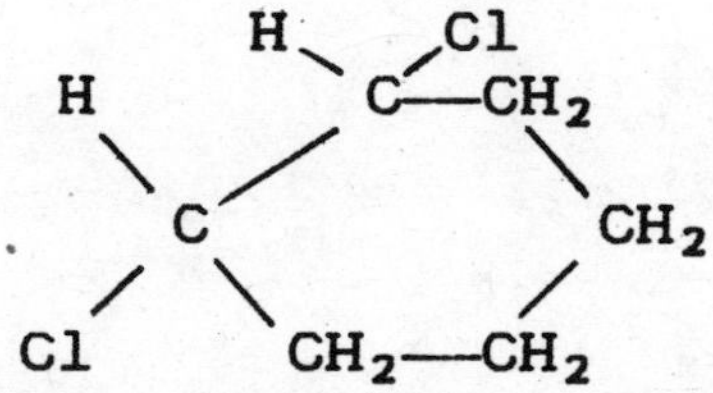

7. In both cases, we have substituted alkanes since the number
   of hydrogens plus halogens is equal to 2n + 2, where n is
   the number of carbons. Thus $C_3H_6Cl_2$ is based upon propane,
   a molecule with two nonequivalent carbons. Thus both Cl's

could be on carbon 1 or both on carbon 2, or one on C-1 and the other on C-2 or C-3. (Any other placement duplicates one of the above and is not a separate isomer):

$CHCl_2$—CH_2—CH_3 is   1,1-dichloropropane
CH_3—CCl_2—CH_3 is   2,2-dichloropropane
CH_2Cl—$CHCl$—CH_3 is   1,2-dichloropropane
CH_2Cl—CH_2—CH_2Cl is   1,3-dichloropropane

C_4H_9Br is a monosubstituted butane; n-butane has 2 nonequivalent carbons at which substitution could occur, as does its isomer 2-methylpropane.

CH_2Br—CH_2—CH_2—CH_3 1-bromobutane
CH_3—$CHBr$—CH_2—CH_3 2-bromobutane

$$CH_3$$
$$|$$
CH_2Br—CH—CH_3 1-bromo-2-methylpropane

$$CH_3$$
$$|$$
CH_3—CBr—CH_3 2-bromo-2-methylpropane

(Note that the substituent —CH_3 group is equivalent to the other methyl groups.)

8.   a)   Aldehyde since it is CHO.

     b)   Alcohol on C-4 and carboxyl group as C-1.

     c)   Phenol group at C-1 and aldehyde at C-2 (or vice-versa).

     d)   Carboxyl group at C-1 and ketone group at C-4.

     e)   Ester group (C—O—C—, with =O on the final C).

     f)   Amide group (—C(=O)—NH_2).

9.   a)   Methanol.

     b)   Ethanol (as in (a), no number is needed as only one compound is possible).

     c)   Methanoic acid (or formic acid).

     d)   2-butanol.

     e)   Propanal.

     f)   1,2-ethanediol (or ethylene glycol).

     g)   Propanone (or acetone).

h)   1-chloro-2-bromopropane.

10. a) AX_4 at carbon since there are 4 groups singly-bonded to C, and no lone pairs. Your diagram should show the carbon as tetrahedral. The oxygen is AX_2E_2 (2 lone pairs) and thus angular.

     b) AX_2E_2 since there are 2 lone pairs on —O— type oxygen. The geometry at —O— should be shown as angular.

     c) AX_3 since C=O counts as only one X. Trigonal planar at C.

     d)   Since the Lewis structure is H—C$\overset{\displaystyle O}{\underset{\displaystyle O^-}{\diagup}}$, it is AX_3 and thus trigonal planar.

     e) AX_3, trigonal planar (see 10(c)).

     f) AX_3, trigonal planar.

     g) AX_3E since there is a lone pair on N. Pyramidal at N.

     h) AX_4, tetrahedral at N.

     i) AX_3E, pyramidal (see 10(g)).

11. As discussed in the text, the geometry is trigonal planar AX_3 at nitrogen as well as carbon since the structure

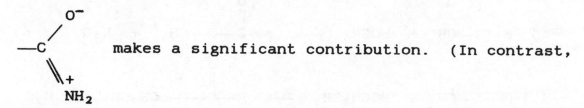

makes a significant contribution. (In contrast,

for —C$\overset{\displaystyle O}{\underset{\displaystyle NH_2}{\diagup}}$, the nitrogen is AX_3E and would be expected to

be pyramidal.) In order that partial double bonds form from C to N and C to O, all of the atoms must be in the same plane.

12. In forming aldehydes/ketones from alcohols, one H atom of the substituted carbon is removed. Thus to determine the appropriate alcohol, add one H to the substituted carbon and one to the doubly-bonded oxygen:

a) $CH_3—CHO \longrightarrow CH_3—CH_2OH$ ethanol

b) $CH_3—\overset{\displaystyle O}{\overset{\|}{C}}—CH_3 \longrightarrow CH_3—\overset{\displaystyle OH}{\overset{|}{CH}}—CH_3$ 2-propanol

c) $\overset{\displaystyle O}{\overset{\|}{\underset{\displaystyle H}{C}}}—\overset{\displaystyle CH_3}{\overset{|}{CH}}—CH_3 \longrightarrow CH_2OH—\overset{\displaystyle CH_3}{\overset{|}{CH}}—CH_3$ 2-methyl-1-propanol

d) $CH_3—\overset{\displaystyle O}{\overset{\|}{C}}—CH_2—CH_2—CH_3 \longrightarrow CH_3—CHOH—CH_2—CH_2—CH_3$
                                                       2-pentanol

13. In each case, H_2O is eliminated.

a) $CH_3\overset{\displaystyle O}{\overset{\|}{C}}—OH + HOCH(CH_3)_2 \longrightarrow CH_3\overset{\displaystyle O}{\overset{\|}{C}}—O—CH(CH_3)_2 + H_2O.$

b) $CH_3\overset{\displaystyle O}{\overset{\|}{C}}—OH + HOCH_2CH_2CH_2CH_3 \longrightarrow CH_3\overset{\displaystyle O}{\overset{\|}{C}}—O—CH_2CH_2CH_2CH_3$
     $+ H_2O$

c) Representing the benzene ring as ϕ, then

$\phi—\overset{\displaystyle O}{\overset{\|}{C}}—OH + HOCH_3 \longrightarrow \phi—\overset{\displaystyle O}{\overset{\|}{C}}—O—CH_3 + H_2O.$

d) $H—\overset{\displaystyle O}{\overset{\|}{C}}—OH + HOCH_2CH_3 \longrightarrow H—\overset{\displaystyle O}{\overset{\|}{C}}—O—CH_2CH_3 + H_2O.$

14. See text:
a) Heat an alkane to 700-800°C in the presence of a Ni catalyst:
     e.g. $CH_4(g) + H_2O(g) \longrightarrow CO(g) + 3H_2(g).$

b) Heat synthesis gas having a 2:1 H_2:CO ratio to 240-260°C under a pressure of 50-100 atm in the presence of a $ZnO/CuO/Al_2O_3$ catalyst:
         $CO(g) + 2H_2(g) \longrightarrow CH_3OH(g).$

15. a) Heating an alcohol in the presence of a Cu catalyst gives an aldehyde
     $CH_3CH_2OH \longrightarrow CH_3—CHO.$

b) Alcohols behave as weak acids in the presence of strong bases:
$$CH_3CH_2CH_2OH \ + \ NaOH \ \longrightarrow \ CH_3CH_2CH_2O^-Na^+ \ + \ H_2O.$$

c) $$2CH_3OH \ + \ 2Na \ \longrightarrow \ 2CH_3O^-Na^+ \ + \ H_2.$$

d) Alcohols behave as weak bases in the presence of strong acids; thus they acccept protons:
$$C_2H_5OH \ + \ HBr \ \longrightarrow \ C_2H_5OH_2^+ \ + \ Br^-.$$

e) Concentrated H_2SO_4 dehydrates alcohols to alkenes; one H is lost from the carbon adjacent to that with the OH group.
$$CH_3CH_2OH \ + \ H_2SO_4 \ \longrightarrow \ CH_2 = CH_2 \ + \ H_3O^+ \ + \ HSO_4^-$$
$$or \ 2CH_3CH_2OH + H_2SO_4 \longrightarrow \ (CH_3CH_2)_2O + H_3O^+ + HSO_4^-.$$

f) $$C_2H_5OH + 3O_2 \ \longrightarrow \ 2CO_2 + 3H_2O$$

g) With a catalyst present, H_2O would add to the double bond, i.e. H to one carbon and OH to the other:
$$CH_3CH = CH_2 \ + \ H_2O \ \longrightarrow \ CH_3CH_2CH_2OH$$
$$or \ \ CH_3CHCH_3$$
$$\qquad\qquad | $$
$$\qquad\qquad OH$$

16. a) The Na^+ and the Br^- combine to form a salt, and the oxygen atom joins to the carbon chain at the position of the lost bromine:
$$C_2H_5ONa \ + \ CH_3Br \ \longrightarrow \ Na^+Br^- \ + \ C_2H_5OCH_3.$$

b) Heating an alcohol in the presence of Cu or Ag results in the loss of H_2, with one H from OH and the other from the carbon bonded to OH, to give an aldehyde or ketone:
$$CH_3CH_2OH \ \longrightarrow \ CH_3CHO.$$

c) Oxidation, using dichromate, of an alcohol gives an aldehyde or ketone:
$$CH_3CHCH_3 \ \longrightarrow \ CH_3CCH_3$$
$$\quad\quad | \qquad\qquad\qquad ||$$
$$\quad\quad OH \qquad\qquad\quad O$$

(Since the product is a ketone, further oxidation to the acid cannot occur.)

d) Hydrogenation of an aldehyde or ketone gives an alcohol, since one H adds to the O and one to the carbon bonded to O; i.e. H_2 adds across the double bond:
$$\quad\quad O \qquad\qquad\qquad\qquad OH$$
$$\quad\quad || \qquad\qquad\qquad\qquad\quad |$$
$$CH_3CH_2CCH_3 \ + \ H_2 \ \longrightarrow \ CH_3CH_2CHCH_3.$$

e) Hydrazine adds to C = O by one H adding to oxygen and the —NH—NH$_2$ group adding to carbon; this product

283

loses water (the OH and the H on the central nitrogen combining):

$$CH_3CH_2\overset{\overset{\displaystyle O}{\|}}{C}CH_3 \ + \ H_2NNH_2 \ \longrightarrow \ CH_3CH_2\underset{\underset{\displaystyle CH_3}{|}}{\overset{\overset{\displaystyle OH}{|}}{C}}\text{—NH—}NH_2$$

$$\longrightarrow \ CH_3CH_2\underset{\underset{\displaystyle CH_3}{|}}{C} = N\text{—}NH_2 \ + \ H_2O.$$

17. a) Oxidation of an aldehyde gives the corresponding acid:
$$CH_3CH_2CHO \ \longrightarrow \ CH_3CH_2COOH.$$

b) Heating CO with NaOH gives the salt of formic acid, since the OH^- adds to the carbon:
$$CO \ + \ NaOH \ \longrightarrow \ HCOO^-Na^+.$$

c) Heating an alcohol and an acid together produces the ester, by H_2O loss

$$CH_3CH_2\overset{\overset{\displaystyle O}{\|}}{C}\text{—OH} \ + \ HO\text{—}CH(CH_3)_2 \ \longrightarrow \ CH_3CH_2\overset{\overset{\displaystyle O}{\|}}{C}\text{—O—}CH(CH_3)_2$$
$$+ \ H_2O.$$

d) Heating an alcohol and ammonia produces an amine and H_2O by replacement of —OH by —NH_2:
$$CH_3OH \ + \ NH_3 \ \longrightarrow \ CH_3NH_2 \ + \ H_2O.$$

e) In water, an amine acts as a weak base:
$$CH_3NH_2 \ + \ H_2O \ \rightleftharpoons \ CH_3NH_3^+ \ + \ OH^-.$$

f) An amine, a base, reacts with HCl to give a salt:
$$CH_3NH_2 \ + \ HCl \ \longrightarrow \ CH_3NH_3^+Cl^-.$$

g) An amine (base) and a carboxylic acid produce a salt which upon heating eliminates H_2O to produce an amide:

$$CH_3\overset{\overset{\displaystyle O}{\|}}{C}\text{—OH} \ + \ H\text{—}NH_2\text{—}CH_2\text{—}CH_3 \ \longrightarrow \ CH_3\text{—}\overset{\overset{\displaystyle O}{\|}}{C}\text{—NH—}CH_2CH_3$$
$$+ \ H_2O.$$

18. a) See Q. 14(b). Overall we obtain
$$CH_4 \ + \ H_2O \ (\longrightarrow \ CO \ + \ 3H_2) \ \longrightarrow \ CH_3OH \ + \ H_2.$$

b) In this case the overall reaction will be
$$a \ CH_4 \ + \ b \ H_2O \ + \ c \ CO_2 \ \longrightarrow \ d \ CH_3OH.$$
Consider the production of 1 mole of CH_3OH (i.e. d = 1). From C atom conservation, we have

284

$$a + c = 1.$$

Similarly for H atom conservation,
$$4a + 2b = 4.$$

Finally, for O atom conservation
$$b + 2c = 1.$$

Solving the three simultaneous equations for the three unknowns gives $a = 3/4$, $b = 1/2$, $c = 1/4$, i.e. after multiplying though by 4,

$$3CH_4 + 2H_2O + CO_2 \longrightarrow 4CH_3OH.$$

Thus in the first step,

$$3CH_4 + 3H_2O \longrightarrow 3CO + 9H_2.$$

One mole of these nine moles of H_2 should be reacted, since one mole of CO_2 is used. Thus one-ninth of the H_2 should be reacted with CO_2.

19. The ester described is that of formic acid, HCOOH, with methanol:

$$\underset{\displaystyle HC-OH}{\overset{\displaystyle O \atop \|}{}} + HO-CH_3 \longrightarrow \underset{\displaystyle H-C-O-CH_3}{\overset{\displaystyle O \atop \|}{}} + H_2O$$

20. a) $CO + 2H_2 \longrightarrow CH_3OH$ methanol

   b) $(CH_3)_2CBr-CH_2BrCH_3$ 2-methyl-2,3-dibromobutane

   c) $(CH_3)_2CH-CH_2CH_3$ 2-methylbutane

   d) Sulfuric acid could dehydrate ethanol molecules to ethene, or by removing H from one alcohol molecule (methanol or ethanol) and OH from another alcohol (not necessarily the same type), it can result in ether formation. Thus a mixture of CH_3OCH_3, $C_2H_5OCH_3$, and $C_2H_5OC_2H_5$ will be produced.

   e) $CH_3CH_2CH_2O^-Na^+$ sodium propoxide.

21. As discussed in the text, to achieve a net replacement of one H by one Cl, one could add Cl_2 to the double bond and then heat the product to eliminate HCl:

$$CH_2 = CH_2 + Cl_2 \longrightarrow CH_2Cl-CH_2Cl$$

$$CH_2Cl-CH_2Cl \xrightarrow{\text{heat}} CH_2 = CHCl + HCl.$$

22. One route would be to first form methanol from methane — see the equations in the solution to Q. 18. The alcohol could then be converted to formic acid by oxidation in acid by an excess of $K_2Cr_2O_7$:

$$CH_3OH \xrightarrow{K_2Cr_2O_7} HCOOH.$$

23. Ethanoate is an ester of ethanoic (i.e. acetic acid); since the ethyl ester is to be produced, we require ethanol

$$CH_3\overset{\displaystyle O}{\overset{\|}{C}}\!\!-\!OH \ + \ HO\!-\!CH_2CH_3 \ \longrightarrow \ CH_3\!-\!\overset{\displaystyle O}{\overset{\|}{C}}\!-\!O\!-\!CH_2CH_3 \ + \ H_2O.$$

To produce ethanol from ethene, we must add H_2O across the double bond. This can be achieved by using a high pressure, a temperature of about 300°C, and a catalyst such as phosphoric acid:

$$H_2C = CH_2 \ + \ H_2O \ \longrightarrow \ CH_3CH_2OH.$$

Half the ethanol so produced should be oxidized to acetic acid, using excess (acidic) $K_2Cr_2O_7$:

$$CH_3CH_2OH \ \longrightarrow \ CH_3COOH.$$

The acid and alcohol should then be combined (see first equation above).

24. See Box 19.2 of the text.

25. a) This alcohol differs from propene by H on one terminal carbon and OH on the middle carbon; thus it can be prepared by adding H_2O to the double bond in propene,

$$CH_3\!-\!CH = CH_2 \ + \ H_2O \ \longrightarrow \ \text{mixture of } CH_3\!-\!CHOH\!-\!CH_3$$
$$\text{and } CH_3\!-\!CH_2\!-\!CH_2OH.$$

b) This tetrabromo compound, minus all its Br, is the alkyne $CH_3\!-\!C \equiv C\!-\!CH_3$, 2-butyne. Thus we react 1 mole of 2-butyne with 2 moles of Br_2, since the halogen adds to triple and to double bonds:

$$CH_3\!-\!C \equiv C\!-\!CH_3 \ \xrightarrow{\ + \ Br_2\ } \ CH_3\!-\!CBr = CBr\!-\!CH_3 \ \xrightarrow{\ + \ Br_2\ }$$

$$CH_3\!-\!CBr_2\!-\!CBr_2\!-\!CH_3.$$

c) This alkene can be made from 2-butyne as well, by simple catalytic hydrogenation.

$$CH_3\!-\!C \equiv C\!-\!CH_3 \ + \ H_2 \ \longrightarrow \ CH_3\!-\!CH = CH\!-\!CH_3.$$

d) To add one Br, one could add HBr to propyne: $CH_3C \equiv CH$ + HBr $\longrightarrow$ mixture of 1- and 2-bromopropenes.

26. a) Comparing reactant with product reveals that each C adds 1 Cl; this is easily accomplished by reacting ethene with Cl_2:

$$CH_2 = CH_2 \ + \ Cl_2 \ \longrightarrow \ CH_2Cl\!-\!CH_2Cl.$$

b) To obtain an acid from its corresponding alcohol, we oxidize an acid with an excess of $K_2Cr_2O_7$:

$$CH_3CH_2CH_2OH \ \xrightarrow{\ K_2Cr_2O_7\ } \ CH_3CH_2\overset{\displaystyle O}{\overset{\|}{C}}\!\!-\!OH.$$

286

c) Ethyl ethanoate is the ester of ethanol and ethanoic acid. To obtain the latter two reactants from ethanal, which is the aldehyde, we must reduce half of it to ethanol and oxidize the other half to ethanoic (acetic) acid. Hydrogenation accomplishes the former, while oxidation by acidic $K_2Cr_2O_7$ does the latter:

$$CH_3-\overset{\overset{\textstyle O}{\|}}{C}-H + H_2 \xrightarrow{\text{Ni}} CH_3CH_2OH$$

$$CH_3-\overset{\overset{\textstyle O}{\|}}{C}-H \xrightarrow{K_2Cr_2O_7} CH_3\overset{\overset{\textstyle O}{\|}}{C}-OH$$

$$CH_3\overset{\overset{\textstyle O}{\|}}{C}-OH + HOCH_2CH_3 \longrightarrow CH_3-\overset{\overset{\textstyle O}{\|}}{C}-O-CH_2CH_3.$$

27. Recall that Br_2 dissociates into atoms when irradiated:
$$Br_2 \longrightarrow 2Br$$
The Br atom can abstract a hydrogen atom from an alkane – either from a CH_3 or a CH_2 group in the case of propane (not specified here):
$$Br + C_3H_8 \longrightarrow C_3H_7 + HBr.$$
The C_3H_7 radical reacts with Br_2 to produce a propyl bromide:
$$C_3H_7 + Br_2 \longrightarrow C_3H_7Br + Br.$$
In addition to HBr and C_3H_7Br, excess Br_2 could react with further H atoms of C_3H_7Br to produce $C_3H_6Br_2$, etc.

28. Ketones are obtained by the oxidation (loss of 2H atoms) of secondary alcohols, which we therefore deduce $C_5H_{12}O$ to be. Possible structures therefore are

$$\overset{\overset{\textstyle OH}{|}}{CH_3CHCH_2CH_2CH_3} \qquad \text{and} \qquad \overset{\overset{\textstyle OH}{|}}{CH_3CH_2CHCH_2CH_3}.$$

29. a) If $pK_b = 3.43$, then $K_b = 10^{-3.43} = 3.7 \times 10^{-4}$. The reaction of the base with water is

	CH_3NH_2	$+ H_2O \rightleftharpoons$	$CH_3NH_3^+$	$+ OH^-$
Initial	0.10		O	O
Equilibrium	0.10-y		y	y.

Since $K_b = [CH_3NH_3^+][OH^-]/[CH_3NH_2]$
thus

$$\frac{y^2}{0.10-y} = 3.7 \times 10^{-4}.$$

Using the approximation $0.10 \gg y$, we obtain
$y = 6.1 \times 10^{-3}$ (i.e. 6.1% ionization).
Thus $[OH^-] = 6.1 \times 10^{-3}$ M, pOH = 2.22, pH = 11.78.
The K_a of $CH_3NH_3^+$, the conjugate acid of CH_3NH_2, is
$10^{-14}/K_b$, i.e. 2.7×10^{-11}, so $pK_a = 10.57$.

b) As a result solely of mixing the two solutions, the
following changes occur to the concentrations:
$[CH_3NH_2] = 0.090$ M $\times$ (24.5 mL/34.5 mL) = 0.064 M
$[HCl] = 0.10$ M $\times$ (10.0 mL/34.5 mL) = 0.029 M.
The base reacts with HCl to produce the conjugate acid:

	CH_3NH_2	+	HCl	$\longrightarrow$	$CH_3NH_3^+$ + Cl^-
Initial	0.064		0.029		0
Final	0.035		0		0.029.

The pH is determined by the equilibrium

	CH_3NH_2	+	H_2O	$\rightleftharpoons$	$CH_3NH_3^+$ + OH^-
Initial	0.035				0.029 0
Equilibrium	0.035-y				0.029+y y

Using the approximation, then
$0.029\, y/0.035 = 3.7 \times 10^{-4}$
$y = 4.5 \times 10^{-4} = [OH]$.
Thus pOH = 3.35 and pH = 10.65.

30. The combustion reactions, balanced, are

$$CH_3OH(\ell) + \frac{3}{2} O_2(g) \longrightarrow CO_2(g) + 2H_2O(\ell)$$

and
$$C_2H_5OH(\ell) + 3 O_2(g) \longrightarrow 2CO_2(g) + 3H_2O(\ell).$$

Thus for methanol
$\Delta H^\circ = \Delta H_f^\circ(CO_2,g) + 2\Delta H_f^\circ(H_2O,\ell) - \Delta H_f^\circ(CH_3OH,\ell)$.
Using the data in the problem and in Table 12.1, we obtain
− 726 kJ mol^{-1} for methanol, and similarly
− 1367 kJ mol^{-1} for ethanol.

31. From the percent mass values, the empirical formula can be
deduced (see Chapter 2):

Moles in 100 g	52.1/12.01	13.1/1.01	3.48/16.00
	= 4.34	= 13.0	= 2.18
Ratio to smallest	1.99	5.96	1.00

Thus the empirical formula is C_2H_6O.
From the P-V-T-m information, the molecular mass M can
be determined via the Ideal Gas Equation (see Chapter 3):
n = PV/RT = 1.00 atm $\times$ 0.153 L/0.0821 L atm $mole^{-1}$ K^{-1} $\times$ 373 K
= 5.00×10^{-3} mole.
Thus M = m/n = 0.230 g/5.00 $\times 10^{-3}$ mole = 46.0 g $mole^{-1}$.

Since the empirical formula mass is (2 x 12.01 + 6 x 1.01 + 16.00 =) 46.08, we conclude that the molecular formula is the same as is the empirical, i.e. C_2H_6O.

There are two stable compounds with this formula, an ether and an alcohol:

$$CH_3—O—CH_3 \qquad \text{and} \qquad CH_3—CH_2—OH.$$

Only ethanol would react with sodium to give H_2 and a salt:

$$2CH_3CH_2OH + 2Na \longrightarrow 2CH_3CH_2ONa + H_2.$$

We can deduce the moles of H_2 produced in this reaction:

$$0.250 \text{ g } C_2H_5OH \times \frac{1 \text{ mole } C_2H_5OH}{46.08 \text{ g } C_2H_5OH} \times \frac{1 \text{ mole } H_2}{2 \text{ moles } C_2H_5OH}$$

$$= 2.71 \times 10^{-3} \text{ moles } H_2.$$

Finally, the volume occupied by this amount of H_2 can be determined from $PV = nRT$, i.e.

$$V = nRT/P = 2.71 \times 10^{-3} \text{ moles} \times 0.0821 \text{ L atm mole}^{-1} \text{ K}^{-1}$$
$$\times 298 \text{ K}/(750/760) \text{ atm}$$
$$= 6.72 \times 10^{-2} \text{ L, i.e. } 67.2 \text{ mL.}$$

32. Boiling points in such compounds are determined to a large extent by the hydrogen bonding that exists between molecules (the greater the H-bonding, the higher the boiling point) and to a lesser extent by London intermolecular forces, which increase the boiling point as the molecular mass (actually the number of electrons) increases. Thus H_2O has the highest boiling point since both its H atoms are involved in hydrogen bonding; methanol and ethanol are next since they each have one H which engages in hydrogen bonding. Finally we have ether, ethane and methane, within which group the boiling point increases with molecular mass.

33. To compare on the basis of equal volumes, consider for convenience 1 cm³ of each; convert this mass to moles, since the thermochemical data is given on a molar basis:

$$0.72 \text{ g nonane} \times \frac{1 \text{ mole nonane}}{128.29 \text{ g ethanol}} = 5.61 \times 10^{-3} \text{ moles nonane}$$

$$0.79 \text{ g ethanol} \times \frac{1 \text{ mole ethanol}}{48.08 \text{ g ethanol}} = 1.71 \times 10^{-2} \text{ moles ethanol}$$

Similarly, for mass comparisons, we take 1 g of each, which corresponds to 7.79×10^{-3} moles nonane and to 2.17×10^{-2} moles of ethanol.

Now deduce the heat energy released per mole of nonane or ethanol; the combustion reactions are

$$C_9H_{20} + 14O_2 \longrightarrow 9CO_2 + 10H_2O(l)$$
$$C_2H_5OH + 3O_2 \longrightarrow 2CO_2 + 3H_2O(l).$$

Thus for nonane,
$$\Delta H_C°(CO_2, 8) = 9\Delta H_f°(CO_2, g) + 10\Delta H_f°(H_2O, l) - \Delta H_f°(C_9H_{20}, l)$$
and for ethanol,

$$\Delta H_c{}^\circ = 2\Delta H_f{}^\circ(CO_2, g) + 3\Delta H_f{}^\circ(H_2O, \ell) - \Delta H_f{}^\circ(C_2H_5OH, \ell).$$
Using the data in Table 12.1 and in the problem, we obtain
−6124 kJ per mole of nonane, compared to −1367 kJ per mole
of ethanol.
Thus the heat released per cm^3 of
  nonane is 5.61×10^{-3} moles $\times$ 6124 kJ/mole = 34.4 kJ
  ethanol is 1.71×10^{-2} moles $\times$ 1367 kJ/mole = 23.4 kJ.
Similarly, the heat released per gram of nonane is
47.7 kJ whereas per gram of ethanol it is 29.7 kJ.

34. Yes, we would expect them to differ since ethanol can
     engage in hydrogen bonding whereas dimethyl ether cannot;
     thus the former has a much higher boiling point (see data
     in Q. 32). They could be distinguished by reaction with
     sodium metal; only the alcohol will react, as detected by
     release of a gas (H_2) − see answer to Q. 31.

35. The combustion and gas law data allows us to deduce the
     molecular formula of the compound; from this we can attempt
     to deduce a structure.
         The empirical formula is determined from combustion
     data using the methodology developed in Chapter 3. Thus:

$$0.512 \text{ g } CO_2 \times \frac{1 \text{ mole } CO_2}{44.01 \text{ g } CO_2} \times \frac{1 \text{ mole C}}{1 \text{ mole } CO_2}$$

$$= 1.163 \times 10^{-2} \text{ moles C} \times \frac{12.01 \text{ g C}}{1 \text{ mole C}} = 0.140 \text{ g C}$$

$$0.209 \text{ g } H_2O \times \frac{1 \text{ mole } H_2O}{18.02 \text{ g } H_2O} \times \frac{2 \text{ moles H}}{1 \text{ mole } H_2O}$$

$$= 2.320 \times 10^{-2} \text{ moles H} \times \frac{1.01 \text{ g H}}{1 \text{ moles H}} = 0.023 \text{ g H}.$$

Thus mass O = 0.256 g − 0.140 g − 0.023 g = 0.093 g O,
i.e. 0.581×10^{-2} moles O.
The ratio of moles C to H to O is 2.00 to 3.99 to 1, so the
empirical formula is C_2H_4O.
    The molecular mass of the compound can be found from
the data for the gas, using PV = nRT. Thus
n = PV/RT = (882/760) atm $\times$ 0.0933 L/0.0821 L atm mole^{-1}
      K^{-1} $\times$ 373 K = 3.54×10^{-3} moles.
Thus M = m/n = 0.156 g/3.54×10^{-3} moles = 44.1 g mole^{-1}.
Since the empirical formula mass for C_2H_4O is 44.06, we
conclude that the molecular formula also is C_2H_4O. The
most likely structure is CH_3CHO, an aldehyde.

CHAPTER 20

1. In these states, I or Xe form polar covalent bonds to a highly-electronegative atom such as fluorine. Thus an oxidation state of +3, for example, implies an atom with a valence of 3. Thus we re-interpret the problem to mean that we are to draw orbital box diagrams for valences of a) 1, 3, 5, 7 and b) 2, 4, 6. We identify the valence with the number of singly-occupied orbitals and promote electrons until this is achieved:

			5s	5p			5d				
a)	+1	$[Kr]4d^{10}$	↑↓	↑↓	↑↓	↑					
	+3	$[Kr]4d^{10}$	↑↓	↑↓	↑	↑	↑				
	+5	$[Kr]4d^{10}$	↑↓	↑	↑	↑	↑	↑			
	+7	$[Kr]4d^{10}$	↑	↑	↑	↑	↑	↑	↑		
b)	2	$[Kr]4d^{10}$	↑↓	↑↓	↑↓	↑	↑				
	4	$[Kr]4d^{10}$	↑↓	↑↓	↑	↑	↑	↑			
	6	$[Kr]4d^{10}$	↑↓	↑	↑	↑	↑	↑	↑		

2. Trigonal bipyramid for AX_5, octahedral for AX_6. Examples of AX_5 are phosphorus pentahalides; for AX_6, sulfur hexafluoride. In SeF_4, there are four bonding pairs and one lone pair on the Se; hence it is AX_4E in type. Thus SeF_4 has the disphenoid shape. BrF_3 is of the AX_3E_2 category; thus it is T-shaped. XeF_4 is of the AX_4E_2 type; hence it is square planar. ICl_2^- is of the AX_2E_3 type, and therefore is linear.

3. In the gas-phase, PCl_5 consists of individual PCl_5 molecules, each of which has the (expected) trigonal bipyramid geometry. In the solid state, however, it consists of tetrahedral PCl_4^+ and octahedral PCl_6^- ions.

4. Such elements have empty d orbitals in the valence shell; promotion of electrons into these orbitals allows for an expansion of the valence shell beyond the eight electrons which can be accommodated in s and p orbitals. Fluorine (and to some extent other highly electronegative atoms) is capable of stabilizing these d orbitals, since it withdraws electrons from the atom.

291

Phosphorus forms pyramidal PF_3 and trigonal bipyramid PF_5 molecules. Sulfur forms disphenoid SF_4, and octahedral SF_6 molecules.

5. Presumably two of the six Cl atoms in I_2Cl_6 are bridging, since we are told its structure is similar to that for $AlCl_3$. In ICl_3, the I atom has five electron pairs (two nonbonding); thus if it accepts one more pair from a Cl atom of the other ICl_3 unit, it has six pairs and an octahedral arrangement. Since the optimum AX_4E_2 geometry is square planar, we expect all the atoms in I_2Cl_6 lie in the same plane, with angles at I and the bridging Cl's of about 90°:

6. Presumably the oxygen atoms are doubly-bonded to the central halogen atom A; thus the valence of A is 5 in AO_2F and 7 in AO_3F. To achieve these values, two or three electrons respectively must be promoted to the d subshell, leaving one and zero lone pairs around A. Thus the Lewis structures are

The number of electron pairs which play a role in determining geometry is four in both cases. Thus AO_2F is an AX_3E molecule with a trigonal pyramid geometry, and AO_3F is AX_4, tetrahedral.

7. The ions involved are XeF_3^+, XeF_5^+, and SbF_6^- which possess respectively 10, 12 and 12 electrons respectively, with geometries called T-shape, square pyramid, and octahedral. The bond angles in the T and square pyramid should be 90° and 180° (or slightly less), and exactly 90° and 180° in the octahedron.

292

8. To decide if a molecule has a dipole, we first deduce its geometry. Using VSEPR theory, we obtain the results below. The molecule has a dipole moment if the A—F dipole vectors do not sum to zero, i.e. if the center of the δ^- charges from the F atoms does not coincide with A:

System	Type	Geometry	Dipole ?
PF_5	AX_5	Trig. bipyramidal	No
SF_4	AX_4E	Disphenoidal	Yes
ClF_3	AX_3E_2	T-shaped	Yes
BrF_5	AX_5E	Square pyramidal	Yes
XeF_2	AX_2E_3	Linear	No
XeF_4	AX_4E_2	Square planar	No

9. In all these examples, the number of electrons at the central atom is quickly computed from its Group Number plus the number of F's, corrected by the net charge.

	System	Pairs at A	Type	Geometry
a)	SiF_6^{2-}	6	AX_6	Octahedral
b)	SiF_5^-	5	AX_5	Trigonal bipyramid
c)	PF_6^-	6	AX_6	Octahedral
d)	SeF_5^-	6	AX_5E	Square pyramid
e)	BrF_4^-	6	AX_4E_2	Square planar
f)	IF_4^+	5	AX_4E	Disphenoidal

10. Similar to Q. 6. The Lewis structures are

(To form 6, 6, and 8 bonds respectively requires the promotion of 3, 3, and 4 electrons, leaving 1, 1, and 0 of the original 4 lone pairs at Xe.) Counting doubly-bonded oxygen as only one active bonding pair X, the types are AX_5E, AX_4E, and AX_5 respectively, so the geometries are square pyramid, irregular tetrahedron, and trigonal bipyramid respectively.

11. In terms of the $XO_m(OH)_n$ classification system, HClO is X(OH), H_3PO_3 is $X(OH)_2O$, $HClO_4$ is $X(OH)O_3$, and H_2SO_4 is $X(OH)_2O_2$. Thus the order of increasing acidity is HClO, H_3PO_3, H_2SO_4, $HClO_4$ since acidity increases with m, the number of doubly-bonded oxygens.

12. a) The unbalanced equation is
$$Cr_2(SO_4)_3 + NaOCl \longrightarrow Na_2CrO_4 + NaCl\ (+ SO_4^{2-}\ compound).$$
In ionic form, and eliminating the spectator ions Na^+ and SO_4^{2-}, we have
$$Cr^{3+} + OCl^- \longrightarrow CrO_4^{2-} + Cl^-.$$
Thus the half-reactions are
$$Cr^{3+} \longrightarrow CrO_4^{2-}$$
which, upon balancing in basic solution, is
$$Cr^{3+} + 8OH^- \longrightarrow CrO_4^{2-} + 4H_2O + 3e^-$$
and $OCl^- \longrightarrow Cl^-$
which upon balancing gives
$$OCl^- + H_2O + 2e^- \longrightarrow Cl^- + 2OH^-.$$
Upon balancing electrons and adding, we obtain
$$3OCl^- + 2Cr^{3+} + 10OH^- \longrightarrow 2CrO_4^{2-} + 5H_2O + 3Cl^-.$$
Adding back the spectator ions, we obtain
$$3NaOCl + Cr_2(SO_4)_3 + 10NaOH \longrightarrow 2Na_2CrO_4 + 5H_2O + 3NaCl$$
$$+ 3Na_2SO_4.$$
(The SO_4^{2-} is associated with Na^+ since it is the only available cation.)

b) The unbalanced reaction is
$$KI + NaClO_3 \longrightarrow I_2 + NaCl\ (+K\ compound).$$
In ionic form we have
$$I^- + ClO_3^- \longrightarrow I_2 + Cl^-.$$
Balancing the obvious half-reactions, we obtain
$$2I^- \longrightarrow I_2 + 2e^-$$
$$ClO_3^- + 3H_2O + 6e^- \longrightarrow Cl^- + 6OH^-.$$
Multiplying the first by three, and adding, we obtain
$$6I^- + ClO_3^- + 3H_2O \longrightarrow 3I_2 + Cl^- + 6OH^-.$$
Adding back the spectator ions, we obtain
$$6KI + NaClO_3 + 3H_2O \longrightarrow 3I_2 + NaCl + 6KOH.$$
(Since $6K^+$ appears on the left, there must be 6 on the right and we associate them with the OH^-.)

c) The oxidation of I^- gives I_2, and the reduction of IO_3^- also produces the element; thus the half-reactions are
$$2I^- \longrightarrow I_2 + 2e^-$$
$$2IO_3^- + 12H^+ + 10e^- \longrightarrow I_2 + 6H_2O.$$
Multiplying the first by five and adding, we obtain
$$2IO_3^- + 10I^- + 12H^+ \longrightarrow 6I_2 + 6H_2O.$$
Dividing all coefficients by two gives
$$IO_3^- + 5I^- + 6H^+ \longrightarrow 3I_2 + 3H_2O.$$

13. Perbromate ion is BrO_4^-, for which we initially obtain the octet structure

The molecule structure at top (Br with four O⁻ groups, 3+ charge):

$$\text{(structure of } BrO_4^{3-} \text{ with } Br^{3+} \text{ and four } O^- \text{ groups)}$$

After expansion beyond the octet at Br, we obtain

$$\text{(structure of } BrO_4^- \text{ with one } O^- \text{ and two } Br=O \text{ double bonds)}$$

    a)   The unbalanced reaction, as stated in the problem, is
$$BrO_3^- + F_2 \longrightarrow BrO_4^- + F^-.$$
In basic solution, the balanced half-reactions are found to be
$$F_2 + 2e^- \longrightarrow 2F^-$$
$$BrO_3^- + 2OH^- \longrightarrow BrO_4^- + H_2O + 2e^-$$
Thus the overall balanced reaction is
$$F_2 + BrO_3^- + 2OH^- \longrightarrow 2F^- + BrO_4^- + H_2O.$$

    b)   The unbalanced reaction, as stated, is
$$XeF_2 + BrO_3^- \longrightarrow Xe + BrO_4^- + F^-.$$
The half-reaction for xenon is
$$XeF_2 + 2e^- \longrightarrow Xe + 2F^-$$
and from part (a),
$$BrO_3^- + 2OH^- \longrightarrow BrO_4^- + H_2O + 2e^-.$$
Overall we obtain, by adding the half-reactions,
$$XeF_2 + BrO_3^- + 2OH^- \longrightarrow Xe + 2F^- + H_2O + BrO_4^-.$$

14.   a)   In cold, aqueous NaOH, chlorine reacts with OH^- as follows:
$$Cl_2 + 2OH^- \longrightarrow Cl^- + ClO^- + H_2O.$$
Thus the overall reaction is
$$Cl_2 + 2NaOH \longrightarrow NaCl + NaClO + H_2O.$$

    b)   In hot, aqueous NaOH the ClO^- (see above) reacts to produce ClO_3^-, and Cl^-, and we obtain overall
$$3Cl_2 + 6NaOH \longrightarrow 5NaCl + NaClO_3 + 3H_2O.$$

15. Upon gently heating, $KClO_3$ decomposes as follows:
$$4KClO_3 \longrightarrow 3KClO_4 + KCl.$$
In the presence of a catalyst such as MnO_2, all the oxygen is expelled instead:
$$2KClO_3 \longrightarrow 2KCl + 3O_2(g).$$

16. a) $PCl_5 + 4H_2O \longrightarrow H_3PO_4 + 5HCl$
i.e. PCl_5, with P in the +5 state, gives the +5 oxoacid.

    b) $IF_5 + 3H_2O \longrightarrow HIO_3 + 5HF$
in analogy with the reaction of ClF_5 with H_2O.

    c) $SF_4 + 2H_2O \longrightarrow SO_2 + 4HF$
i.e. the +4 fluoride yields the +4 oxide.

d) $Br_2 + H_2O \longrightarrow HOBr + HBr$
   in analogy with the reaction of Cl_2 with H_2O.

17. Hypochlorous acid can be made by reacting Cl_2 with water:
    $$Cl_2 + 2H_2O \longrightarrow HOCl + H_3O^+ + Cl^-.$$
    The chloride is removed from solution, and the equilibrium
    shifted to the right in the reaction above, by adding one
    mole of Ag_2O (eg. as $AgNO_3$) per 2 moles of Cl_2:
    $$Ag_2O + 2Cl^- + H_3O^+ \longrightarrow 2AgCl(s) + H_2O + OH^-.$$
    Multiplying the initial equation by two and adding, we
    obtain
    $$2Cl_2 + Ag_2O + 3H_2O \longrightarrow 2HOCl + 2AgCl(s) + H_3O^+ + OH^-.$$
    Since $H_3O^+ + OH^- \longrightarrow 2H_2O$, then
    $$2Cl_2 + Ag_2O + H_2O \longrightarrow 2HOCl + 2AgCl(s).$$
    If an attempt is made to further concentrate the solution,
    the acid decomposes.

18. a) By analogy with the reactions of chlorine, we expect
       Br_2 and OH^- when hot to form a mixture of Br^- and
       BrO_3^-, by disproportionation; the unbalanced equation is
       $$Br_2 \longrightarrow Br^- + BrO_3^-.$$
       After balancing, the half-reactions (in base) are
       $$2e^- + Br_2 \longrightarrow 2Br^-$$
       $$Br_2 + 12OH^- \longrightarrow 2BrO_3^- + 6H_2O + 2e^-.$$
       Thus overall the balanced equation is
       $$6Br_2 + 12OH^- \longrightarrow 10Br^- + 2BrO_3^- + 6H_2O.$$
       After dividing all coefficients by 2, we have
       $$3Br_2 + 6OH^- \longrightarrow 5Br^- + BrO_3^- + 3H_2O.$$

    b) Here presumably Br_2 is acting as an oxidizing agent,
       and becomes bromide ion:
       $$Br_2 + 2H_2O \longrightarrow Br^- + O_2.$$
       After balancing, the half-reactions are
       $$2e^- + Br_2 \longrightarrow 2Br^-$$
       $$H_2O_2 \longrightarrow O_2 + 2H^+ + 2e^-.$$
       Thus overall we have
       $$Br_2 + H_2O_2 \longrightarrow 2H^+ + 2Br^- \text{ (i.e. 2HBr)} + O_2.$$

    c) Presumably here HBr and KH_2PO_4 are formed:
       $$KBr + H_3PO_4 \longrightarrow HBr + KH_2PO_4.$$

    d) As discussed in the text, SO_2 reduces IO_3 to iodine;
       the balanced ionic equation (see regular methods above)
       gives
       $$2IO_3^- + 5SO_2 + 4H_2O \longrightarrow I_2 + 8H^+ + 5SO_4^{2-}$$
       and after adding spectator ions, we obtain
       $$2NaIO_3 + 5SO_2 + 4H_2O \longrightarrow I_2 + Na_2SO_4 + 4H_2SO_4(aq).$$

19. a) HOBr is hypobromous acid.

    b) Since OCl^- is the hypochlorite ion, $Ca(OCl)_2$ is
       calcium hypochlorite.

c) Since BrO_3^- is the bromate ion, $KBrO_3$ is potassium bromate.

d) Since ClO_2^- is the chlorite ion (see Table 20.4), $KClO_2$ is potassium chlorite.

e) Since ClO_4^- is the perchlorate ion, $Mg(ClO_4)_2$ is magnesium perchlorate.

f) HIO_3 is iodic acid.

g) $HBrO_4$ is perbromic acid.

h) H_5IO_6 is paraperiodic acid.

20. Iodic acid is HIO_3. Since dehydration means loss of H_2O,
$$2HIO_3 \longrightarrow H_2O + I_2O_5$$
$$I_2O_5 \longrightarrow I_2 + 5/2O_2,$$
i.e. $2I_2O_5 \longrightarrow 2I_2 + 5O_2$.
I_2O_5 could be formed by H_2O loss from $2HIO_3$, to yield an oxygen-bridged compound:

$$O = \overset{..}{I} - O - \overset{..}{I} = O.$$
$$\quad \| \qquad \qquad \|$$
$$\quad O \qquad \qquad O$$

21. Balancing each reaction, eg. $ClO^- \longrightarrow Cl^-$, in acid gives
$$ClO_3^- + 6H^+ + 6e^- \longrightarrow Cl^- + 3H_2O$$
$$ClO_2^- + 4H^+ + 4e^- \longrightarrow Cl^- + 2H_2O$$
$$ClO^- + 2H^+ + 2e^- \longrightarrow Cl^- + H_2O.$$

22. The normal valence for both O and S is 2; to achieve a higher valence, promotion to the (empty) d subshell of the valence shell must occur. Oyxgen has no valence-shell d subshell whereas sulfur does, so SF_4 can form, but OF_4 cannot exist.

23. Using a sample size of 100 g, we obtain

	I	Cl
Moles in 100 g	54.5/126.90	45.5/35.45
	= 0.429	= 1.28
Ratio	1	2.98

Thus the empirical formula is ICl_3.

24. In calculating oxidation numbers, count each F as −1 and each O as −2, and ensure that the sum of the numbers equals the charge on the ion. Thus we obtain
a) +5 for Cl in ClO_3^-.

b) +3 for Br (and −1 for F) in BrF_3.

c) +7 for Cl in $HClO_4$.

d) +3 for Cl in ClO_2^-.

e) +4 for Cl in ClO_2.

f) +7 for I in H_5IO_6.

25. $2ClO_3^- + 12H^+ + 10e^- \longrightarrow Cl_2 + 6H_2O$.

If Fe^{2+} is to supply electrons, it must be oxidized to Fe^{3+}:
$Fe^{2+} \longrightarrow Fe^{3+} + e^-$.

The overall equation, in which e^- is balanced, is then
$10Fe^{2+} + 2ClO_3^- + 12H^+ \longrightarrow Cl_2 + 10Fe^{3+} + 6H_2O$.

26. A disproportionation reaction is an oxidation-reduction reaction in which some fraction of a reactant is oxidized and the remainder is reduced, forming two different products. Examples listed in this chapter of the text include
$Cl_2 + 2H_2O \longrightarrow HOCl + H_3O^+ + Cl^-$
$Cl_2 + 2OH^- \longrightarrow Cl^- + ClO^- + H_2O$ (and similarly for I_2)
$3ClO^- \longrightarrow 2Cl^- + ClO_3^-$ (and similarly for IO^-)
$3Cl_2 + 6OH^- \longrightarrow 5Cl^- + ClO_3^- + 3H_2O$ (and similarly for I_2)
$4KClO_3 \longrightarrow 3KClO_4 + KCl$
$6XeF_4 + 12H_2O \longrightarrow 2XeO_3 + 4Xe + 3O_2 + 24HF$.

27. To calculate the amount of $NaHSO_3$, we need the balanced reaction; the unbalanced process is
$IO_3^- + HSO_3^- \longrightarrow I_2 + SO_4^{2-}$.
Balancing via half-reactions gives
$2IO_3^- + 5HSO_3^- \longrightarrow I_2 + 5SO_4^{2-} + 3H^+ + H_2O$.
After adding back the spectator ions, we obtain
$2NaIO_3 + 5NaHSO_3 \longrightarrow I_2 + 3NaHSO_4 + 2Na_2SO_4 + H_2O$

$$50,000 \text{ g } NaIO_3 \times \frac{1 \text{ mole } NaIO_3}{197.89 \text{ g } NaIO_3} \times \frac{5 \text{ moles } NaHSO_3}{2 \text{ moles } NaIO_3}$$

$$\times \frac{104.06 \text{ g } NaHSO_3}{1 \text{ mole } NaHSO_3} = 65.7 \text{ kg } NaHSO_3.$$

If an excess of $NaHSO_3$ is added, it reduces I_2 to I^-.

28. See Q. 24 for method.
a) +2   b) +4   c) +6   d) +4   e) +6   f) +8

29. Kr and Xe can promote electrons into the d subshell of the valence-shell, and thereby achieve an electron configuration with singly-filled orbitals so that bonds can be formed. In contrast, neon has no d subshell in the valence shell and thus cannot promote electrons and cannot form molecules.

298

30. We can deduce the empirical formula of each compound from the percent composition information, using a 100 g sample size. The molecular formula is then obtained using the molar mass information. For A, moles Xe = 53.5 g/131.30 g mole^{-1} = 0.408 moles, whereas moles F = 46.5/19.00 = 2.45. Thus the ratio of moles F to Xe is 2.45/0.408 = 6.00 to 1, and the empirical formula is XeF_6. Since the empirical formula mass is 245.8 and the molar mass is 245, we conclude that the molecular formula for A is XeF_6.

Similarly for C, moles Xe = 73.2/131.30 = 0.558, moles O = 26.8/16.00 = 1.68, so moles O/Xe = 3.01 to 1 and the empirical formula is XeO_3. Again the molar mass equals the empirical formula mass, so the molecular formula also is XeO_3. For B, the moles Xe = 58.8/131.80 = 0.446, moles F = 34.0/19.00 = 1.79, and moles O = 7.2/16.00 = 0.450, so ratio F/O/Xe = 4.01/1.01/1; thus the empirical formula is $XeOF_4$. Since the molar mass is equal to the empirical formula mass, the molecular formula also is $XeOF_4$.

The first reaction is balanced if it is assumed that HF is a product:
$$XeF_6 + H_2O \longrightarrow XeOF_4 + 2HF.$$
Similarly the second reaction also produces HF:
$$XeOF_4 + 2H_2O \longrightarrow XeO_3 + 4HF.$$
The geometry of XeF_6 is distorted octahedron since it contains 7 pairs. XeO_3 contains hexavalent Xe, which requires three electrons promoted from its s^2p^6 configuration; therefore one lone pair remains and XeO_3 is an AX_3E system with a pyramidal geometry. $XeOF_4$ is a square pyramid – see solution to Q. 10.

31. The Lewis structure for XeO_3 has all XeO bonds as double, so $3E(Xe = O)$ is the $\Delta H°$ of the reaction
$$XeO_3(g) \longrightarrow Xe(g) + 3O(g).$$

To determine the $\Delta H°$, we need to deduce $\Delta H_f°$ for $XeO_3(g)$. The equation given in the problem is the reverse of the formation reaction for $XeO_3(g)$; thus $\Delta H_f°(XeO_3,g)$ = + 402 kJ. We also are told that
$$XeO_3(s) \longrightarrow XeO_3(g) \qquad \Delta H° = + 80 \text{ kJ}.$$
Since
$$80 = \Delta H_f°(XeO_3,g) - \Delta H_f°(XeO_3,g)$$
$$= \Delta H_f°(XeO_3,g) - 402$$
then $\Delta H_f°(XeO_3,g) = 482.$

From the data supplied, $\Delta H_f°(O,g)$ = 249.1 kJ, and we know $\Delta H_f°(Xe,g)$ = 0. Thus the $\Delta H°$ for the top reaction is 0 + 3x (249.1) – 482 = 265.3 kJ, and hence each $E(Xe = O)$ = 88 kJ. This is much less than the double bond (or even single bond) energies in Table 12.2, (presumably because so much energy is needed to promote electrons in Xe before bonds can be formed), and thus XeO_3 is a reactive compound. Since its formation from Xe(g) and $O_2(g)$ is endothermic, it should be able to easily form these elements.

299

32. The half-reaction involving xenon is
$$XeO_3 \longrightarrow Xe$$

which upon balancing becomes
$$XeO_3 + 6H^+ + 6e^- \longrightarrow Xe + 3H_2O.$$
For the half-reaction
$$Mn^{2+} \longrightarrow MnO_4^-$$
which upon balancing becomes
$$Mn^{2+} + 4H_2O \longrightarrow MnO_4^- + 8H^+ + 5e^-.$$
Multiplying the first reaction by 5 and the second by 6 to balance the electrons, and adding, gives
$$5XeO_3 + 6Mn^{2+} + 9H_2O \longrightarrow 5Xe + 6MnO_4^- + 18H^+.$$

1. We can deduce electron configurations for these ions by generating those for the neutral atoms and then subtracting the number of electrons appropriate to the ion. Recall that in ion and compound formation, the ns electrons are ionized <u>prior</u> to the $(n-1)d$.
   a) Since Cr is $[Ar]4s^13d^5$ (i.e. an exception), after loss of three electrons Cr^{3+} is $[Ar]4s°3d^3$.

   b) Ni is $[Ar]4s^23d^8$ (since Ni is the eighth transition element in the series), so Ni^{2+} is $[Ar]3d^8$.

   c) Cu is $[Ar]4s^13d^{10}$ (another exception) so Cu^+ is $[Ar]3d^{10}$.

   d) Co is $[Ar]4s^23d^7$, so Co^{2+} is $[Ar]3d^7$.

   e) Au is $[Xe]6s^24f^{14}5d^9$, so Au^{3+} is $[Xe]4f^{14}5d^8$.

   f) Fe is $[Ar]4s^23d^6$, so Fe^{3+} is $[Ar]3d^5$.

2. See Q. 1 for methodology.
   a) $[Ar]4s^23d^2$ for Ti.

   b) $[Ar]4s^13d^5$ for Cr.

   c) $[Ar]4s^23d^6$ for Fe.

   d) $[Ar]4s^23d^8$ for Ni.

   e) $[Ar]4s^23d^{10}$ for Zn.

   f) See 1(e).

   g) $[Xe]4f^{14}5d^{10}$.

   h) See 1(a).

   i) See 1(d).

3. As in Q. 1, we can deduce the number of d electrons by first deducing the neutral atom electron configuration and then removing electrons, first from the 4s (except for Ag^+) and then from the 3d, until the ion charge is satisfied.
   a) 9, since neutral Cu is $...4s^13d^{10}$.

   b) 5, since Fe is $...4s^23d^6$.

c) 5, since Mn is ...$4s^23d^5$.

d) 10, since for Ag and Ag^+ the 4d level is part of an inner shell.

e) 2, since V is $4s^23d^3$.

f) 2, since Ti is $4s^23d^2$.

4. To deduce the oxidation number of the transition metal, we apply the principle that the sum of the oxidation numbers (times the element subscripts) over all atoms must equal the charge on the ion (if any). Further, we recall the following familiar ion charges: +1 for K and Na, -2 for O, +1 for H, -2 for SO_4, -1 for Cl, OH, and CN, and zero for NH_3.

a) Since K + 4O's = +1-8 = -7, Mn is +7.

b) Since 2K + 7O's = +2-14 = -12, the sum for 2Cr's = 12, and Cr = +6.

c) Each CN is -1 and the sum must be -1, so Ag is +1.

d) The sum from 2Cl is -2, so Cr is +3 in order that the sum is +1.

e) +3 for Cr.

f) +2 for Co.

g) +6 for Mn.

h) +3 for Mn since OH is -1.

i) +5 for V.

j) Since both O and SO_4 are -2, Ti is +4.

5. Method is identical to that in Q. 4.
    a) +3 for Fe.

b) Since H_2O is neutral, Co is +3.

c) +3 for Al.

d) +1 for Ag since NH_3 is neutral.

e) +2 for Fe.

f) +3 for Fe.

6. Since [Ar] contains 18 electrons, we have 4, 7, and 9 electrons to allocate beyond an argon core. Each will use two in the 4s and the remainder in 3d, so

22 electrons	$[Ar]4s^23d^2$
25 electrons	$[Ar]4s^23d^5$
27 electrons	$[Ar]4s^23d^7$.

Loss of both 4s electrons is possible in all cases, and thus each atom could display the +2 state. The +3 and +4 states also are possible for all three, corresponding to loss of 1 or 2 3d electrons (in addition to the 4s pair). The elements of Z = 25 and 27 could as well lose 3, 4 or 5 d electrons, yielding +5, +6, and +7 states. Loss of further electrons by the Z = 27 case is possible but unlikely, due to the high core charge attracting the electrons.

7. In all cases, O is -2 and the sum is the ion charge. Thus

a) Cr is +6 in CrO_4^{2-}.

b) Cr is +6 in $Cr_2O_7^{2-}$.

c) Mn is +6 in MnO_4^{2-}.

d) V is +5 in VO_4^{3-}.

e) V is +4 in VO^{2+}.

f) Fe is +6 in FeO_4^{2-}.

8. a) There are 3 NH_3 ligands, 2 H_2O and one Cl^-.

b) The Co is +2, since the sum of it and Cl^- must be +1.

c) If Co is +2, and there are three Cl^- ions, the ion charge would be +2-3 = -1.

9. The coordinated ions and molecules are those which lie within the square brackets. Each NH_3 and Cl coordinates at one site and each en at two. Thus the coordination number for $[Zn(NH_3)_4]Cl_2$ is 4, for $[Co(NH_3)_3Cl_3]$ is 3+3=6, for $[Co(NH_3)_5Cl]Cl_2$ is 5+1=6, for $[Cr(en)_2Cl_2]^+$ is 2x2+2=6, and for $K_2[FeCl_4]$ is 4.

10. Following the convention used in the text, $C_2O_4^{2-}$ and en are shown as O⌒O and N⌒N respectively. Presumably the geometry is octahedral in all cases, since given that NH_3, halides and CN^- are monodentate and $C_2O_4^{2-}$ and en bidentate, each metal is six-coordinate.

a) trans $[Cr(NH_3)_4Cl_2]^+$ The Cl's are trans to each other.

303

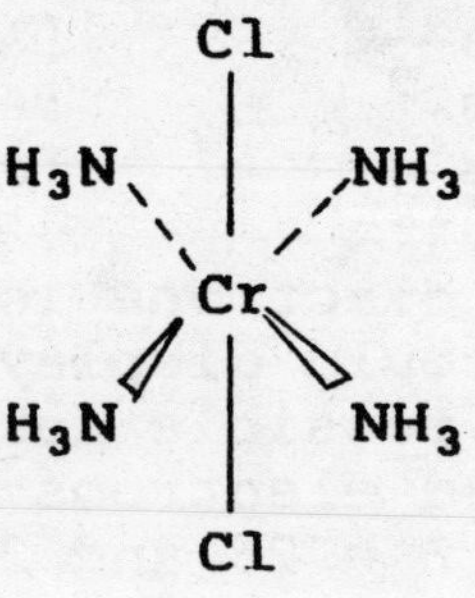

a)

b) $[Co(C_2O_4)_3]^{3-}$ is

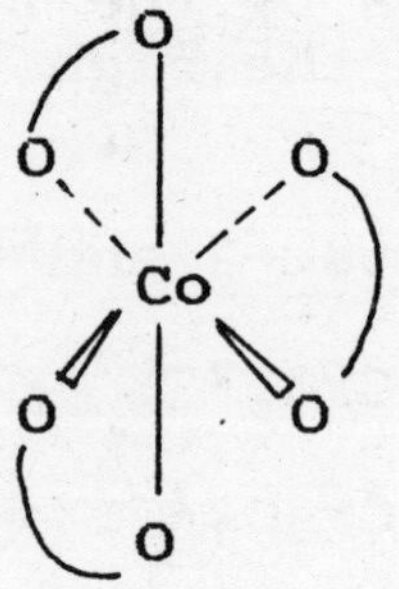

c) $[Cr(C_2O_4)Br_4]^-$ is

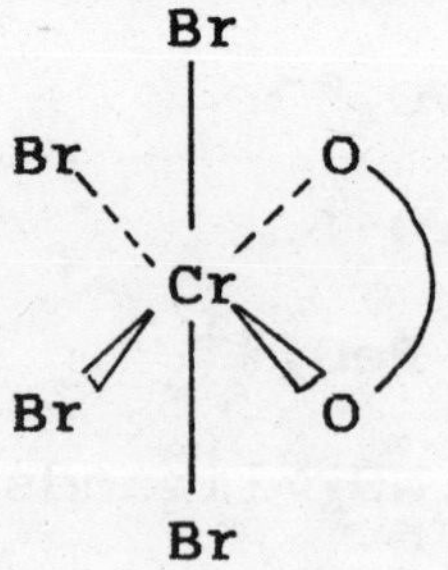

d) cis $[Pt(en)_2(CN)_2]^{2-}$ is

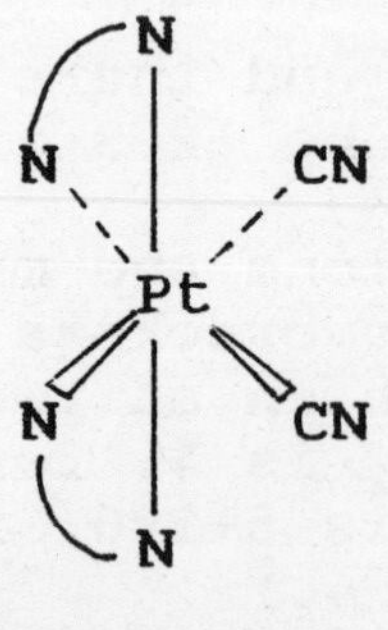

11. Using the nomenclature rules in the text and the ligand
    names in Table 21.9, we obtain

    a) trans-Dichlorotetramminechromium(III) ion (where we
       know Cr is +3 since the net charge is +1 and each Cl is
       −1). (Note that di is used to signify the presence of
       2 Cl and tetra is used to signify four NH_3's.)

    b) Trioxalatocobaltate(III) ion (where we know Co is +3
       since each oxalate is 2− for a total of 6− but the net
       charge is 3−. The ate ending is used since the charge
       on the complex is negative.)

c) Tetrabromooxalatochromate(III) ion (since each Br is -1 and C_2O_4 is -2.)

d) cis-Dicyanodiethylenediamineplatinate(O) since en is neutral and each CN is -1, so the platinum is neutral as well. The -ate ending is still used because the complex is negatively-charged.

12. The moles of AgCl equals the moles of Cl^- not bound covalently to Pt; in all cases the NH_3 is bound covalently as a ligand. Thus the formulas are $[Pt(NH_3)_6]Cl_4$, $[Pt(NH_3)_5Cl]Cl_3$, $[Pt(NH_3)_4Cl_2]Cl_2$, $[Pt(NH_3)_3Cl_3]Cl$, and $Pt(NH_3)_2Cl_4$ respectively.

13. The red form must have SO_4 bound as a ligand but not Br since it was free to precipitate; thus the formula is $[Co(NH_3)_5SO_4]Br$. The violet compound contains Br as ligand since it does not precipitate, but not SO_4^{2-} since it does. Thus its formula is $[Co(NH_3)_5Br]SO_4$. Your structures should show the octahedral arrangement of $5NH_3$ and one ligand around the Co in each case.

14. a) As discussed in Box 21.2, Ag^+ forms a soluble complex ion with the thiosulfate ion; thus AgCl dissolves by forming $Ag(S_2O_3)_2^{3-}$:
$$AgCl(g) + 2S_2O_3^{2-} \longrightarrow Ag(S_2O_3)_2^{3-} + Cl^-$$

b) If 3 mol AgCl are obtained, then clearly three moles of Cl^- ion must have been available; thus $[Cr(en)_2Cl_2]Cl$ was transformed into a material with all three, not just one, Cl as counterions. One possibility for the final product is $[Cr(en)_2(H_2O)_2]Cl_3$, with H_2O's replacing the Cl ligands:
$$[Cr(en)_2Cl_2]Cl + 2H_2O \longrightarrow [Cr(en)_2(H_2O)_2]Cl_3$$

c) With NH_3, Ni^{2+} like many other transition metals forms a soluble complex ion; by analogy with the ion for Co,
$$Ni(OH)_2(s) + 6NH_3(aq) \longrightarrow Ni(NH_3)_6^{2+} + 2OH^-.$$

d) Presumably it turns deep blue due to formation of $CoCl_4^{2-}$:
$$Co^{2+} + 4Cl^- \longrightarrow CoCl_4^{2-}.$$

15. Presumably calcium oxalate dissolves since the calcium forms a stable complex ion with EDTA and the salt of this ion is soluble.

16. The total number of valence-shell electrons in 2 (from Zn $4s^24p°$) + 4 x (6 + 1) + 2 (for the net charge), for a total of 32. All of these are required to obtain an octet of electrons about each oxygen (2 bonding, 2 lone pairs), thus leaving no lone pairs for zinc:

$$
\begin{array}{ccc}
\text{HO} & & \text{OH} \\
& \diagdown \diagup & \\
& \text{Zn} & \\
& \diagup \diagdown & \\
\text{HO} & & \text{OH}
\end{array}
$$

Since the average number of electrons at Zn here is 4, compared to 2 in the atom, its formal charge is -2. Since it is an AX_4 system, it should be tetrahedral.

17. Since it is early in the transition metal series, Cr uses all six of its 4s and 3d electrons here in compound formation; thus it forms six bonds and has no lone pairs:

$$
\begin{array}{ccc}
\text{O} & & \text{Cl} \\
\diagdown\diagdown & & \diagup \\
& \text{Cr} & \\
\diagup\diagup & & \diagdown \\
\text{O} & & \text{Cl}
\end{array}
\qquad \text{(lone pairs on O, Cl not shown)}
$$

Thus it is an AX_4 system, and should be tetrahedral.

18. As the charge on the transition metal becomes increasingly positive, its effective electronegativity increases and its demand for electrons in XO bonds increases. Now for an oxide to be acidic, it must be able to add H_2O and release one of the hydrogens as H^+. The polarity of the O—H bonds, in the sense $O^{\delta-}-H^{\delta+}$, increases with positive charge on X since X is withdrawing more and more electrons from O, making the oxygen demand on hydrogen all the greater. Thus we conclude that acidity should increase with the oxidation state of the metal.

19. The electronegativity increases and thus the ionic character of its bonds, in the sense $M^{\delta+}X^{\delta-}$, decreases as its oxidation state increases. An excellent example is chromium; all its +6 state compounds are predominately covalent whereas its +3 compounds are ionic.

20. The strength of the metallic bonding, and hence the melting point of the solid, increases from Sc to Cr since more and more 3d electrons are present and are involved. However, as the nuclear charge increases the 3d begin to behave as core electrons and are less able to engage in bonding. These two trends oppose each other, with the result that metallic bonding is maximized near the middle of the series of ten transition elements, not at the right.

21. a) The basic and ionic oxide will be Cr_2O_3 since in it the oxidation state of Cr is relatively low (+3).

b) The covalent and acidic oxide will be that of a high
    oxidation state - here CrO_3.

c) CrO_3 is an oxidizing agent since here Cr is in the +6
    state.

d) Cr_2O_3 is a reducing agent since Cr is in a low
    oxidation state.

22. According to the text, $Fe(H_2O)_6^{3+}$ is pale violet; thus the
    solid $Fe(NO_3)_3 \cdot 6H_2O$ must consist of the $[Fe(H_2O)_6](NO_3)_3$
    system. In acidic solution, $Fe(H_2O)_6^{3+}$ must be present,
    since adding nitric acid to the aqueous solution of the
    salt turns it violet. In neutral solution, then,
    $Fe(H_2O)_6^{3+}$ presumably would lose one or more protons to
    become $Fe(H_2O)_5(OH)^{2+}$, etc. which are yellow.

23. Copper exists as $Cu(H_2O)_4^{2+}$ in aqueous copper sulfate
    solution. When concentrated HCl is added, Cl^- ions can
    replace one or more of the H_2O ligands. If concentrated
    ammonia is added, NH_3 can replace the Cl^- and H_2O ligands
    to give $Cu(NH_3)_4^{2+}$. Addition of CN^- presumably would yield
    a Cu complex with CN^- ions, eg. $Cu(CN)_4^{2-}$.

24. In both cases, the metals dissolve to give solutions of the
    +2 ions, and H_2 is released:
    $Co + H_2SO_4 \longrightarrow Co^{2+} + SO_4^{2-}$ (i.e. aq $CoSO_4$) + H_2
    $Ni + H_2SO_4 \longrightarrow Ni^{2+} + SO_4^{2-} + H_2$.
    The cobalt solution is the pale pink color of $Co(H_2O)_6^{2+}$,
    whereas the nickel solution is green due to $Ni(H_2O)_6^{2+}$.
    Upon addition of NaOH, the hydroxide precipitate forms:
    $Co^{2+} + 2OH^- \longrightarrow Co(OH)_2(s)$ (pink)
    $Ni^{2+} + 2OH^- \longrightarrow Ni(OH)_2(s)$ (green).

25. Note that the relevant chemistry of Fe and Cu required to
    answer this problem is found in Chapter 9 for the most part.
    a) Only Zn as Zn^{2+} gives a colorless solution.

    b) The +2 state is common to all.

    c)   i) A blue hydroxide is formed by Cu in its +2 state.
         ii) White hydroxides are formed by +2 ions of Mn, Fe,
              Zn.
        iii) Green hydroxides are formed by Ni and Cr in +2
              states.

    d) Both Fe^{2+} (see Chap. 9) and Ni^{2+} give green solutions.
        However only Fe^{3+}, obtained by oxidation of Fe^{2+} by
        H_2O_2, gives an insoluble hydroxide which is red-brown

    e) Both Mn^{2+} and Co^{2+} give pink solutions, but only Co^{2+}
        becomes blue when some of the H_2O's in $Co(H_2O)_6^{2+}$ are
        replaced, in this case by chloride ion.

307

f) Both Cr and Mn form the +6 state - examples are CrO_3 and salts of CrO_4^{2-} and $Cr_2O_7^{2-}$, and salts of MnO_4^{2-}.

g) To solve this problem, one must devise a test to which the response of Mn^{2+} and of MnO_4^- will be obviously different to the observer. The formation of a precipitate and the decoloration of a solution are easily-observable properties to use in this connection. For example, adding strong base should produce a white precipitate, $Mn(OH)_2$ with Mn^{2+} but no precipitate with MnO_4^{2-}. Alternatively, the pink color should disappear if a reducing agent is added to MnO_4^- but not to Mn^{2+}, since MnO_4^- is an oxidizing agent whereas Mn^{2+} is not.

26. Presumably $Cr_2O_7^{2-}$ is reduced to Cr^{3+}; the unbalanced half-reaction is
$$Cr_2O_7^{2-} \longrightarrow Cr^{3+}.$$
After balancing (acid solution), we obtain
$$Cr_2O_7^{2-} + 14H^+ + 6e^- \longrightarrow 2Cr^{3+} + 7H_2O.$$

a) Presumably SO_2 is oxidized to sulfate, SO_4^{2-}, for which the balanced half-reaction is
$$SO_2 + 2H_2O \longrightarrow SO_4^{2-} + 4H^+ + 2e^-.$$
Trebling this reaction and adding to the chromate process, we obtain
$$3SO_2 + Cr_2O_7^{2-} + 2H^+ \longrightarrow 3SO_4^{2-} + 2Cr^{3+} + H_2O.$$

b) The $C_2H_5OH \longrightarrow CH_3CHO$ half-reaction, balanced, is
$$C_2H_5OH \longrightarrow CH_3CHO + 2H^+ + 2e^-.$$
Trebling and adding to the chromate process, we obtain
$$Cr_2O_7^{2-} + 3C_2H_5OH + 8H^+ \longrightarrow 2Cr^{3+} + 3CH_3CHO + 7H_2O.$$

c) The $I^- \longrightarrow I_3^-$ half-reaction, balanced, is
$$3I^- \longrightarrow I_3^- + 2e^-.$$
Trebling and adding, we obtain
$$Cr_2O_7^{2-} + 14H^+ + 9I^- \longrightarrow 2Cr^{3+} + 7H_2O + 3I_3^-.$$

27. By difference, the mass of sulfur is 0.905-0.540 = 0.365 g. Thus the moles of Fe and S in the sample are 0.540/55.85 = 0.00967 and 0.365/32.06 = 0.0114 respectively, i.e. 1.00 to 1.18. There is no set of small integers which yields exactly this ratio. The closest formula is $Fe_{11}S_{13}$. Presumably the compound is a nonstoichiometric version of FeS, with some of the Fe^{2+} sites occupied by Fe^{3+} ions, since this type of compound is known to be formed by iron. Thus it is unlikely that the experiment itself is inaccurate, though this can't be ruled out completely.

28. The reaction is
$$Ni(s) + 4CO(g) \rightleftharpoons Ni(CO)_4(g).$$

$$2.50 \text{ g Ni} \times \frac{1 \text{ mole Ni}}{58.71 \text{ g}} \times \frac{1 \text{ mole Ni(CO)}_4}{1 \text{ mole Ni}}$$

$$= 0.0426 \text{ mole Ni(CO)}_4.$$

From $PV = nRT$, $V = nRT/P$

$\quad\quad\quad\quad = 0.0426 \times 0.0821 \times 353/2$

$\quad\quad\quad\quad = 0.62 \text{ L}.$

Decomposing this amount would produce four times as much CO, i.e. $4 \times 0.0426 = 0.170$ moles. Thus

$\quad\quad V = nRT/P$

$\quad\quad\quad = 0.170 \times 0.0821 \times 298/1$

$\quad\quad\quad = 4.2 \text{ L}.$

29. From the PVT information for the H_2, we can deduce the moles of it and from it the moles of Zn (since Cu is not soluble in dilute sulfuric acid):

$\quad\quad Zn + H_2SO_4 \longrightarrow ZnSO_4 + H_2.$

$n = PV/RT = ((756-23.8)/760) \times 0.1028/0.0821 \times 298$

$\quad\quad\quad\quad = 0.00405 \text{ moles}.$

Thus the brass sample must contain 0.00405 moles Zn, which is equivalent to 0.265 g of it. Thus the percent Zn of the sample is $(0.265/0.50) \times 100\% = 53\%$, and by difference the Cu content is 47%.

30. Recall that 1 metric ton, i.e. 1 tonne, is 1000 kg. Thus the nickel content is $0.18 \times 1000 \times 1000 \text{ g} = 1.8 \times 10^5$ g. Since 1 mole Ni gives 1 mole NiS, we convert mass to moles Ni, and moles NiS to mass NiS:

$$1.8 \times 10^5 \text{ g Ni} \times \frac{1 \text{ mole Ni}}{58.71 \text{ g Ni}} \times \frac{1 \text{ mole NiS}}{1 \text{ mole Ni}} \times \frac{90.77 \text{ g NiS}}{1 \text{ mole NiS}}$$

$$= 2.8 \times 10^5 \text{ g NiS}.$$

31. $\text{Percent Co} = \dfrac{\text{Mass Co in 1 mole}}{\text{Molar mass}} \times 100\%$

$$= \frac{58.93 \times 100}{1357.57} = 4.34\%$$

$$1.0 \times 10^{-6} \text{ g Vitamin B}_{12} \times \frac{4.34 \text{ g Co}}{100 \text{ g Vitamin B}_{12}} = 4.3 \times 10^{-8} \text{ g}.$$

Thus the body requires 4×10^{-8} g of cobalt per day.

32. First convert the solubility to a molar basis:

$$5.6 \times 10^{-6} \text{ g Cr(OH)}_3 \times \frac{1 \text{ mole Cr(OH)}_3}{103.03 \text{ g (Cr(OH)}_3}$$

$$= 5.4 \times 10^{-8} \text{ mole } Cr(OH)_3.$$

Dissolving this amount of $Cr(OH)_3$ produces the same number of moles of Cr^{3+}, and three times as much OH^-; i.e. 1.6×10^{-7} moles.

The dissociation reaction is

$$Cr(OH)_3 \underset{\longleftarrow}{\longrightarrow} Cr^{3+} + 3OH^-$$

Since $K_{sp} = [Cr^{3+}][OH^-]^3$

then $K_{sp} = (5.4 \times 10^{-8} \text{ M})(1.6 \times 10^{-7} \text{ M})^3$

          $= 2.2 \times 10^{-28}.$

33. From Table 21.3, the density of Cr is 7.19 g cm^{-3}. First find the volume, in cm^3, of the layer and then convert it to mass:

$$(100 \text{ cm})^2 \times 0.01 \text{ cm} = 100 \text{ cm}^3 \times \frac{7.19 \text{ g}}{1 \text{ cm}^3} = 719 \text{ g}.$$

The reaction of coating is
$$Cr^{3+} + 3e^- \longrightarrow Cr.$$
From the mass of Cr, we can deduce moles Cr, then moles e^-, and then C:

$$719 \text{ g Cr} \times \frac{1 \text{ mole Cr}}{52.00 \text{ g Cr}} \times \frac{3 \text{ moles } e^-}{1 \text{ mole Cr}} \times \frac{96500 \text{ C}}{1 \text{ mole } e^-}$$

$$= 4.00 \times 10^6 \text{ C}.$$

At 1.5 C per second, the time needed is 4.00×10^6 C $\times 1$ s$/1.5$ C $= 2.7 \times 10^6$ seconds, i.e. one month! The coating is thin due to the time required to plate the steel and due to the relatively high cost of chromium.

34. The equilibrium is

$$Ag_3PO_4(s) \rightleftarrows 3Ag^+ + PO_4^{3+}$$
and thus
$$K_{sp} = [Ag^+]^3[PO_4^{3-}].$$
If S is the solubility, then in water $[Ag^+] = 3S$ and $[PO_4^{3-}] = S$, so
$$(3S)^3S = 1.8 \times 10^{-18}$$
$$S = 1.6 \times 10^{-5} \text{ M}.$$
$[Ag^+] = 3S +$ the contribution from $AgNO_3$, which dominates, so
$$[Ag^+] \approx \text{ that of } AgNO_3.$$
Thus $S = 1.8 \times 10^{-18}/[Ag^+ \text{ from } AgNO_3]^3.$
For a 0.0010 M $AgNO_3$ solution, $S = 1.8 \times 10^{-9}$ M.

CHAPTER 22

1. The fundamental unit of the silicates is the SiO_4 tetrahedron. In aluminosilicates, some of the Si atoms are replaced by Al^-.

2. An example of a silicate with a layer structure is talc, $Mg_3(Si_2O_5)_2(OH)_2$. (Kaolinite is also an example.) The layer anion has the empirical formula $Si_2O_5{}^{2-}$, since it corresponds to two $SiO_4{}^{4-}$ chains which share three oxygen atoms per silicon; thus the number of oxygens per two Si atoms is not eight but five (see text Figure 22.5(c)).

3. An amphibole is a silicate which contains two chains of SiO_4 tetrahedra joined by sharing oxygen atoms on alternate tetrahedra, giving a double chain with the empirical formula $Si_4O_{11}{}^{6-}$.

4. The three principal components of glass are sodium carbonate, calcium oxide or carbonate, and silicon dioxide in the form of white sand.

5. Like a solid, glass is hard and does not deform or flow to any significant extent. Like the liquid, its viscosity increases as it is cooled.

6. Photochromic glass is glass which darkens upon exposure to bright sunlight, but which becomes clear again in indoor light. The glass contains AgCl or AgBr; this salt is decomposed by light to give finely-divided black silver crystals. In the absence of bright light the adjacent Ag and halogen atoms recombine to reform silver halide.

7. See Figure 10.22c in the text for a sketch of the unit cell of diamond (a face-centered cube). Since there is an atom at each lattice point, and four more located one-fourth the way along the body diagonals, there are a total of 8 atoms in each unit cell. Each atom forms a covalent bond to each of its four nearest neighbours. The quantitative aspects of the problem are handled by methods similar to those in Chapter 10. Thus we obtain:

$$\text{Cell volume} = (545 \times 10^{-12} \text{ m})^3$$
$$= 1.62 \times 10^{-28} \text{ m}^3$$

$$\text{Density} = \frac{8 \text{ atoms} \times 28.09 \text{ g mol}^{-1}}{6.022 \times 10^{23} \text{ atoms mol}^{-1} \times 1.62 \times 10^{-28} \text{ m}^3}$$

$$= 2.30 \times 10^6 \text{ g m}^{-3}$$

311

$$= 2.30 \text{ g cm}^{-3}$$

The body diagonal $= 545\sqrt{3}$ here
$$= 944 \text{ pm}$$

But for this type of structure, the body diagonal is four times the length of a bond.

Thus Si–Si bond length $= 944/4 = 236$ pm
and the silicon atom radius is $236/2 = 118$ pm.

8. Presumably the ring contains alternating Si and O atoms; thus the remaining eight oxygen atoms are bonded to individual Si atoms (two each); the eight negative charges are reasonably associated with these eight oxygen atoms. Thus we obtain

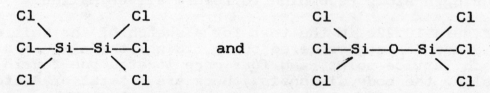

Each ring oxygen then possesses two lone pairs (not shown) and each O^- has three (not shown).

9. The charges for the common ions are +1 for K, and +2 for Ca, Mg, Zn, Ba and −1 for OH. We obtain the charge for the Si unit by charge balance.
    a) $Ca^{2+}Mg^{2+}[SiO_3{}^{2-}]_2$; silicate chain anion
    b) $K^+[AlSi_3O_8{}^-]$; aluminosilicate chain derived from $(SiO_3{}^{2-})_3$.
    c) $(Ca^{2+})_2Zn^{2+}(Si_2O_7{}^{6-})$; disilicate anion
    d) $Ba^{2+}Ti^{4+}(Si_3O_9{}^{6-})$; cyclic anion
    e) $Al^{3+}(Si_2O_5OH^{3-})$; chain anion
    g) $Ca^{2+}(Al_2Si_2O_8{}^{2-})$; infinite 3D aluminosilicate structure

10.

```
   Cl           Cl                    Cl              Cl
     \         /                        \            /
  Cl—Si——Si—Cl          and        Cl—Si—O—Si—Cl
     /         \                        /            \
   Cl           Cl                    Cl              Cl
```

Si_2Cl_6O will have a dipole moment since the SiOSi angle is less than 180° (oxygen is AX_2E_2 here) and the net dipoles of the $SiCl_3$ units will not directly oppose each other and cancel as they do in Si_2Cl_6.

11. The $Si_6O_{18}{}^{12-}$ ion has an Si/O/charge ratio which is 1.5 times the cyclic ion discussed in Q. 8; thus we expect it too is a ring of six alternating Si and O atoms with two O^- ions per Si. See Section 22.3 for a diagram of this silicate anion, which is found in the mineral called beryl.

316

12. In zone refining, a short segment of a metal rod is heated until it melts. Since impurities are more soluble in the molten metal than in the solid, they concentrate in the liquid as the rod is moved through the heater, with the melted zone moving along as well. Thus the impurities eventually become concentrated at the end of the rod, which is then allowed to solidify and cut off.

13. Silicon does not have a graphite-like allotrope since it would have to contain SiSi double bonds and they are weak relative to two Si—Si bonds, and would be very reactive.

14. Silicones are synthetic polymers containing chains or/and rings of alternating Si and O atoms. See Figure 22.7 for diagrams of typical silicones. Silicones are excellent electrical insulators, good lubricants, water-repellent, nontoxic, heat resistant, and remain fluid until low temperture. The solid silicones retain their rubbery properties even at low temperatures.

15. The carbon analogs of silicones are ketones. The latter are small molecules and contain C = O bonds, whereas silicones are polymers which contain Si—O bonds, since carbon has a much greater tendency to form double bonds than does silicon.

16. Silanes are more reactive than alkanes because silicon has accessible, empty valence-shell d orbitals and thereby can bond to attacking reagent molecules whereas carbon cannot do so due to the nonexistence of 2d orbitals.

17. Few compounds containing Si = Si are known since double bonds between elements in this period are weak and reactive.

18. From the Ideal Gas Equation $PV = nRT = mRT/M$, and since $d = m/V$, we obtain

$$
\begin{aligned}
M &= dRT/P \\
&= 1.23 \times 0.0821 \times 273/1 \\
&= 27.6
\end{aligned}
$$

Since boron has an atomic mass of 10.8 and hydrogen of 1.0, the only possibility is B_2H_6.

19. Aluminum chloride and fluoride, in the solid state, are ionic solids (since the electronegativity difference is large) and thus a relatively high temperature is required to convert them to liquids or gas. In contrast, BF_3 and BCl_3 form molecular solids in which the monomer units are held together by weak forces – hence their melting and boiling points are relatively low.

20. In its behaviour as an acid, $B(OH)_3$ acquires an OH^- group from H_2O and releases the H^+ to another H_2O, forming $B(OH)_4^-$ and H_3O^+. Aluminum can do likewise. To behave as a base, however, OH^- must be released to the solution or

the system must accept protons H^+. Aluminum hydroxide can accept H^+ (from water or acids), converting one or more of its OH^- groups to H_2O; ultimately the ion $Al(H_2O)_n^{3+}$ is formed and is stable (see Chapter 9). However B is more electronegative than Al, and loses OH^- (or allows protons to bond to OH^-) less readily; thus it does not behave as a base.

21. Lewis acids accept electron pairs (from Lewis bases). Thus examples are

$$F_3B \ + \ :NH_3 \longrightarrow F_3\overset{-}{B}\!-\!\overset{+}{N}H_3$$

$$F_3B \ + \ :\!\overset{..}{O}R_2 \longrightarrow F_3\overset{-}{B}\!-\!\overset{+}{\overset{..}{O}}R_2$$

$$F_3B \ + \ F^- \longrightarrow BF_4^-.$$

22. Borax is $Na_2[B_4O_5(OH)_4]\cdot 8H_2O$. Its structure is shown in Figure 22.13 of the text. It can be used as a water softener because it is a weak base and because the borates of calcium and magnesium are insoluble, so it can remove Ca^{2+} and Mg^{2+} from water.

23. Limestone is $CaCO_3$ (see Box 22.1).
Gypsum is $CaSO_4\cdot 2H_2O$ (see Box 22.1).
Silica is SiO_2.
Bauxite is Al_2O_3 (see Box 22.1).
Pyrite is FeS_2 (see Box 22.1).
Beryl is $Be_3Al_2Si_6O_{18}$.
Talc is $Mg_3(Si_2O_5)_2(OH)_2$.

24. Acid strength increases with m in $XO_m(OH)_n$ systems; since the acids listed correspond to m=0,1,2, and 3 respectively, the acidity should increase from $Si(OH)_4$ through to O_3ClOH_3 as observed.

25. In a three-center bond, one electron pair holds together three (rather than the usual two) nuclei. An example is the B_2H_6 molecule, in which two hydrogen atoms bridge the BH_2 groups; each BH_{bridge} B interaction is a three-center bond.

CHAPTER 23

1. a) An addition polymer is one prepared by the successive addition of monomer units. Examples include polyethene and polystyrene.

   b) Condensation polymers are those formed through condensation reactions in which monomers are joined into polymer chains by the elimination of small molecules such as water. Examples include the polyamides and polyesters - e.g. nylon, Dacron (Mylar) and Kodel.

   c) An α-amino acid is a molecule which possesses a CO_2H group and an NH_2 group on the same carbon. Examples include all those in Table 23.2.

   d) A sugar is a monosaccharide or a disaccharide; examples include glucose, fructose, and sucrose.

   e) A polypeptide is a polymer which is a polyamide, and which has the repeating unit $-NH-CHR-C(=O)-$ with different groups R found along the chain. Any protein is an example of a polypeptide.

2. See the text and Table 23.1 to answer these questions.
   a) Teflon is $\cdots-CF_2-CF_2-\cdots$, and is made from $CF_2 = CF_2$.

   b) Saran is not mentioned in the text.

   c) PVC is polyvinyl chloride, $\cdots-CH_2-CHCl-\cdots$, and is made from $CH_2 = CHCl$.

   d) Nylon (see text) is made from hexane dioic acid, $COOH-(CH_2)_6-COOH$, and 1,6-hexanediamine, $NH_2-(CH_2)_6-NH_2$.

   e) Dacron (see text) is made from 1,2-ethanediol and 1,4-benzene dicarboxylic acid.

3. a) Propene, $CH_3-CH = CH_2$, will give an addition polymer with a CH_3 group on every second carbon:

   $$n\ CH_3-CH = CH_2 \longrightarrow \cdots-CH_2-CH(CH_3)-CH_2-CH(CH_3)-\cdots$$

   b) This monomer is 1,3-butadiene and as stated in the text gives polybutadiene, $\cdots-CH_2-CH = CH-CH_2-\cdots$.

315

c) See text Section 23.1 for structure; these molecules condense to give Nylon-66.

d) See text Section 23.1 for structure; these molecules condense to give Dacron.

4. When 1,3-butadiene polymerizes, we obtain a system in which the originally-single C—C bond becomes a double bond. Thus the structure for the polymer of the 2-methyl derivative is

$$\cdots-CH_2-\underset{\underset{CH_3}{|}}{C} = \underset{\underset{H}{|}}{C}-CH_2-\cdots$$

with a trans orientation of the chain around each double bond.

5. The repeating unit is —CH_2—$CH(CN)$—; thus we could form this from the monomer $CH_2 = CH(CN)$ by addition polymerization.

6. In the elimination of methanol, CH_3OH, presumably we combine the OH unit of one molecule with the CH_3O of the other to produce an oxygen bridge between the units; thus we obtain

$$\cdots-CH_2-CH_2\underset{}{\left(O-\underset{\underset{||}{O}}{C}-CH_2-\underset{\underset{||}{O}}{C}-O-CH_2-CH_2\right)}O-\cdots$$

The repeating unit is shown inside the parentheses.

7. These acids produce H_3O^+ which presumably can destroy the polymeric nature of Nylon by attacking the basic N atoms in the chain and subsequent addition of water:

$$\cdots-\underset{\underset{||}{O}}{C}-\underset{\underset{|}{H}}{N}-(CH_2)_6-\cdots + H_3O^+ \longrightarrow \cdots-\underset{\underset{||}{O}}{C}-\underset{\underset{|}{N^+}}{\underset{H}{}}-(CH_2)_6-\cdots + H_2O$$

$$\longrightarrow \cdots-\underset{\underset{||}{O}}{C}-OH + \overset{+}{H_3N}-(CH_2)_6-\cdots$$

Since the system is depolymerized into soluble monomers, the nylon stockings are observed to dissolve in acid.

8. To undergo addition polymerization, a molecule must contain a multiple bond, normally a C = C bond. (In the process a double bond within a monomer is converted to single bonds which join monomer units together.)

9. A nucleotide is prepared by the condensation of phosphoric acid, a sugar, and a nitrogen base.

10. a) Alanine is $CH_3CH(NH_2)COOH$.

    b) Glycine is $CH_2(NH_2)COOH$.

    c) Aspargine is $NH_2C(O)CH_2CH(NH_2)COOH$.

    d) Glutamic acid is $HOOC(CH_2)_2CH(NH_2)COOH$. It alone of four is dicarboxylic since it alone has two COOH groups.

11. α- and β-glucose differ only in the orientation of one OH group with respect to the six-membered ring; see Figure 23.3.

12. These nitrogen bases are just the right size and shape to form hydrogen bonds that will link them together in pairs (guanine with cytosine, and adenine with thymine) at the same distance between the chains on which they are bound.

13. Starch is a mixture of polymers of α-glucose, whereas cellulose is a straight-chain polymer of β-glucose.

14. Since each glucose unit has lost an H_2O in the process of polymerization, the repeat formula for the "residue" is $C_6H_{12}O_6 - H_2O = C_6H_{10}O_5$, the molar mass of which is 162.16 g. The molecular mass is 162.16 u; thus the number of glucose residues is

$$\frac{2.57 \times 10^5 \text{ u}}{162.16 \text{ u/residue}} = 1580 \text{ residues.}$$

15. For each of the three components, there could be six possibilities, so the total number would be 6^3, i.e. 216. However we should divide this number by two, as the sequence ABC is identical to CBA in the tripeptide. Thus there could be 108 different tripeptides.

16. The order in which amino acids occur in a peptide is called its primary structure. The protein's conformation is called its secondary structure. The form of the folded chain of the protein is called its tertiary structure.

17. The reactant molecules fit into a cavity in the structure of the enzyme protein; since the reactant molecules are held in the correct orientation for reaction, the reaction occurs rapidly. The enzyme behaves as a catalyst.

CHAPTER 24

1. Recall that the leading superscript gives the mass number = protons + neutrons, whereas the subscript is the atomic number = protons only. Thus the Li isotope has 3 protons and 3 (= 6−3) neutrons, and C has 6 and 7 respectively, Zr 40 and 54, and Ba has 56 and 81.

2. Same as Q. 1 except that we must find the number of protons from the type of element. Since from the Periodic Table the atomic number of Ne is 10, the number of protons is 10 and in this isotope the number of neutrons is 12 (= 22−10). Similarly the values for ^{88}Sr isotope are 38 and 50 respectively, for ^{92}Sr they are 38 and 54, for W they are 74 and 106, and for Cm they are 96 and 146.

3. Beta decay involves loss of e^-, so Z increases by 1 without a change in mass number. Since Z = 36 corresponds to Kr, the new isotope is $^{80}_{36}$Kr. For positron emission, Z decreses by 1 without a mass change; thus we obtain $^{80}_{34}$Se. Electron capture similarly leads to $^{80}_{34}$Se since Z decreases by one without a change in mass.

4. Loss of two beta particles produces an increase of two in the atomic number without a change in mass number; thus Z = 92 and we obtain $^{233}_{92}$U.

5. a) Since e^- is lost, Z increases by one, giving $^{32}_{16}$S.

   b) Since Z decreases by one without a change in mass number, then to conserve charge the particle must have a charge of +1 and zero mass number, i.e. a positron, $^0_1$e.

   c) Same as (b), i.e. $^0_1$e.

   d) Since the mass number decreases by 4, the new value is 218 − 4 = 214. Since Z decreases by 2, the new value is 87 − 2 = 85, i.e. At. Thus we obtain $^{214}_{85}$At.

   e) To conserve charge, Z must increase to 27 (Co) but the mass number is unchanged; thus we obtain $^{59}_{27}$Co.

   f) Z increases by 1; thus the particle must be $_{-1}^0$e since the mass number is unchanged.

6. In all cases, compare the sum of the mass numbers on the two sides of the equation to deduce the mass number of the unknown particle as the difference; similarly compare the atomic numbers to obtain the charge on the particle.

    a) To equate mass numbers, that for the particle must be 1 (= 36−35); to equate charge, that for the particle must also be 1 (= 18−17). Thus the particle is a proton, $_1^1p$.
    b) Similarly, we obtain $_1^2H$.
    c) Similarly, we obtain $_{11}^{23}Na$.
    d) Similarly, we obtain $_2^3He$, since a gamma particle has neither charge nor a nonzero mass number.

7. Method is identical to Q. 6.
    a) $_{15}^{32}P$.   b) $_3^7Li$.   c) $_{36}^{81}Kr$.

    d) $_2^4He$.   e) $_{38}^{93}Sr$.   f) Isotope mass 263, Z = 106.

8. Since Z = 32 for Ge, and positron emission changes Z (only) by −1, the product is $_{31}^{66}Ga$.
    $$_{32}^{66}Ge \longrightarrow {}_{31}^{66}Ga + {}_{1}^{0}e$$
    Since nuclei decay by first-order processes
    $$\ln (N_0/N) = kt$$
    $$\ln (50.0/N) = 0.277 \ h^{-1} \times 12.5 \ h$$
    $$= 3.4625.$$
    Taking antiln, we obtain
    $$50.0/N = 31.90$$
    so $N = 1.57$, i.e. 1.57 g remains.
    We could have obtained the same result more easily by noting that 12.5 h is exactly 5 half-lives, so the fraction left is $0.5^5 = 0.03125$.

9. The number of disintegrations per second per gram is $95/50.0 = 1.90$, whereas living carbon has 15.3. For first-order decay, we have
    $$\ln (N_0/N) = kt$$
    so $\ln (15.3/1.90) = (0.693/5730 \ y)t$
    $$2.086 = 1.209 \times 10^{-4}t$$
    $$t = 1.725 \times 10^4 \ years.$$
    Thus the casket is made from wood which was alive about 17000 years ago.

10. If 1.0% of the activity remains, $N_0/N = 100/1 = 100$.
    For first-order disintegration, we have
    $$n (N_0/N) = kt$$
    $$\ln (100) = (0.693/30.2 \ y)t$$
    so $t = 201 \ y.$
    Thus it will take 201 years to reduce the radioactivity to 1% of its initial value.

11. Methodology is identical to Q. 9.

$$\ln (15.3/2.4) = (0.693/5730\ y)t$$

so $\quad t = 15300\ y.$

The artists lived about 15000 years ago.

12. The $^{35}_{17}Cl$ nucleus contains 17 protons, each of mass 1.00728 when isolated, and 37-17 = 18 neutrons, each of mass 1.00866. Thus the total mass of the elementary particles is 35.27964, which is 0.31074 greater than the isotope mass quoted in the question. We convert this loss of mass, Δm, into kilograms using the conversion factor given in the text, and calculate ΔE:

$$\Delta E = c^2\Delta m = (2.998 \times 10^8\ m\ s^{-1})^2 \times 0.310740 \times \frac{1.66 \times 10^{-27}\ kg}{1u}$$

$$= 4.64 \times 10^{-11}\ J.$$

The total binding energy is 4.64×10^{-11} J, which on a per nucleon basis is $(4.64 \times 10^{-11}\ J/35\ nucleons) = 1.33 \times 10^{-12}$ J/nucleon.

13. The methodology for each part is identical with that in Q. 12. Thus we obtain:

a) $\Delta m = 0.16700\ u$, $\Delta E = 2.49 \times 10^{-11}$ J, or 1.25×10^{-12} J/nucleon.

b) $\Delta m = 0.58370\ u$, $\Delta E = 8.71 \times 10^{-11}$ J, or 1.36×10^{-12} J/nucleon.

c) $\Delta m = 0.55956\ u$, $\Delta E = 8.35 \times 10^{-11}$ J, or 1.37×10^{-12} J/nucleon.

d) $\Delta m = 1.81032$, $\Delta E = 2.70 \times 10^{-10}$ J, or 1.20×10^{-12} J/nucleon.

14. The change in mass is given by

$$\Delta m = 2 \times 2.01410 - 3.02603 - 1.00866 = -0.00649\ u.$$

We convert from a 2 atom of D basis to 1 mole of D:

$$\frac{0.00649\ u}{2\ atoms\ D} \times \frac{6.022 \times 10^{23}\ atoms\ D}{1\ mole\ D} = 3.91 \times 10^{-21}\ u/mole\ D$$

We then proceed to find ΔE as in Q. 12

$$\Delta E = c^2\Delta m = (2.998 \times 10^8\ m\ s^{-1})^2 \times \frac{3.91 \times 10^{21}\ u}{1\ mole\ D} \times \frac{1.66 \times 10^{27}\ kg}{1\ u}$$

$$= 5.84 \times 10^{11}\ J/mole\ D\ atoms.$$

In contrast, the amount of energy that could be obtained by burning, in oxygen, one mole of D_2 would presumably be the same as that for burning one mole of H_2, which from Table 12.1 is 285.8 kJ/mole $H_2(\ell)$, i.e. 1.43×10^5 J/mole D atoms.

CHAPTER 25

1. The number of planar nodes is ℓ, so for ℓ=0 there are no planar nodes; since the toal number of nodes is n-1, the number of spherical nodes is 2. For ℓ=2, there are two planar nodes and zero spherical ones. For n=3, ℓ=3 is impossible since ℓ must be an integer from zero to n-1. The n=3, ℓ=0 orbital is usually designated 3s (since ℓ=0 is given the symbol s) and the n=3, ℓ=2 is designated 3d.

2. The number of planar nodes is equal to ℓ (and the number of spherical ones is n-ℓ-1 since the total number is n-1).

3. For n=3, ℓ=0 we have s orbitals which are spherical and possess two spherical nodes.
    For n=3, ℓ=1 we have p orbitals which have two lobes and possess one spherical node each, plus one planar node.
    For n=3, ℓ=2 we have d orbitals which have no spherical nodes but two planar nodes.

4. Phosphorus has three singly-occupied atomic orbitals, all of them 3p, with which it can form bonds. Thus the molecule should be pyramidal, with HPH angles of 90°. Similarly H_2S should be angular, with a 90° angle.

5. Since there are four equivalent C—Cl bonds in a tetrahedral orientation, the carbon atom uses sp^3 hybrid orbitals in CCl_4.

6. To a first approximation, the geometry at the nitrogen is tetrahedral since there are four pairs of electrons at N(VSEPR). Thus nitrogen uses four sp^3 hybrid orbitals, three of them to form bonds to fluorine and one to contain the lone pair.

7. At each oxygen there are four electron pairs - two bonding and two nonbonding. To a first approximation, each oxygen is sp^3 hybridized, with two hybrid orbitals used for bonding (one to H, one to the other oxygen) and two used for lone pairs.

8. The hybridization at the methyl carbon is sp^3, since four single bonds are formed. The hybridization at the other two carbons is sp, since each forms two single bonds. The remaining two 2p orbitals on each carbon are unhydridized and are used to form pi bonds between the pair of atoms.

9. As in Q. 8, the hybridization at the methyl group is sp^3. Since the central carbon forms sigma bonds to methyl, H, and O it is sp^2 hybridized. The remaining 2p orbital on carbon and the parallel 2p on oxygen overlap to form a pi bond; hence the CO bond is a double bond.

10. As in Q. 8 and 9, the hybridization at the methyl group is sp^3, and as in Q. 9 that at the central carbon is sp^2 since sigma bonds are formed to its H and the two carbons. The hybridization at the third carbon also is sp^2, since it forms sigma bonds to two H atoms and to the central carbon. The central and third carbons each use parallel 2p orbitals to form a pi bond between them.

11. Since NO_3^- and CO_3^{2-} are isoelectronic, the description for NO_3^- is identical to that given in the text for CO_3^{2-}. The nitrogen forms three sp^2 hybrid orbitals using its 2s and two of its 2p orbitals; each of the hybrids is directed at one of the three oxygen atoms which are at 120° to each other in the NO_3 plane. Each oxygen uses a 2p orbital to bond to a nitrogen hybrid to form a sigma orbital. The $2p_z$ orbital on each atom, i.e. that on N and one from each O combine to form four delocalized pi molecular orbitals, the three stablest of which are doubly-occupied.

12. In ClF_3, one chlorine 3p electron is promoted to 3d. Thus there are electorns in one 3s, three 3p, and one 3d orbital on chlorine. Hybridization of the five orbitals yields five sp^3d hybrids which have a trigonal bipyramid shape. Since ClF_3 is AX_3E_2, three of the hybrids bond to F and two are lone pairs. Similarly, for SF_4 four of the sp^3d hybrids bond to F and one is a lone pair.

13. The $2p_z$ orbitals overlap sideways with each other to form a pi bond; if the CH_2 group is rotated 90°, the 2p orbitals of the pi bond no longer overlap each other and thus the pi bond is destroyed. Thus there is no free rotation about a double bond since it would completely destroy the pi bond if it occurred.

14. Since $AlCl_3$ should be an AX_3 system, at the Al atom the 3s orbital and two of the 3p orbitals hybridize to form three sp^2 hybrids in a plane at 120°; each sp^2 hybrid forms a single bond to a singly-occupied 3p orbital on a chlorine. Hence the $3p_z$ orbital in $AlCl_3$ is empty.
   The structure of Al_2Cl_6 is known to be bridged:

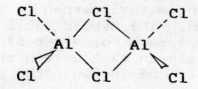

Since the geometry is tetrahedral around each Al, it forms sp^3 hybrid orbitals and uses them to bond to four Cl atoms. The bridging chlorine atoms presumably use sp^3 hybrid orbitals to form bonds to the Al atoms; the other two sp^3 hydrids each contain a lone pair.

15. The Lewis structures here are

$$:C \overset{+}{\equiv} \overset{-}{O}: \qquad :C \equiv \overset{-}{N}: \qquad \overset{-}{:C} \equiv \overset{-}{C}:$$

Presumably each triple bond is composed of a sigma bond plus two pi bonds. Thus each atom forms two sp hybrid orbitals, one of which contains a lone pair and the other of which forms a sigma bond to the other atom. The $2p_y$ orbitals of the two atoms combine to form one pi bond, and the $2p_z$ orbitals combine to form the second pi bond.

16. a) The valence-shell electron configuration for Sn is s^2p^2, i.e. two singly-occupied p orbitals and an s lone pair. Each of the two singly-occupied p orbitals can form a bond with the singly-occupied p orbital of a chlorine. Thus the bond angle should be 90°.

b) If the orbitals containing electrons are hybridized, we obtain three sp^2 orbitals at 120° - two are singly-occupied and bond to chlorines and the other is a lone pair. Thus the bond angle is about 120°.

c) For three pairs of electrons at Sn, VSEPR predicts a trigonal planar arrangement of pairs and an angular geometry with a 120° angle. Thus it is in better agreement with the hybrid orbital model.

17. A double bond consists of one sigma and one pi bond. A triple bond consists of one sigma and two pi bonds. Each pi bond is the combination of sideways-overlapping p orbitals, one on each atom.

18. a) Using the methods developed in earlier chapters, we obtain

b) The sigma framework here at carbon is the hybridization of the 2s and two 2p orbitals to give three sp^2 hybrid orbitals, each of which forms a single sigma bond, with either the 1s of H or a p orbital on oxygen. The $2p_z$ orbitals of the carbon and two oxygens combine to form three π orbitals, two of which are occupied by an electron pair.

19. In general, the more nodes an orbital has, the higher its energy. For an atomic orbital, there are n-1 nodes.

20. The diagram for the x^2-z^2 orbital should look similar to that for the x^2-y^2 orbital in the text (p. 870, Fig. 25.32d) except that there are lobes in the z direction rather than the y. Similarly for the y^2-z^2 orbital, there are lobes along the y and z axes. The signs of the lobes along the z axis for the x^2-z^2 and y^2-z^2 differ; thus if they are combined, the clouds disappear (cancel) in the z direction, and leave an orbital with clouds in the x and y directions only.

CHAPTER 26

1. a) Water, since the molecules have more freedom in the liquid.

    b) A solution, since the ions have more freedom in solution.

    c) The collection, since it is random.

    d) Raw rubber, since the chains are not held in fixed positions relative to each other as they are in vulcanized rubber.

    e) Shuffled cards, since the arrangement is more random.

2. a) Positive entropy change, increased disorder since a gas is formed from a liquid.

    b) Negative entropy change, decreased disorder since the moles of gas decreases.

    c) Positive entropy change, increased disorder since the moles of gas increases.

    d) Same as (b).

    e) Same as (c).

    f) Positive entropy change, increased disorder as the ions have a larger volume in which to travel.

3. a) $\Delta S > 0$ since the moles of gas is increased.

    b) $\Delta S < 0$ since the moles of gas is decreased.

    c) Same as (b).

    d) $\Delta S > 0$ since the ions have more freedom in solution.

4. Attachment of free H_2O molecules to the ion will decrease the entropy, but the H_2O molecules are not originally free - they are hydrogen-bonded to each other, and the order associated with such bonding is lost when they become bound to the ion. Thus there are entropy changes of each sign in the process

$$Al^{3+}(g) + nH_2O(\ell) \longrightarrow Al(H_2O)_n^{3+}(aq).$$

The overall value ΔS will be small. Even if ΔS is negative, the process can still be spontaneous if $\Delta S_{surroundings} > 0$ due to a heat release by the process.

5. a) If the system moves to lower energy, heat q is expelled and thus $\Delta S_{surroundings} > 0$. The reaction will be spontaneous <u>unless</u> the system entropy decreases to a greater extent than is offset by q/T.

    b) If $\Delta S_{sys} > 0$ and the process is spontaneous, $\Delta S_{total} > 0$ and thus any decrease in $\Delta S_{surroundings}$ must be smaller in magnitude than ΔS_{sys}.

6. a) $\Delta S_{sys} < 0$ since the moles of gas decrease.

    b) $\Delta S_{sys} < 0$ since the moles of gas decrease.

    c) $\Delta S_{sys} > 0$ since the moles of gas increase.

    d) $\Delta S_{sys} > 0$ since the moles of gas increase.

    e) $\Delta S_{sys} < 0$ since the moles of gas decrease.

    f) $\Delta S_{sys} > 0$ since the moles of gas increase.

7. In each case, $\Delta S°$ is calculated from the equation
    $$\Delta S° = \text{Sum } S°(\text{products}) - \text{Sum } S°(\text{reactants})$$
    where the $S°$ values are taken from Table 26.1.

    a) $\Delta S° = S°(CO_2, g) - S°(C, graphite) - S°(O_2, g)$
          $= 213.7 - 5.8 - 205.0$
          $= 2.9 \text{ J K}^{-1} \text{ mol}^{-1}$.

    b) $\Delta S° = 2S°(CO_2, g) + 3S°(H_2O, \ell) - S°(C_2H_5OH_3 \ell)$
          $- 3S°(O_2, g) = -138.5 \text{ J K}^{-1} \text{ mol}^{-1}$.

    c) Similarly, $\Delta S° = 289.8 \text{ J K}^{-1} \text{ mol}^{-1}$.

    d) Similary, $\Delta S° = 166.3 \text{ J K}^{-1} \text{ mol}^{-1}$.

8. The method of $\Delta S°$ calculation is identical to Q. 7.

    a) $\Delta S° = S°(CaO, s) + S°(CO_2, g) - S°(CaCO_3, s)$
          $= 158.9 \text{ J K}^{-1} \text{ mol}^{-1}$
        $\Delta S° > 0$ since the number of moles of gas increases due to the reaction.

    b) $\Delta S° = 2S°(BrF_3, g) - S°(Br_2, \ell) + 3S°(F_2, g)$
          $= -175.5 \text{ J K}^{-1} \text{ mol}^{-1}$
        $\Delta S° < 0$ since the moles of gas decrease.

    c) $\Delta S° = 2S°(CO_2, g) - 2S°(CO, g) - S°(O_2, g)$
          $= -172.8 \text{ J K}^{-1} \text{ mol}^{-1}$
        $\Delta S° < 0$ since the moles of gas decrease.

d) $\Delta S° = S°(CO,g) + S°(H_2,g) - S°(C,graphite) - S°(H_2O,\ell)$
$= 236.4$ J K^{-1} mol^{-1}
$\Delta S° > 0$ since the moles of gas increase.

e) $\Delta S° = S°(NaCl,s) - 2S°(Na,s) + S°(Cl_2,g)$
$= -253.1$ J K^{-1} mol^{-1}
$\Delta S° < 0$ since the moles of gas decrease.

9. Methodology is identical to Q. 8; thus only answers are given.

a) $\Delta S° = +11.1$ J K^{-1} mol^{-1}.

b) $\Delta S° = +24.7$ J K^{-1} mol^{-1}.

c) For $P_4(s)$, $S° = 4S°(P,white,g)$ so
$\Delta S° = -958.4$ J K^{-1} mol^{-1}.

d) $\Delta S° = -549.4$ J K^{-1} mol^{-1}.

e) $\Delta S° = -326.2$ J K^{-1} mol^{-1}.

10. For the reaction,
$\Delta H° = 2\Delta H_f°(Fe,g) + 3\Delta H_f°(CO,g) - \Delta H_f°(Fe_2O_3,g) - 3\Delta H_f°(C,s,graphite)$
and similarly for $\Delta S°$ and $\Delta G°$, we obtain
$\Delta H° = +492.5$ kJ mol^{-1}
$\Delta S° = +542.6$ J K^{-1} mol^{-1}
$\Delta G° = +330.6$ kJ mol^{-1}.

The value of $\Delta H° - T\Delta S°$ at T = 298 K is (after conversion of $\Delta S°$ to kJ K^{-1} mol^{-1}) easily calculated to be 331 kJ mol^{-1}, i.e. equal to the calculated $\Delta G°$. Since $\Delta S° > 0$ the entropy change favors the reaction but since $\Delta H° > 0$ it is disfavored by the enthalpy change. The latter dominates since $\Delta G° > 0$.

11. To answer the questions, we calculate both $\Delta G°$ and $\Delta H°$:
$\Delta G° = 2\Delta G_f°(HCl,g) - \Delta G_f°(H_2,g) - \Delta G_f°(Cl_2,g)$
$= 2\Delta G_f°(HCl,g)$
$= 2 \times (-95.3$ kJ mol$^{-1})$
$= -190.6$ kJ mole^{-1}; the reaction is spontaneous.

$\Delta S° = 2S°(HCl,g) - S°(H_2,g) - S°(Cl_2,g)$
$= 2 \times 186.8 - 130.6 - 223.0$
$= +20.0$ J K^{-1} mol^{-1}.

Now $\Delta G° = \Delta H° - T\Delta S°$, so the contribution from the entropy is $-T\Delta S°$, i.e. -298 K $\times$ 20 J K^{-1} mol$^{-1} = -5.96$ kJ mol^{-1}. Thus the enthalpy $\Delta H°$, which must be -184.6, makes a much larger contribution to $\Delta G°$ than does the entropy term $-T\Delta S°$.

12. We can obtain $\Delta G°$ from the $\Delta G_f°$ values in Table 26.2. Note that $\Delta G_f° = 0$ for an element in its standard state.

a) $\Delta G° = 3\Delta G_f°(CO_2, g) + 4\Delta G_f°(H_2O, g) - \Delta G_f°(C_3H_8, g) - 5\Delta G_f°(O_2, g)$

$= 3 \times (-394.4) + 4 \times (-228.6) - (-23.4) - 5 \times 0$

$= -2074.2 \text{ kJ mol}^{-1}$.

Spontaneous, since $\Delta G° < 0$.

b) $\Delta G° = 2\Delta G_f°(NO_2, g) - \Delta G_f°(N_2O_4, g)$

$= 2 \times 51.3 - 97.8$

$= 4.8 \text{ kJ mol}^{-1}$.

Not spontaneous, since $\Delta G° > 0$.

c) $\Delta G° = 2\Delta G_f°(CH_2Cl_2, \ell) - \Delta G_f°(CH_4, g) - \Delta G_f°(CCl_4, \ell)$

$= 2 \times (-67.3) - (-50.8) - (-65.3)$

$= -18.5 \text{ kJ mol}^{-1}$.

Spontaneous, since $\Delta G° < 0$.

13. The $\Delta G°$ for decomposition will in each case be minus the $\Delta G_f°$ for the compound, since the $\Delta G_f°$ vaues for the elements are zero. Thus $\Delta G°$ is negative, and the reaction is spontaneous, only for NO_2. Thus it shows the greatest tendency to decompose.

14. In each case, we obtain $\Delta G°$ from
$\Delta G° = \text{Sum } \Delta G_f°(\text{products}) - \text{sum } \Delta G_f°(\text{reactants})$
and recalling that $\Delta G_f° = 0$ for any element in its standard state, i.e. for $Cl_2(g)$, $F_2(g)$, $Br_2(\ell)$, $Zn(s)$, $Pb(s)$, $Fe(s)$ and $Al(s)$ in the present context. Data is from Appendix 2.

a) $\Delta G° = +324.0 \text{ kJ mol}^{-1}$.

b) $\Delta G° = -70.4 \text{ kJ mol}^{-1}$.

c) $\Delta G° = -423.6 \text{ kJ mol}^{-1}$.

d) $\Delta G° = +839.8 \text{ kJ mol}^{-1}$.

Since the production of F_2 by Cl_2 is not spontaneous, but that of Br_2 by Cl_2 is spontaneous, we conclude that in oxidizing power $F_2 > Cl_2 > Br_2$. No comparison can be made between Zn and Fe as reducing agents from examples (c) and (d), as different oxidizing agents are involved in the two reactions.

15. We can obtain K_p from $\Delta G°$ via the equation
$\Delta G° = -RT \ln K_p$.

Now from the data in Appendix 2, it follows that
$\Delta G° = -142.0 \text{ kJ mol}^{-1}$.

Thus the reaction is spontaneous at 298 K (since $\Delta G° < 0$), and
$$K_p = e^{-\Delta G°/RT} = e^{+57.3} = 7.7 \times 10^{24}.$$
The units of K_p are atm^{-1}.

16. We can obtain K_p from $\Delta G° = -RT \ln K_p$ if we can calculate $\Delta G°$ at 700K. Since we are told that $\Delta H°$ and $\Delta S°$ are independent of temperature here, we can evaluate the required $\Delta G°$ from $\Delta G° = \Delta H° - T\Delta S°$. From the data in the Appendix,

$$\Delta H° = +172.5 \text{ kJ mol}^{-1}$$
$$\Delta S° = +175.7 \text{ J K}^{-1} \text{ mol}^{-1}$$

$$\begin{aligned}\Delta G° &= \Delta H° - T\Delta S°\\ &= 172.5 - 700 \times 175.7/1000\\ &= 49.5.\end{aligned}$$

Now
$$\begin{aligned}K_p &= e^{-\Delta G°/RT}\\ &= e^{-49,500/8.314 \times 700}\\ &= e^{-8.51}\\ &= 2.0 \times 10^{-4}.\end{aligned}$$

17. Using methodology identical to that in Q. 15, we obtain
$$\Delta G° = +37.2 \text{ kJ mol}^{-1}$$
and thus $K_p = 3.1 \times 10^{-7}$ atm.

18. By the usual methods,
$$\Delta G° = -4.8 \text{ kJ}$$
$$K_p = e^{-\Delta G°/RT} = e^{+4800/8.31 \times 298} = 6.9.$$

19. a) $$\begin{aligned}\Delta G° &= \Delta G_f°(CO_2,g) + 2\Delta G_f°(H_2O,g) - \Delta G_f°(CH_4,g) - 2\Delta G_f°(O_2,g)\\ &= -800.8 \text{ kJ}.\end{aligned}$$
Since $\Delta G°$ is negative, the reaction is spontaneous.

b) $$K_p = e^{-\Delta G°/RT} = e^{+800,800/8.31 \times 298} = e^{323} = 10^{140}.$$

c) The mixture can remain unreacted for long periods of time since the activation energy required to start the process is substantial and is not normally available except in the form of a spark, etc.

20. a) To decide if the reaction is spontaneous, we calculate $\Delta G°$:
$$\begin{aligned}\Delta G° &= 2\Delta G_f°(CO_2,g) + 4\Delta G_f°(H_2O,\ell) - 2\Delta G_f°(CH_3OH,\ell) - 3\Delta G_f°(O_2,g)\\ &= -1404.8 \text{ kJ mol}^{-1}.\end{aligned}$$
Since $\Delta G° < 0$, the reaction is spontaneous.

b) We obtain K from
$$\Delta G° = -RT \ln K.$$
Thus $\ln K = -\Delta G°/RT = 567.0$
and $K = e^{567} = 10^{246}.$

c) Products are favored since $K \gg 1$.

d) Since the number of moles of gas decreses, incresed pressure favors formation of more products (Le Chatelier's Principle).

e) $\Delta H°$ is negative here since we know that burning methanol produces heat; thus increasing the temperature favors the reactants (by Le Chatelier's Principle).

21. a) Since $\Delta G° \gg 0$, very little C_2H_2 will be present in an equilibrium mixture of $C(s)$, $H_2(g)$, and $C_2H_2(g)$ at room temperature; thus it is not a practical route for C_2H_2 synthesis.

b) To decide whether the reaction becomes more or less spontaneous at higher temperatures, we need to compute $\Delta H°$ and $\Delta S°$ (which we can take to be relatively temperature-independent); using data in Appendix B, we obtain
$$\Delta H° = \Delta H_f°(C_2H_2,g) = 2\Delta H_f°(C, \text{graphite}) - \Delta H_f°(H_2,g)$$
$$= + 228.0 \text{ kJ mol}^{-1}$$
$$\Delta S° = S°(C_2H_2,g) - 2S°(C,\text{graphite}) - S°(H_2,g)$$
$$= + 58.6 \text{ J K}^{-1} \text{ mol}^{-1}.$$
Since $\Delta G° = \Delta H° - T\Delta S°$ and both $\Delta H°$ and $\Delta S°$ are positive, it follows that $\Delta G°$ becomes less positive, i.e. the reaction becomes more spontaneous, as the temperature increases.

c) Using $\Delta H°$ and $\Delta S°$ from part (b), we obtain
$$\Delta G° = \Delta H° - T\Delta S°$$
$$= 228.0 \text{ kJ mol}^{-1} - 1200 \text{ K} \times (58.6/1000) \text{ kJ K mol}^{-1}.$$
$$= + 157.7 \text{ kJ mol}^{-1}.$$
Now
$$\Delta G° = - RT \ln K_p \text{ so}$$
$$K_p = e^{-\Delta G°/RT} = e^{-15.8} = 1.4 \times 10^{-7}.$$

22. For the $N_2O_4(g) \rightleftharpoons 2NO_2(g)$ reaction, at equilibrium
$$K_p = P_{NO_2}^2/P_{N_2O_4}.$$
Substituting the partial pressures mentioned in the problem, we obtain

$$\frac{P_{NO_2}^2}{P_{N_2O_4}} = \frac{(0.020 \text{ atm})^2}{0.040 \text{ atm}} = 0.010 \text{ atm}.$$

Since the reaction quotient is much less than the K_p value of 6.9, the reaction is not at equilibrium. Much more of the N_2O_4 will dissociate to NO_2.

23. We can compute ΔG from $\Delta G = RT \ln(Q/K_p)$.
For the reaction conditions,

$$Q = P_{CO_2}^2/P_{CO}^2 P_{O_2} = (0.02 \text{ atm})^2/(0.02 \text{ atm})^2(0.02 \text{ atm})$$

$$= 50 \text{ atm}^{-1}.$$

We obtain K_p from
$$K_p = e^{-\Delta G°/RT}.$$
Here $\Delta G° = -514.4$ kJ, so $K_p = 10^{90}$.
Thus $\Delta G = 8.31$ J K^{-1} mole^{-1} x 298 K x $\ell n(50/10^{90})$
$= -503.5$ kJ mole^{-1} i.e. less negative than is $\Delta G°$.
Since ΔG is negative, the reaction will proceed from left to right.

24. a) $\Delta G° = 2\Delta G_f°(CH_3OH,\ell) + 3\Delta G_f°(O_2,g) - 2\Delta G_f°(CO_2,g)$
$- 4\Delta G_f°(H_2O,\ell)$
$= +1404.8$ kJ.

b) Similarly, $\Delta G° = -788.8$ kJ.
If the reactions were coupled, then
$\Delta G° = +1404.8 - 788.8$
$= +616.0$ kJ.
Since $\Delta G°$ is positive, the coupled reaction is not spontaneous.

25. The entropy of the surroundings ΔS_{surr} decreases in an endothermic reaction, for which ΔH_{system} is positive
$$\Delta S_{surr} = -\Delta H_{system}/T$$
because energy that was dispersed in the surroundings is transferred to the system. Such a reaction cannot proceed unless there is a sufficiently positive entropy increase in the system so that $\Delta S_{universe}$ is positive. Now at higher temperature $\Delta H_{system}/T$ becomes smaller so that the entropy decrease in the surroundings is smaller and thus the $\Delta S_{universe}$ becomes more positive; in other words the reaction is favoured by increasing temperature.

26. According to the second law of thermodynamics the entropy of the universe must increase in any spontaneous process, i.e., $\Delta S_{universe} = \Delta S_{system} + \Delta S_{surroundings} > 0$. $\Delta S_{surroundings}$ is increased by the dispersal of heat energy transferred from the system. $\Delta S_{surr} = -\Delta H_{system}/T$. ΔS_{system} is increased by an increase in the disorder or randomness of the system with which is associated an increased dispersal of the energy of the system.
$\Delta S_{system} + \Delta S_{surroundings} > 0$
$-\Delta H_{system}/T + \Delta S_{system} > 0$
$-T\Delta S_{system} + \Delta H_{system} < 0$
but $\Delta G = \Delta H - T\Delta S$
so $\Delta G < 0$
Thus we see that a spontaneous reaction, in which there is a sufficient dispersal of energy in the system or in the surroundings or both so that $\Delta S_{universe} + \Delta S_{system} = S_{surr} > 0$, will have a negative free energy change.

27. To reduce an oxide to the metal, we must reverse the reactions shown in the problem; $\Delta G°(1500°C)$ is positive for Al, Fe, and Pb. To make the reduction feasible, we must couple the process with a reaction for which $\Delta G° < 0$. Consider the oxidation of carbon to CO and to CO_2:

$$2C(s) + O_2(g) \longrightarrow 2CO(g) \qquad \Delta G° = -500 \text{ kJ}$$

$$C(s) + O_2(g) \longrightarrow CO_2(g) \qquad \Delta G° = -380 \text{ kJ}.$$

Consider coupling either of the reactions with the Al reaction; in both cases we multiply the above reactions by three so that the moles of O_2 are the same:

$$6C + 3O_2 \longrightarrow 6CO \qquad \Delta G° = -1500 \text{ kJ}$$
$$3C + 3O_2 \longrightarrow 3CO_2 \qquad \Delta G° = -1140 \text{ kJ}.$$

Since these $\Delta G°$ values are not as negative as is the positive $\Delta G°$ (of 2250 kJ) for $Al_2O_3 \longrightarrow Al$, we conclude that the combined reaction has $\Delta G° > 0$ and will not proceed.

For FeO and PbO reduction, only one mole of O_2 is involved. These processes are feasible using either CO or CO_2, since the $\Delta G°$ values of +250 and +120 kJ for Fe and Pb production respectively are less in an absolute sense than is the $\Delta G°$ for $C \longrightarrow CO$ or $C \longrightarrow CO_2$. Coupling either oxidation with the FeO or PbO reduction therefore yields a spontaneous reaction.

The reduction of CuO to Cu is almost spontaneous even without CO or CO_2 production since $\Delta G° = 0$. Using carbon would make $\Delta G° << 0$ and increase the yield considerably.